Take Time

Take Time to think . . . It is the source of
    power.
Take Time to play . . . It is the secret of
    perpetual youth.
Take Time to read . . . It is the fountain
    of wisdom.
Take Time to pray . . . It is the greatest
    power on earth.
Take Time to love and be loved . . . It is a
    God-given privilege.
Take Time to be friendly . . . It is the road
    to happiness.
Take Time to laugh . . . It is the music of
    the soul.
Take Time to give . . . It is too short a day
    to be selfish.
Take Time to work . . . It is the price of
    success.
Take Time to do charity . . . It is the key
    to heaven.

Joe Kotcka

BROTHERHOOD OF SILENCE

The Story of an Anti-Communist Underground

BROTHERHOOD
of
SILENCE

The Story of an
Anti-Communist Underground

by STEFAN ILOK
with LESTER TANZER

ROBERT B. LUCE, INC.

Washington, D. C.

Library of Congress Catalog Card Number: 62-21923

MANUFACTURED IN THE UNITED STATES OF AMERICA

VAN REES PRESS   •   NEW YORK

To the brave men and women
of all the Undergrounds
within the Communist empire
who fight in silence and anonymity
to remain captains of their souls.

Table of Contents

Prologue

I am called Stefan Ilok. It is not my real name, but it is one by which I am known to the Slovak Underground. I would like to tell you about that Underground, about its people, the way they work and live, and the things they do in their struggle to regain freedom from their Communist masters.

I first became engaged in clandestine activities during World War II, when I held an important position in a Slovakian economic institution. From this relatively immune position, I was able to organize a network that managed to shelter many Jews from persecution or help them escape to countries outside Fascist rule. With the assistance of sympathizers in the State Police, for example, I obtained false papers for many Jews showing that they were not Jews at all.

In 1944, I began working with a branch of the French Resistance, known as "Arc-en-Ciel" or "Rainbow," protecting French officers who had escaped from German camps by supplying them with false identity papers. That year, armed with diplomatic status, I left Slovakia and headed across Hungary and Yugoslavia for Italy, where I planned to negotiate with the American Army for arms and food for the Slovak insurgents who had resisted the Nazis. In my car were several escapees masquerading as Slovaks.

We never got past Yugoslavia. There we were arrested by the German Secret Service. Eventually I wound up in a concentration camp at Mauthausen in Austria. I was sentenced to death as a *judenfreund,* a "friend of the Jews," one who helped Jews escape the fate the Nazis had in store for them. Less than a week before I was to die, however, the camp was stormed and liberated by General George Patton's Third Army. But that is another story.

Upon my return to Czechoslovakia, I was distressed to learn of the inroads the Communists had made there. Two officials whom I had previously dismissed because of Communist leanings had now become members of the new government, ostensibly a coalition government but Communist-dominated. Quickly I got in touch with anti-Communist leaders in Slovakia. Because we were certain a Red *coup* would come we decided to organize a resistance movement. To start with, its personnel would come from the anti-Communists among the insurgents who fought the Nazis. But the Underground quickly grew as Slovaks discovered the true meaning of communism.

Because of the foreign contacts I had made during my career, it was decided that I should represent the Underground abroad. I was to alert and arouse the West to support Slovakia's cause, to raise money for the Underground and to serve as a liaison between the Underground and the free world.

I was stationed first in Vienna, then in Paris. Later I came to the United States. Here I have been based ever since, though my travels on behalf of the Slovak Underground take me back to Europe several times a year. Through an elaborate courier system, I have been able to serve as a means of transmitting vital information from behind the Iron Curtain to the West, and for passing on assignments from the West to the Slovak Underground.

Through these trips to Europe, and through the flight of Slovaks to the United States, I have met many of the people whose exploits appear on the following pages—Filip Polhora, Jan Baar, Father Michael, Peter Dub, Jozef Maryan, Olga Gazdova and others. Most of the stories were told to me by the actual participants; some by people who knew and worked with the chief characters of this book. Of the many stories and events with which I am familiar, I have selected those which best describe the structure and operations of the Underground.

To protect the individuals involved, many of whom are still fighting communism, I have used assumed names in most cases. Occasionally, the locations and times of certain events have also been altered where it was necessary to avoid disclosures that might compromise the Underground's members. But each character in this book actually existed, or still lives. Each story is a true one, described as accurately as the narrators can remember. In some cases, scenes and conversations that are known to have occurred have had to be reconstructed in part out of the information available.

To understand the Slovaks' fight, you will need to know something of Slovakia. Struggling for freedom is an old story in my native land. A glance at a map of Europe will demonstrate Slovakia's strategic location, an accident of geography and history that has made the country a continual prey for those who lust for empire. Slovakia, the eastern half of Czechoslovakia, is situated at the very heart of Europe.

To most Americans, Slovakia is an integral part of Czechoslovakia. Yet for more than eleven centuries Slovakia was a land apart. Not until the end of World War I were the Czechs and Slovaks merged into one nation. If the Slovaks had their way today, I have no doubt that they would prefer to break away and regain their own independent nationhood.

More than a thousand years ago, the Slovaks were first among the Slavic peoples to achieve sovereignty, even before the Czechs, Poles, Serbs and Russians entered the scene of civilized Europe. Along the banks of the Danube, the Nitra and the Morava Rivers, the Great Moravian Empire was created as a kind of buffer zone between the Carolingian and Byzantine empires. From the year 800 on, the Slovaks had their own princes and kings, waged wars as one nation, exchanged embassies with Constantinople and Rome, made alliances with neighboring peoples and tribes of Slavic ancestry, and became the first Slavic nation to adopt Western culture and religion.

xi

But early in the tenth century, the Moravian Empire was destroyed. Beset by continual warfare against the Germans to the west, the Slovaks were overwhelmed in 907 by Mongolian hordes from the east and fell under Mongol rule. Ever since then, Slovakia has been a battleground, a strategic pawn in the seemingly perpetual wars among Germans, Turks, Tartars and Magyars, as the Mongols later came to be called. And yet, through it all, the Slovaks never lost their national consciousness, their culture or their language.

I first learned of Slovakia's history from my mother's lips. As a child during World War I, when Slovakia was a part of the Austro-Hungarian Empire, I became aware that most of the land in our country was owned by Austrians, who spoke a strange tongue called German. Nor did I understand the language of the police and other local officials, who spoke to my parents in Hungarian. In our own home, and in our church, we spoke Slovak. Becoming conscious that I was different from the people who ruled us, I asked Mother why this was so. Over the following weeks and months, she told me tale after tale of Slovak history, of our origins, our ancient independence, our national heroes who, even after Slovakia was no longer a separate entity, became the underground leaders of their day. Starting with nothing but their hands and their wills, they organized bands of resistance, forged their own armor, gathered in food, planned strategy and sometimes outwitted the oppressors. Many were the times when, along with my playmates, I would re-enact the heroic stories my mother told me in the rugged Carpathian mountains that surrounded our town.

Yet the centuries without freedom had taken their toll. Under the Austro-Hungarian monarchy, the Slovaks gradually began losing their sense of national uniqueness. They were in danger of falling into oblivion as a people. And then they were brought back to life in 1918. It was Woodrow Wilson, President of the United States, who wrought the miracle with his insistence on self-determination by all the peoples subjugated by the Dual Monarchy. To him and to the American people belong Slovakia's national survival.

It was Wilson's idea that the Slovaks and the Czechs unite as equal partners in a federated Czechoslovakia. Only when he was informed that the Czechs and Slovaks had reached certain agreements guaranteeing equal status to both partners did he recognize the new nation.

But one year later the political marriage of the Slovaks and Czechs was on the rocks, for the more numerous Czechs sought to dominate Slovakia. To Wilson, then in Paris for the Versailles conference, came the aggrieved Slovak leaders. He heard their pleas, then told them:

I must concentrate on the Covenant [for the League of Nations] for unless we secure it there will be no tribunal before which we can bring for rectification any mistakes or any inequalities in the treaty that may be revealed when it is put into practice. . . . On the other hand, I give you my word that when the League convenes in November, I will bring your grievances before it and I have no doubt that they will be promptly remedied and a better settlement arrived at.

At that time, Wilson did not have the remotest idea that the Senate would reject both the Versailles Treaty and the Covenant, or that when the League assembled the United States would not be a member.

So it happened that the Slovak case was never heard. Between 1918 and 1938, Slovaks lived under the sway of the Czechs. It is little wonder then that when Hitler, in an effort to divide and conquer Czechoslovakia, offered Slovakia its independence, the Slovaks accepted. On March 14, 1939, Slovakia realized her thousand-year-old dream of freedom. Or so she thought.

The Hitler years are not a period of which all Slovaks are proud. Some of the leaders of the new nation embraced the cruel, racist philosophy of the Führer, even though the decent people of the land recoiled in horror. Independence proved illusory, for it depended on the fortunes of its grantor.

In 1945 Slovakia was buried again by invaders from the East, this time the armies of communism, and forced into an unhappy marriage once more with the Czechs. But the Slovaks did not give in meekly. Having tasted freedom, even if diluted and temporary, they were bent on regaining mastery over themselves. It was out of this will to independence, to nationhood, that the Underground was born anew.

Book I THE SECRET STATE

In the beginning the Underground believed that the overthrow of Slovakia's Red rulers was just around the corner. If only it could reach its tentacles everywhere, if only it could flex its muscles, the Underground thought, then it might topple the Communist regime—if not by itself, then with the help of the West, which would surely come to the aid of the Underground when it saw how deep, how successful the Resistance was.

The Underground organized itself as a secret state within a state. It had its own general staff and army, the guerillas; its own communication system, built around the couriers; its own labor unions, intelligence network, and division of psychological warfare. In those early days of Communist enslavement, the main task of the Underground was to rouse the people; to sabotage Red plants, to harass Communist troops and trains—and to keep alive....

1. The Prince of Couriers

FILIP POLHORA flattened himself against the bare earth as the searchlight swept past him. The night was moonless, but the faint radiation on the dial of his watch told him that Karol's information, so far at least, was correct. It took the searchlight exactly thirty seconds to sweep a full circle.

Filip raised himself to a crouching position. Ahead of him, perhaps fifty yards away, was the Iron Curtain itself—in this instance, the eastern embankment of the Morava River. Here the Communists had built a high levee with a dual purpose in mind: to keep the Morava from inundating the low-lying farmlands in the state-controlled buffer zones—and to keep the citizens of Slovakia from leaving the "workers' paradise."

It occurred to Filip that the Reds had been unsuccessful in either case. The levee had been sabotaged last Spring when the farmers decided they would rather drown their crops than see them shipped to the Soviet Union. And the levee had not kept Filip and other couriers of the Underground from completing their missions.

To his right, Filip made out the dim outlines of the watchtower where the searchlight was located. Besides the light it contained, if Karol was correct, two machine guns, a Lieutenant Koterba and a Sergeant Gursky.

Filip forced himself to breathe slowly and softly while he listened intently for sounds to his left. Soon they came. First he heard the panting of the dogs, the fierce hungry dogs straining at their chains. Fear clutched at his stomach, as always. Lying perfectly still, he waited, watching the footpath at the

3

base of the levee. The dogs came into view, lurching forward, and dragging with them two troopers of the State Security Police, the SNB.

His eyes strained through the murky light as the dogs and troopers drew abreast of his hiding place. For a fleeting instant, Filip wished he could shrink to the size of an ant. The ants of this world, he thought, had no trouble crossing the Iron Curtain or any other man-made barrier.

As the second trooper came closer, Filip slowly exhaled. He permitted himself the luxury of a smile. The trooper was Juraj, a respected member of the Communist Party and a stalwart defender of the border.

Juraj was also a loyal member of the anti-Communist Underground.

Juraj tapped his fellow trooper on the shoulder, and pointed to a spot further along the footpath on the far side of the watchtower. "Halt!" Juraj shouted to an imaginary trespasser. He brought his carbine up to his shoulder and opened fire. As Juraj ran forward, the other trooper followed with the dogs. Immediately the searchlight swung away from the area in which Filip was lying and the machine guns in the watchtower began chattering.

Filip arose and started running in the same motion. Reaching the footpath, he leaped across it to the embankment and swiftly climbed up the side. At the top, he discovered the earth had been raked clean so that the footprints of anyone crossing it would show clearly in the searchlight's beam.

Peering quickly toward the watchtower, Filip was silently grateful for Karol's spadework and Juraj's diversionary tactics. The border guards were busily wasting ammunition on a phantom.

Filip pulled a lady's fan from his pocket. Spreading it wide open, he dragged it across the earth behind him as he crossed the top of the levee, neatly obliterating any signs of his passage.

The searchlight started back toward him as he scrambled down the far side of the embankment into the icy waters of the Morava, a quarter mile wide at this point. Beneath the surface, he held his breath and counted. Ten seconds . . . twenty . . . thirty . . . forty. . . . He came up gasping. The light had moved on. Filip swam toward the far shore, cursing himself for splashing. Each time the light came near, he ducked under.

By now, the men in the watchtower realized they had been firing at shadows. They moved their sights toward the erratic currents in the Morava made by Filip Polhora. "Please, God," Filip prayed, "let me through this time." Numb from the bitter cold of the river, he kept on swimming.

Bullets sent up spray only inches from him as Filip reached the west bank. He slithered out of the water, crouched forward, and propelled himself at a dead run straight ahead. He had left Slovakia and reached Austria. Behind him the machine guns were still chattering.

Filip felt no elation at having crossed the Iron Curtain. His heart was still beating like a triphammer from the naked fear of having escaped death by inches. Neither did he relax his vigilance. He was still too near the border for comfort.

Filip ran until he reached a clearing in the Austrian forest. There, chest heaving, he fell to the ground and became violently ill.

When the nausea passed, Filip removed his wet clothes and changed into a drab business suit, a loose-fitting shirt and a pair of shoes which had been carefully cached in a hollow tree stump on the Austrian side of the Morava. The clothes he had been wearing were wrung out and placed in the stump, for he might need them again on the return trip.

He walked swiftly past a path that led away from the river, remembering Karol's warning. "The path is a trap," Karol had said. "Many couriers follow paths like it because they are tired from crawling through the mud and from swimming up the river. But it is on those paths that many of them are caught. Remember, the Reds offer 1,500 schillings for every courier who is betrayed and too many people are looking for that money."

5

The route Karol had shown him took him through woods and over rocks. The night was pitch black and not a single star could be seen to guide him, but Filip had memorized the map and he had an excellent sense of direction. Every step of the way he expected to hear the challenge of a border guard or a shot. But luck was with him. By eight o'clock in the morning, he reached a railroad station.

For the first time, Filip relaxed. It was easy to lose himself among the workers who crowded the depot and he knew the language well enough not to attract attention when he bought a ticket to Vienna. Money for the ticket had been placed in a pocket of the suit he wore. Cigarettes and matches were also left in the coat pocket, and Filip enjoyed a smoke as he waited for the train. There was enough money left over for a meal as well. He bought a cup of coffee, some dark bread and cheese, and ate solemnly as befits a man who could not afford to be impatient. It was the first food he had taken in over twenty-four hours.

In Vienna, he took a streetcar to the American zone. He got off the car more than a half mile from his destination and walked circuitously the rest of the way to a drab house in a neighborhood of drab houses. He knocked on the door twice.

The door opened a crack and unfriendly eyes looked him over.

"Come in." It was a command, not an invitation. Filip walked in carefully, keeping his hands in plain sight. The door slammed shut behind him. Two men, one on either side, carefully frisked him for weapons. A young woman, dark-eyed with jet black hair, indolently pointed a Beretta automatic at Filip's midsection.

"Your name?" barked the short, stocky man on Filip's left.

"George Baltay," Filip said evenly.

"Where are you from?" demanded the slim man on his right.

"I come from Bratislava," Filip said.

6

"You are six minutes late," the woman remarked almost casually.

"No," said Filip without looking at his watch, "I think I am only four minutes late."

The woman smiled and the Beretta disappeared from sight. "Welcome, Mr. Baltay," the woman said, "we were expecting you." She moved forward to shake Filip's hand and the other two men slapped his back.

"You weren't followed here, were you?" the taller man asked.

Filip shook his head. "I don't think so."

"Have any trouble at the border?" the woman wanted to know.

Filip's smile was mirthless. "None to speak of. I'm here."

The first half of Filip Polhora's mission was almost over.

The courier is the bloodstream of the Underground, and Filip Polhora, in his late twenties, was known as the Prince of Couriers. He had the body of an athlete, supple, slender and erect. His face was thin and unlined, his hair dark. He was neither handsome nor ugly; his face in repose was a pleasant one and except for the dark brown eyes that seemed to pierce you when seen up close it was a face that blended into others in a crowd. Its lack of distinctive features made it easily adaptable to simple disguises.

Filip was born in Eastern Slovakia but raised in Bratislava, the capital of Slovakia. There, at the University, he studied engineering. Filip was inclined to be something of a dilettante, dabbling in acting, athletics and whatever other whim came over him. He had the reputation of a ladies' man, but his devil-may-care approach to life attracted many male friends, too. Not until the Russians came to Slovakia did Filip show his true mettle.

At the time the Soviet troops marched into Slovakia, Filip was visiting his aunt and uncle in the eastern portion of the country. The soldiers, like conquerors throughout history, looted wherever they went. They raped thousands of women, young and old alike, and in their wake they left disease. Filip drove a horse-drawn cart and he took many of the women from the villages to the hospital at Prešov. He saw hundreds of women waiting at the door of the hospital, begging to be cured. Sometimes the hospital was able to help them,—usually it was crowded and turned women away.

One day Filip was driving a girl who couldn't have been more than twelve. She was so ravaged with disease that she could hardly sit up. All the way to Prešov she lay on the straw at the bottom of the cart. Each time Filip turned around to look at her, he saw her eyes trained on him. They were big, brown and afraid. They reminded him of the eyes of a dog that has been hurt and does not know what is wrong. Once the girl asked, "Will they make me all right at the hospital?"

Filip mumbled a comforting answer, with tears in his eyes. The hospital was crowded but it took the girl in. Filip could not wait, however. He never did find out whether the child had been cured, but the experience marked a turning point in his life. He went back to school for a time, but shortly afterward he returned to his home and spoke with people who had connections with the Underground. They told him that as an athlete he might best serve the Underground as a courier. And so he attended the "school" for couriers, a small cottage in a wooded mountain ravine in the High Tatras where he went through an intensive course with several other young men.

Filip was warned against gambling, against heavy drinking. He was warned to beware of attractive girls, for women were among the Communists' most effective tools in betraying the Underground. He was trained to run until he was exhausted, until his chest was bursting, his legs leaden and his mind numb. And then he was forced to keep on running, another step, another minute, another mile. He learned how to swim rivers in zero weather with his clothes on, pushing a package ahead on a cake of ice. And when he crossed the river, he learned to run with the clothes frozen stuck to him, because if he did not

8

keep going he would die. He was trained to go without food, to hide for a week if he had to, in the heat of summer or the cold of winter.

The courier, Filip was taught, usually travels by normal means—railroad, bus or private car. He is protected by false identity papers and his own wits. Sometimes he knows the man he is to meet, sometimes not. If he does not know his contact, he is given a general description. He is told how the man will dress, whether he wears glasses, whether he has a mustache or any other distinctive marks on his face. The courier is also told certain signs a contact may make to indicate danger, warning him not to approach.

The courier might be told before the mission starts that "X wears his wristwatch on the outside of his wrist. If it is on the inside, stay away from him." Or "X wears a handkerchief in his breast pocket with three folds in it. If there are only two folds, you must not speak to him." Or "X always buttons every button of his coat. If one button is open, there is danger."

The signals of danger cannot be anything spectacular. No obvious gesture, or motion of eyes or lips. They must seem entirely natural to an unfriendly observer.

Filip learned there were two broad classes of couriers. The "internal" couriers worked largely within their own country, acting as links between the various units of the Underground. The "external" couriers regularly passed through the Iron Curtain, carrying information to the West and back or bringing needed supplies to Slovakia. Most of Filip's assignments took him across the Iron Curtain, but he was occasionally asked to perform risky missions within Slovakia, too.

At the beginning, Filip was given easy tasks. His first job was simply to contact an Underground intelligence agent near the Polish border who kept count of the food shipped by the Reds out of Slovakia over a railroad line that passed through the town. Similar reports were received from every border town and were compiled by the Underground into a complete picture of the extent to which the Soviets were robbing Slovakia of its food, while Slovaks went hungry.

Filip's assignments after that grew increasingly difficult and dangerous. On his first trip across the Iron Curtain, Filip was shot in the leg by border guards firing blindly. Weak from the loss of blood, he crawled a mile to a safer place and lay hiding for an entire day. Only because a farmer to whose house he dragged himself was an Underground liaison did Filip escape certain capture and death.

Filip's latest mission began in Prešov. One of the Underground's largest secret radio stations broadcast throughout Eastern Slovakia from a hidden site in the nearby High Tatra mountains. Rudolf Maly, reporter for the Underground, was broadcasting one day, warning the people of the latest moves of the Communists to trap the freedom fighters:

"The State Security Police, in cooperation with the Communist Regional Committees, has completed the training of about 2,000 *agents provocateurs*. They pose as representatives of the Underground, pretending that they have been sent into our country from Underground headquarters in Austria and Germany.

"These *agents provocateurs* will call on you. They will mention the name of a friend or relative of yours who is in the West, for the Communists have compiled detailed lists of these people. These Red agents will know what your friend or relative looks like. They will know his habits, his personal mannerisms. They will say that your relative has asked them to get in touch with you. They will try to get you to talk about the Underground.

"You must be careful at all times. Do not speak to anyone unless you are certain who he is. It is better to say nothing than to say something that might betray the Underground. We know who these agents are. If anyone approaches you, give his name to someone you know and trust. We can investigate, and if he is a Red agent, we can take care of him."

Maly turned to another subject:

10

"In the Danube and Morava River areas, new permits for fishing are now granted only to Communists who sign a written declaration for the Security Police swearing to denounce any person who is seeking to escape. If you plan to try to cross into Austria do not ask for help from these fishermen.

"And now," Maly continued, "I will read the latest list of known spies in the City of Prešov. First is Jozef Vavro, manager of the Stehra printing plant. He is an informer for the Communist Party. Next is . . ."

But as Rudolf Maly spoke, the broadcast began to fade, and finally stopped. Tubes in the transmitting station had burned out. No radio tubes could be purchased in Slovakia without Communist authorization. They would have to be bought in Austria.

Filip Polhora was summoned to Prešov. It was ten days later when he arrived, his first trip to Eastern Slovakia since he had become a courier. He stood bareheaded across the street from the old, rambling house where he was to meet his contact. For a long time he gazed thoughtfully at the structure. It had been built, Filip was sure, well before the Renaissance, for its facade was obviously of Moorish design. An open archway high up in its windowless structure attested to the massive strength of the house. The walls were at least three feet thick.

There it stood, thought Filip, an everyday landmark for generations and generations of Slovaks. In places its stucco coating had fallen away, revealing the sturdy bricks and cobblestones with which the original builder had fashioned it. But it still stood. Not all the wars in Europe's history had destroyed it. Its attackers had been beaten off and were long since reduced to dust in graveyards all over Europe, Asia and Africa. Now, in 1952, the house was still there, symbol of Slovakia's will to be free, or so it seemed to Filip.

Inside the house, Filip was directed to an upstairs room. There, in an unused boudoir, he met Rudolf Maly and a man known as Captain Tilka, the chief of the courier school in which Filip was first trained. Tilka rushed to grip Filip's hand.

11

"It's good to see you again," he said with a smile that quickly faded. Tilka was a slight man, his closely-cropped dark hair tinged with white. His bearing stamped him as a military man and he spoke in a precise, clipped manner.

"The Underground movement here is in great danger, Filip, because our radio station has gone off the air. Already the Reds are spreading rumors that our station was captured, that I am in prison and that Rudolf has been executed. They are claiming that the Underground has been smashed.

"Now we know that the people don't believe any of these things as yet. But doubts may begin to arise if we don't get the radio transmitter back on the air. It is absolutely imperative that we get the truth to the people, or there will be chaos. Nobody will know what to believe."

Tilka explained what had happened and what was needed. He handed Filip a tiny slip of paper, listing the technical specifications of the tubes and other transmitting equipment that would have to be bought in Austria. "You will furnish this list to our people in Vienna," he said, "wait for delivery of the equipment and then return it to us."

Tilka reached into a pocket and removed a metal cartridge, about the size and shape of a medicine capsule. "Filip, this mission is so important that we must take extreme measures to protect the list. Put it inside the capsule."

Filip folded the paper until it was small enough to stuff into the bottom half of the capsule, then screwed on the top. "Is this watertight?" he asked.

"It is," replied Tilka. "Also fireproof. Unfortunately, you are not. The capsule will get to Vienna if you do. I think it will be safe enough if you carry it taped to your navel until you get to the border zone. Then you must carry the capsule rectally and remove it only after you are safely in Austria."

Filip nodded.

"Good," said Tilka. "Now down to business. From this moment on you are George Baltay. You are a machinist in the Slovak Mills in Bratislava. Here is your identity card and your

12

dossier. Read it over and find out what makes you tick, George."

For the next three days, Filip taught himself to think and behave as Baltay. He learned the names of scores of workers in the Slovak Mills, their jobs, what they looked like and how they acted. He could tell anyone who asked him whether Jan Dubny smoked a pipe or cigarettes; he knew how much wine Imrich Breza drank and in which Bratislava cafés; he could describe with facility the exact mechanical operation of each machine in the shop George Baltay worked in. He also learned the family history of the Baltays until it seemed his own family history.

At last Filip felt he was ready and reported back to Captain Tilka. The courier chief immediately went into his favorite routine, pretending to be a Red security trooper who had stopped Filip for questioning. "Your name?" he barked.

Filip looked meekly at his feet. "I am called George Baltay," he mumbled.

"Where are you from?"

"Bratislava, sir."

"Where do you work?"

"I work in the Slovak Mills."

"What do you do there?"

"I am a machinist."

"Do you know a man there named Imrich Dubny?"

Filip looked puzzled. "No sir. I know a Jan Dubny, but no Imrich Dubny."

Tilka went on for fifteen minutes. At last he stopped and permitted himself a thin smile. "Good, Filip. Now your route." He laid a well-worn map of Slovakia on the table and spread it smooth.

Pointing, Tilka said, "The entire border area of Zahorie, where you will cross the Curtain, is swarming with Communist agents."

Filip had no reason to doubt this intelligence. He could, in

13

fact, scarcely recall a time when Zahorie, the low-lying farm-land area along the Morava River, had not been crowded with Red agents, informers, secret police and other hazards. As an Iron Curtain buffer zone, Zahorie was one of the areas in Slovakia from which the population of entire villages had been exiled, its possessions confiscated and the farms turned over to trusted Communists.

After an intensive briefing, Filip departed. He took a train to Bratislava and from there another to Malacky, in Zahorie. It was dark when he reached Malacky and began walking through the fields toward Levary, a village some five miles away. Twice he hid from border patrols until he finally reached his first objective, a farmhouse where he would get up-to-the-minute information on the safest spot to cross the Morava.

At precisely 2 A.M., he knocked softly on the door. Exactly five times. A man answering to the name of Karol Danko, if Captain Tilka were correct, should open the door.

The door opened. Captain Tilka had been wrong.

Standing in the doorway was a young woman, her willowy figure silhouetted in the soft light of a candle on a table behind her. As his eyes became accustomed to the light he could see her hair was the color of October wheat. Her eyes were blue, bright blue. She smiled at Filip and bade him enter.

Panic fought in Filip with the sudden joy he felt the instant he set eyes on her. Repeatedly it had been drummed into his head: do not trust yourself to a woman; the courier is a dedicated man; you have no time for love. Why did he think of love? he wondered. His next thought was to turn and run. It could be a trap. Yet he was unable to move away from the girl.

"You are Mr. Baltay," she said. "Come in. We are expecting you." Her voice was soft and inviting. Casually brushing his hand against his thigh to make sure the knife was in place, Filip walked in behind her.

14

An elderly man entered the room through another door, his hands empty, Filip noted carefully. "George Baltay?" the old man asked.

"Yes."

"I am Karol Danko." A few phrases passed between them and then Danko nodded. "Good. Leonora, fetch us some tea and lace it with rum. And take your time about it. We have business together."

Filip relaxed. Leonora, he thought. Her name meant "light." How apt, Filip reflected, such a lovely thing amid the dark gloom of the Communist buffer zone. Filip turned to Danko. His hair was iron grey and his shoulders slumped forward from years of toil in the fields. His hands were gnarled and his clothes were the nondescript garb of the working farmer. Only his searching eyes hinted that he was something else, a man who lived by his wits, smart enough to occupy a border-zone farm as a trusted Communist while serving as host to couriers of the Underground.

Danko was all business. He described in detail the route Filip would take to the border. "You must understand," he said, "that you must follow my directions precisely if you are to get through. I will accompany you as far as the canal which is between this house and the Morava. Here is a map. Study it carefully and get some rest. We'll start at eight tonight. Now, if you don't mind, I'll go to bed. My daughter will see to your needs. Good night."

Filip shook the outstretched hand warmly. "Good night," he replied, "and thank you. You are most kind."

Leonora returned with the tea. It was so hot it scalded Filip's tongue, and the rum so strong it made his eyes water. But Filip nodded his thanks to Leonora.

"And then," said Filip, "the Communists were marched off into the forest, naked as the day they were born."

Leonora laughed merrily. Filip beamed at her enjoyment of

15

his tale. For hours now, he had been telling her of his experiences and those of the Underground. Something about her made him want to tell of himself. Perhaps it was her air of natural innocence, an attitude that Filip, an urbane sort himself, at first thought was affected but came gradually to realize was not. Though Leonora could not have been more than twenty, she must have met many couriers as the daughter of a buffer-zone Underground contact. Yet she maintained the wide-eyed wonder of seeing things afresh and Filip found it strangely appealing.

Never before had Filip told so much of himself to a woman. His reluctance had disappeared with her encouragement. He found her a marvelous audience, a girl who seemed to find everything he had done brave, noble, enchanting or charming. Filip was entranced at how easily she slipped into his moods as the stories varied.

He found himself eager to tell her of his life, of his childhood, his ambitions and dreams. But somewhere a cock crowed and Filip, startled, realized it was no longer night. "But how boorish of me," he said. "I've kept you up all night. Forgive me, Leonora."

She smiled. "Tonight I need no sleep," she said, looking away from his face.

He arose and took her hand. "Leonora," he said, "I have no right to ask you anything, nor to say this to you, but . . ."

"No, Filip," she interrupted, placing her other hand gently on his lips. Her blue eyes were grave now. "I think I know what you want to say. You are a courier. Your duty is to Slovakia. So is mine." She lowered her eyes, then brought them up to meet his. "Please make no promises. Who knows what will be tomorrow? You will be gone soon, but perhaps, someday . . ."

Filip removed her hand from his lips and kissed it.

Later, they sat on the floor before the hearth, content merely to be together, not speaking. Leonora's father came out of his room, smiled when he saw them and then went out to perform his chores.

Filip and Leonora stared into the fire. "In a way," Filip said, "I'm sorry. God knows I wasn't looking for this. It will be difficult but I have to leave tonight and I don't know when I can return. And what if they catch me? What then?"

"Hush," said Leonora as she stood up. Pretending to be stern, she forced Filip to leave the fireside. "You will have breakfast with us and then you will go to bed. You need all the sleep you can get before you leave." After they had eaten, she sat on the edge of his bed, stroking his black hair, then rubbing the stubble on his cheeks. Filip soon fell asleep. Quietly, Leonora slipped out of the room. She knelt beside her own bed and prayed for the courier who had suddenly entered her life.

A few minutes before eight that night she awakened him. Out of long habit, he sprang up quickly, alert for danger. He saw Leonora and smiled. "I dreamed of you," he whispered.

"I thought so," she said. "You were smiling."

"Is everything ready?"

"Yes." Leonora handed him a Luger and a loaded ammunition clip. Filip examined the weapon thoroughly and nodded, slipping the clip into place. Leonora's father entered the room and beckoned to Filip. "We must leave," he said. "I will wait outside for you."

Filip took Leonora into his arms. "God be with you, my Leonora."

"And, you, Filip Polhora."

He left abruptly. It was the only way to lessen the pain of departing. Outside, Karol Danko led Filip through a vegetable garden shadowed by trees and shrubs, into a rutted lane leading to a forest. Every few minutes they stopped, listening for Communist patrols. The forest floor was swampy and their feet and legs were soon drenched.

At length they reached the canal. The old man poked into a clump of bushes and took out a long pole. "You look athletic," he remarked. "Vault over the canal with this, then hide the

17

pole in the bushes on the other side. God be with you, my son."
Danko shook his hand, then disappeared into the night.

Filip's timetable called for spending five days in Vienna. He explained his mission to the trio that had greeted him. All three, Olga Gazdova, Stefan Zubak and Eugen Olsansky, were exiles from Slovakia. They had fled Communist rule but instead of continuing West to begin a new life, as so many of their countrymen did, they chose to remain in Austria to serve the Underground.

While Zubak, the short, husky member of the trio, sought out the tubes and radio equipment, Filip remained in hiding. He was visited by other Slovak exiles who gave him messages to take back to the Underground, some personal, some official.

Rain beat down heavily and steadily, and the Vienna radio announced that the Morava River was flooding over. His new friends urged him to remain until the waters receded. "You'll never get across the river when it's flooded this bad," Olga warned.

"I have to," Filip replied. "We must get the radio station back on the air. I'll get across the river somehow."

Filip's nerves were taut when he left. He stuffed the radio equipment into a large canvas bag of a type that a workman would normally carry. But the equipment would be a dead giveaway if he were stopped and searched. The return trip called for double the vigilance he had exercised in getting to Vienna.

The journey began well. He took a streetcar to the railroad station, and a train to Drossing, a town near the Slovak border. Despite his anxiety, he maintained a bland, untroubled exterior. That was part of his courier training. Never seem conspicuous. If he traveled on a railway car filled with people on a holiday, Filip would appear gay and carefree. If, as sometimes happened, Filip found himself in a funeral procession, he could weep as copious tears as the bereaved family.

Even in unfamiliar cities, Filip always walked purposefully, and at the same pace as others on the street, for the Communist police were quick to spot anyone who looked uncertain of his surroundings. So it was that Filip strode at a steady pace, neither too quick nor too slow, when he stepped off the train at Drossing. As he walked into the waiting room, a middle-aged man he had never seen before approached him, his hands outstretched and a grin on his face.

"Ah, George. It's good to see you again," the stranger said.

Filip smiled back, as if greeting a long lost friend. He put his bag down and the two embraced, as a Soviet soldier, a member of the Army of Occupation, eyed them suspiciously from a distance.

"Radio," the stranger muttered under his breath.

"Tubes," Filip answered.

As they walked away from the depot, Filip's contact, whose name was Kosik, quietly told him he must exercise special caution. Three couriers had been shot down trying to cross the border in the last week and everywhere along the Slovak side of the Morava, the border patrol forces had been reinforced.

But there was still danger on the Austrian side. Two soldiers were now following Filip and Kosik out of the depot. The rain and the darkness were a help, however. Filip and Kosik walked unconcernedly for a few blocks until the latter poked Filip and whispered "Now!"

The two vaulted a low wall, zigzagged through gardens and back streets until they were certain they had shaken their pursuers. Out of breath and exhausted from running, they hid for several hours in an old barn until they were rested. There was no sign of the police when they emerged. But the incident, Filip was certain, would be reported and prod the border patrol on the Slovak side to redouble their alert.

At the water's edge, Filip saw a scene of utter desolation. The muddy water raced between tree trunks a quarter mile inland from what was normally the riverbank. Kosik pulled out a flat rubber object, folded over several times, from the pack on his back. He raised it above his head as he and Filip waded through the current beyond the trees to the river itself. Kosik tugged at the rubber until a hissing sound came from it. The hissing seemed so loud that Filip looked around nervously, expecting a shot to be fired at them. But no challenge came, and soon the rubber boat was inflated.

Filip gingerly stowed the radio equipment aboard, then he and Kosik hopped in. The two men paddled for their lives. Ordinarily, they would have paddled slowly with their hands so as not to betray their presence by any noise. But the raging, black waters drowned out the sound of their paddles pulling through the churning river. The swirling current sent them dizzily downstream. Tree trunks came at them out of the darkness and whirlpools tore at their fragile craft. In a matter of minutes they had lost all sense of direction and any course they tried to steer the boat in was sheer guesswork. The only consolation, Filip thought, was that the turbulent currents and the blackness of the night should help them escape detection.

Kosik's paddle bumped against something hard and suddenly the rubber craft was hurled onto the shore. The two quickly leaped out, grabbed the radio equipment and deflated the craft.

"Are we in Slovakia or Austria?" Filip whispered

Kosik shivered. "I don't know."

They started forward, crouched against the rain. The underbrush tore at their clothing and the torrential downpour swept the landscape blind ahead of them. After what seemed to Filip hours of aimless wandering, Kosik threw out his arm in a silent signal to Filip. Both men dropped flat. Peering into the darkness, Filip made out the form of a border guard.

"Halt!" the guard shouted. "Hands up."

So, Filip thought, we are in Slovakia.

As the guard advanced, Filip staggered to his feet, shouting "Hello, hello, hello. Do you have any wine with you?" He put on a supercilious grin, hoping it was properly alcoholic.

The guard, astonished by what seemed like a pair of drunks

wandering around in the rain in the middle of the night, lowered the sights of his submachine gun. He was careful to keep his distance as he looked first at Kosik, then at Filip, unsure of just what to do.

Filip began a crazy dance step, whirling madly and singing gaily. Kosik followed Filip's lead, but the uneven footing proved too much for him. He fell down in a heap.

Muttering in disgust the border guard started toward Kosik. He turned his back on Filip for an instant. It was the last mistake he ever made.

Filip drew his knife and plunged it expertly into the man's back. He fell on his gun, his mouth trying unsuccessfully to produce a sound.

Filip wiped the blood from his knife on the guard's green tunic and carefully sheathed it. "I think," he told Kosik, "we had better hurry. He may have a friend nearby. They often work in pairs."

Kosik nodded. He did not trust his voice.

Kosik had spotted a landmark. "We are a long way downstream from Karol Danko's house," he told Filip. "We're near the village where my brother lives. You'd better go to him."

Damn, thought Filip. He had been looking forward to seeing Leonora again if only for a few hours. And he was barely inside the Iron Curtain. There was still an uncomfortably long way to go before the Underground radio could resume operation.

Kosik scribbled his brother's name and address on a piece of paper. He added a terse note asking the brother to take Filip in until it was safe for him to resume his journey. Kosik took Filip's Slovak workclothes out of his knapsack. The latter changed out of the suit he had worn in Austria, which was then buried. "I must return to Austria now," Kosik said. "Good luck, Baltay."

Filip smiled thinly. He had forgotten for a moment that he was George Baltay, machinist from the Slovak Mills, Bratislava, even to other members of the Underground. He waved farewell to Kosik and started out for the village where Kosik's brother lived.

It was raining as hard as ever. Filip was already wet through his new attire. He was tired from lack of sleep and his innards growled for food. At that moment he thought he would be glad to trade in George Baltay's identification card for a cigarette.

On the outskirts of the village, Filip paused when he saw the steeple of the church. More than likely, he reflected, the Reds had converted it into a storehouse for grain, or ammunition. It was also a good bet that the Reds had used the church for their barbaric orgies. They took particular pleasure in defiling churches.

By the time he found the house where Kosik's brother lived the rain had stopped and he was feeling a bit better. He knocked on the door, but there was no answer. The sound of footsteps on the street came closer. It might be a Red patrol, Filip thought. He tried the handle and it turned. Filip entered quietly and closed the door behind him.

He struck a match in the dark room. A young man, rubbing his eyes and clad in pajamas, came into the room. He looked at Filip, fear jarring his eyes open. "Who the hell are you?" he asked indignantly when he saw that Filip did not wear the uniform of the SNB, the dreaded Security Police. Filip handed him the note from Kosik.

Kosik's brother lighted a lamp and read the note. His hands were unsteady. His face paled and he began to scream: "Police! Police!"

Drawing out his Luger, Filip pressed the front of the barrel against Kosik's Adam's apple. Biting out the words, he warned, "If you don't quiet down I will kill you."

Kosik kept on shouting. It was more than ordinary fear, it seemed to Filip. Kosik was close to hysteria. Something must have happened in the village, Filip thought. He smashed the pistol across Kosik's chin and Kosik toppled to the floor.

Filip searched the room and found a package of cigarettes and a box of matches. Gratefully, he lit one with a hand that trembled slightly and pocketed the rest. After a few puffs, he filled a pitcher with water from the sink and sloshed it across Kosik's face.

Kosik's eyes opened. Filip stood over him with the Luger drawn. "Are you going to scream any more?"

Kosik shook his head.

"All right," said Filip, "you can get up." As Kosik arose, Filip asked, "What's the matter with you? Your brother told me you were reliable. Have you turned Communist all of a sudden?"

Kosik's eyes filled again with fear. "No," he grumbled, "but you'll have to get out of here. They killed a courier in the village tonight. They think he had a companion. The police are hunting for him everywhere. For God's sake, get out of here before they find you and kill me." He began to sob.

In disgust, Filip walked out the back door of Kosik's house. He scurried through the garden into a patch of woods and burrowed behind a large bush. Three times Communist police patrols passed the tiny wooded area, only a few feet from Filip's hiding place. Filip covered the bag with his left hand and held the Luger, with the safety off, in his right, but the police passed by each time without finding him. The rain started up again and fell the rest of the night.

Filip awoke with a start. It was dangerous to sleep, particularly while holding a loaded automatic, but fatigue can sometimes be stronger than resolution. Dawn, thankfully, had come. And the rain had stopped.

A murmuring noise from the direction of the village square caught Filip's ear. He double-checked the Luger and prepared for the worst. Then he relaxed. The sounds were made by a band of workers, trudging along the road toward the railroad depot. Within moments, Filip had slithered his way into their ranks. Dirty, unshaven, his clothing rumpled, Filip blended into the crowd of workmen. His bag, containing the precious radio parts, could easily pass for a workman's tool bag.

There were police at the station but they did not stop Filip.

He bought a ticket to Bratislava and boarded the train with the others. Entering a compartment where a window seat was vacant next to a gypsy woman, he sat down, making sure to fall on the edge of her voluminous skirt that protruded onto his seat. She pulled her skirt loose and rearranged the folds, as Filip had hoped. As she spread out the skirt, it fell onto Filip's lap and completely covered the bag, which he had wedged between them.

Filip dozed fitfully most of the way to Bratislava. He handed his ticket to the gypsy and asked her to give it to the conductor. When the conductor collected the tickets, he presumed the pair was traveling together. He paid no attention to the dirty, rain-soaked man sleeping in the corner.

The train rattled onward, jerking Filip awake every time it stopped. At last it slowed down for the approach to Bratislava, and Filip came fully awake. He stretched voluptuously, looking forward to a few hours rest before continuing his journey.

He reached for the bag. But it was gone. So was the gypsy woman.

Filip almost gave way to panic. To come this far, only to fail. He cursed himself for forgetting the old saying: "Shake hands with a gypsy, then count your fingers."

Outwardly, however, Filip displayed no emotion. There were others in the compartment. He arose slowly and left the compartment casually. In the corridor, he swiftly looked both ways. Toward the front, he caught sight of a flashing striped skirt, disappearing into the next car. Moving as quickly as he could without seeming to race, he caught up with the gypsy halfway through the car. She was still clutching the bag, walking unconcernedly as if the bag were her own, and unaware that Filip was behind her.

Moving only inches away, Filip shoved the nose of the Luger into the base of her skull and reached for the bag with his free hand. "If you make any noise," he said in a barely audible whisper, "I will kill you."

She relinquished the bag, but started to raise her voice.

24

"Shut up!" Filip ordered. He moved the Luger to the small of her back and shoved her down the corridor. Fortunately, the first compartment he tried was empty and he pushed the gypsy woman into it.

The train was noticeably slowing down as it threaded its way into the Bratislava station. Filip slammed the door behind him, reached over and pulled down the shade, while keeping the pistol trained on the woman.

He had to decide quickly. Was she just a common thief, or did she mean real trouble? He opened the bag and rummaged through it quickly. Everything seemed in order. The woman obviously had not had the time to go through the bag.

Out of the corner of his eye, Filip saw a swift movement. The gypsy had a knife in her hand and lunged toward Filip, aiming the point for his stomach. Filip sidestepped, grasping her arm as the knife whisked past his side.

The train stopped with a jolt and Filip and the gypsy were thrown to the floor. Filip landed on top, dropped the bag and wrested the knife from her hand. She began to scream, "Police! Police!"

Filip's choice had been made for him. Reluctantly, he plunged the knife into her chest and the screaming stopped with a gurgle. He wiped the blade clean on her skirt, pocketed the knife, gathered up the bag and walked nonchalantly into the corridor, closing the door behind him.

Two workmen were nearby, looking at him quizzically. Had they heard the scream? Filip grinned sheepishly. "She seemed friendly at first," he said with a shrug of the shoulders, "but I guess one must not get too fresh too soon even when they seem to encourage you." The workmen chuckled along with Filip as they joined the crowd leaving the train.

Steam hissed from the underside of the railroad cars as Filip trudged along the platform toward the depot. As it cleared, Filip saw that an unusual number of police were studying the passengers as they filed along the ramp.

Were they looking for him, or someone else? Fearing the

25

worst, Filip thought fast. The only way out was to use diversionary tactics. To his right and a few paces ahead, Filip spotted a well-dressed man, wide of girth and laden with luggage and parcels. The next time a cloud of steam temporarily enveloped Filip and his fellow passengers, he quickly came up beside the struggling fat man. As if by accident Filip jostled his victim. His right foot darted out between the obese man's legs.

With an enormous clatter, the unsuspecting victim fell to the ground, his luggage and packages scattering every whichway. The noise quickly drew a crowd. Immediately, the police came running to see what had happened and to restore order. Filip, like the other passengers, crowded around, ostensibly for a look at the accident. "What happened?" he asked one of the policemen.

Police in many ways are pretty much the same everywhere, even behind the Iron Curtain. The one Filip addressed could not be bothered with answering bystanders' questions. "Keep moving." He shouted. "Stand back!"

Filip shrugged philosophically and followed orders. He kept moving, right out of the Bratislava depot, while the police busied themselves with the unfortunate fat man.

At his hideout in Bratislava, Filip was able to clean up and rest till evening. His sleep was a troubled one, though. He dreamed of Leonora. It was a nightmare of border police, of stabbing and of pistol-whipping, with Leonora always in the background, watching on in horror as Filip miraculously came through the violence unscathed. Filip awoke an hour before he needed to, and stared at the ceiling, forcing himself to adjust to the near sanity of reality.

At last he struggled upright and lit a cigarette, staring dully out the window at the brick wall facing it. His underground contact at the hideout, Andrej Vrba, came into the room with a tray of food and snapped on the light. "Eat well, Filip. God knows how long before you'll have another chance."

Filip nodded dumbly and forced himself to eat. Surprisingly

the food tasted good. He had been sure anything he ate would taste of ashes.

"There has been a slight change of plans," Andrej told him.

"Oh," Filip responded between mouthfuls of stew.

Andrej smiled mischievously. "It seems the depot of Bratislava is hardly the safest place for you to begin another journey."

"So?" Filip tried to look surprised but he was not at all sure he had carried it off.

"Yes," said Andrej. "Somebody killed a Communist agent posing as a gypsy on the very train you came in on."

Thank God, thought Filip, the killing had not been in vain. "Is that right?" said Filip, taking another bite of meat.

"And," Andrej went on, "somebody tripped up a visiting Communist functionary from Prague, right alongside the same train. The poor commissar is in the hospital with contusions and abrasions and a fractured dignity."

Filip barely managed to swallow the bite he had been chewing on. "You don't say."

Andrej grinned at him. "You don't talk much, do you, Filip?"

Filip smiled innocently. "Do you think I should?"

When Andrej stopped laughing, he told Filip he was to take a taxi to the next station beyond Bratislava. From there he was to board the train that went through the Low Tatra mountains to Košice, just twenty-five miles south of Prešov.

Filip patted the bag with the radio equipment. "Come along, little bag," he said. "We still have some traveling to do." Andrej shook his head in mock dismay.

In the taxi, driven by an Underground member, Filip sat back at ease. He had been furnished with a fresh suit, he had shaved and washed, and felt like a new man. At the tiny railway station beyond Bratislava, he bought his ticket for Košice, and boarded the train without incident.

Filip felt fairly safe on the train. After all, his papers as

George Baltay were in order. Now he had a new letter from the Communist boss of the Slovak Mills, stating that he was on a business mission for the mills to Košice. Furthermore, he wore a Communist emblem in his lapel and he had picked up a copy of the local Communist newspaper to read as he traveled. Several of his fellow passengers, noticing the paper, eyed him with ill-concealed hatred.

Once inside the Košice depot, however, the illusion of safety vanished. The State Security Police were methodically checking all luggage and carefully scrutinizing the identity cards of all the passengers. The Communist intelligence forces, it occurred to Filip, must have expected some effort would be made to revive the Underground's secret radio, figured out the trouble was mechanical and planted police at all the main railroad depots near Prešov.

Filip nevertheless queued up meekly with the rest of the passengers as they filed past the checkpoint. To do otherwise, of course, would have been even more dangerous. Most of the passengers, Filip noticed, were on edge. Many of them, perhaps, feared they would be discovered in the petty smuggling of food, medicine and money that goes on everywhere behind the Iron Curtain. Almost to a man, Filip discerned, they had something to hide and the idea of having the police look through their effects made them all nervous. Filip felt sure they would panic in a moment if something went wrong.

Suddenly Filip had the answer. A few feet before the portable table the police had set up for their inspections was a newsstand piled high with papers. From his pocket, Filip pulled out a package of cigarettes and a wooden matchbox. He lit his cigarette, dropping the flaming match into the matchbox and lightly tossed the box onto a stack of newspapers.

As a tiny column of flame leaped up, Filip grabbed the arm of the woman on line in front of him. Quietly, but with alarm in his voice, he said, "Look!" and pointed at the fire.

Filip had figured her reaction properly. She screamed

"Fire!" and pandemonium descended on the depot. Passengers, station agents and police began running in every direction as the flames, now shooting higher, licked sharply at the newsstand.

It was an isolated fire, endangering no one, but the tensions built up among the passengers by the long wait and the police scrutiny exploded at the sight of the flames. The police were no longer in control. It was a case of every man for himself. Dozens of people were trampled as the crowd fled blindly for the exits.

Filip managed to be among the first to reach the street. He walked casually away from the station.

Seven blocks from the depot, he spotted an inconspicuous black sedan parked midway in the street. Two men sat in the front seat. Filip walked toward the car and when he drew abreast of it he stopped and switched the bag, for no apparent reason, from his left to his right hand.

The driver leaned out the window and murmured a single word: "Radio."

Filip responded: "Tubes."

Without another word, he climbed into the rear seat and the car slid smoothly away into the night.

He was driven to Sabinov, north of Prešov, in the Carpathian mountains. There he said farewell to the Underground driver and his cohort. A short walk brought him into the woods.

Following a trail marked out so that no one who did not know what to look for would even have realized the route was there, Filip came, after several miles, to a divergence in the path, marked by a mammoth outcropping of rock. There he sat down, wearily, awaiting his next contact.

For the first time in what seemed years, he had time to think of Leonora, and the memory assuaged the pain and tension he had gone through. Filip was about to light a cigarette when a rifle barrel appeared over the top of the rock. Warily he stood up and raised his hands slowly over his head.

A voice behind him said: "Radio."

Filip smiled. "Tubes."

At the guerilla camp where the clandestine radio station was then located, there was great rejoicing when Filip arrived with the tubes and other equipment. Rudolf Maly, the chief broadcaster, was beside himself with joy. Filip was given a hero's welcome, but as soon as he could decently quit the festivities, he did so, and dropped exhausted onto a bunk the guerillas had provided for him. He fell asleep immediately, and if he dreamed he did not remember when he awoke.

All that day, the guerillas stuck close to their mountainside cave, preparing to strike camp at night. They had already been at the site for four days waiting for Filip, and their leader, whose name was Stevko Novak, reasoned that was long enough to remain in any one place with Red patrols constantly on the move in the mountains, looking for Resistance fighters. The wisdom of Novak's decision became apparent when runners came in late that afternoon with word a Communist patrol was headed toward the hideout.

Novak grinned. The short, powerfully built guerilla turned toward Filip, with a crafty look in his eyes. "Let us prepare a fitting reception for them."

The guerillas set about their tasks expertly and with a minimum of noise. By the time the Communist patrol had penetrated the valley below their cave, Novak had a roaring fire going just outside the entrance. It was in plain view of the Communist troops.

On either side of the cave the guerillas had deployed themselves, at a safe distance away, hiding in the trees. Signs of habitation were left strewn about the cave entrance, inviting the Communist patrol to take a look inside.

From behind a rock overlooking the cave mouth, Filip watched with Novak as the Red patrol spotted the fire and cautiously advanced toward the cave, their rifles drawn and ready to shoot.

Novak stifled a laugh as the Red leader warily peered into the cave. Then he motioned his men to follow him inside.

A puff of orange flame shot out of the cave entrance, then soared high into the air. A thick cloud of black smoke rolled skyward. Filip squinted as the shockwave reached them. "Mines?" he asked.

Novak nodded, grinning. "Mines. The whole place was booby trapped. I can't understand why they never learn, but I enjoy it all the same."

Early the next morning, Novak's small guerilla band had reached their new camp site. It was an excellent location for broadcasting. Rudolf Maly, footsore and not used to the hit-and-run tactics of guerilla life, grumbled at the long march and complained his feet would never be the same.

Filip looked at him levelly. "Your feet do not matter, Rudolf Maly. It is your voice that counts. Is it all right?"

Maly grasped Filip's hand and shook it. "You are right Filip. Nothing could be less important to Slovakia than my aching feet. And my voice, as you hear, is well enough to complain. But if you don't mind, I will make my broadcast sitting down. And with my shoes off."

Filip smiled. "I will join you," he said, and promptly sat down and took off his own shoes as Maly checked out the radio equipment.

All over Eastern Slovakia that day, there were smiles on the faces of the partisans of freedom and scowls on the faces of Communist officials. Rudolf Maly was back on the air, which proved that the Underground was still in business. Maly had not been captured, nor was the Underground crushed, as the Communists would have had the people believe.

2. The Guerilla

IT WAS THE cruelty of the conquering Soviet troops that also started Jan Labuda on the path to guerilla leadership. Labuda was a peasant who owned a prosperous twenty-acre farm in the village of Solna Bana, located in a pleasant valley of the Vihorlat Mountains in Eastern Slovakia. He, his wife Zuzka, and their daughter Anicka, lived in a white-washed farmhouse that had been in the family for generations. In the fall of 1944, Anicka was sixteen, and her mother had stored away the soft pillows and the downy mattresses and quilts that would be part of her dowry on her wedding day, which would not be far off.

Jan Labuda was in his fortieth year, a sturdy man, with powerful peasant's hands and a slow peasant's walk and movement. His shoulders were wide and his rib cage was enormous. His black hair was thick, coarse and flecked with grey. The crops had been good and his barn was well-stocked for the winter. He was as content as a man could be under the Nazi occupation.

Yet the year was one of confusion and unrest. Many men had already gone into the mountains to fight in the first, ill-organized partisan resistance to the Nazis. There were reports that the Red Army was driving at the gates of the Carpathian Mountains, that soon they would storm through the passes and bring liberation to Slovakia and the entire Danube Valley.

In the early fall, the Nazis had drafted men, women, even children, into forced labor groups to construct trenches and other fortifications against the Soviets. Then, on a golden October day, Nazi officials came to Jan Labuda's village. They ordered him, his wife and daughter, and his neighbors to leave their homes. The village was to be destroyed so that nothing would be left in the path of the Soviets.

The villagers could take with them only a few belongings. With a cart, a couple of horses, a cow or two and some pigs, Labuda joined his neighbors in the trek away from the farms they had worked all their lives. As they looked back, above the dust of the road, they could see everything burning behind them—homes, farms, crops, even the pillows and quilts of Anicka's dowry.

Jan and his family found refuge in his mother-in-law's home, some twenty-five miles further west. He got a job as a wood-cutter in the hills; and as winter came and the snow, gathering first on the mountain crests, crept slowly into the valley, Jan went sometimes of an evening to the inn.

Men spoke in whispers of the progress of the Red Army. It was storming the Carpathian passes, forcing the Nazis back. Partisans were helping the rout of the Germans by cutting rail lines, wrecking bridges, destroying tunnels. Now and then a weather-beaten man might drop into the inn, where he would be strangely silent, and when he left the whisper was that he was one of the "mountain lads." Liberation, it was said, was near at hand. Labuda's old friend, the displaced mayor of Solna Bana, told him:

"Do not worry, Jan. You will see. The Soviets will come, and they will make the Nazi swine pay for everything they have done. The Soviets are our protectors, our big brothers."

It was heartening talk and Labuda and the others believed it because they wanted to believe it. They were ready to welcome the Red Armies, to meet them indeed as friends and brothers.

The morning of Christmas Eve that year was one of almost unbearable excitement. There was gunfire in the distance. Villagers greeted each other with broad smiles. "They will be here tonight, or surely tomorrow," the word went around. "This will be a Christmas we will never forget."

Jan left early for his work in the forest, planning to come home early to greet the liberators. His wife Zuzka and his mother-in-law were busy making heaping piles of *pupacky*, the poppy-seed cakes, and the dried mushroom soup that were a part of their Christmas Eve tradition.

Zuzka's eyes were shining and she cried "Ah, we will show them that we Slovaks know how to welcome our brothers! Oh, Jan, what a Christmas this will be." Her words were repeated in every cottage in the village as the reception for the Red Army was prepared.

While Jan worked in the hills, the sound of gunfire rolled closer. In late afternoon, he cut a little Christmas tree, and started home. It was snowing and dusk was falling as he came near the village. In the distance he could see figures moving quickly in the street and he knew they must be Red soldiers. He walked faster. But then, as he neared his mother-in-law's house, he heard screams. He began to run.

The door of the cottage was open. His mother-in-law lay on the floor. Her body was beaten and it lay still. One Red soldier was holding Labuda's wife. She had been beaten so that her face was no longer recognizable. A second soldier was raping her. In a corner, Anicka was fighting off a third soldier with a piece of firewood. Her skirt was ripped and the lace on her blouse was shredded.

With a roar, Labuda swung his axe. He crushed the skulls of two of the Reds. The third ran out of the house. Jan turned toward his wife, but in that moment, as he held her, she died. There was no time to mourn, no time to do anything but cover the faces of the dead women, take Anicka's arm, and run with her into the snow and the darkness before the soldier who had escaped could return with other "liberators."

And so began Jan Labuda's passion, a passion that burned at the start in a fierce, flaming hatred; and later hardened into a cold, calm determination to do anything he could to destroy the Communists.

34

At first, as Jan and his daughter tramped through the hills that terrible Christmas, his mind was numbed and dazed. They found shelter somehow, he could not remember how or where, and slowly as his mind cleared, the need for personal revenge filled it.

He did not dare to go back to the village even for the funerals, if there were funerals. But gradually, after he found a cave for himself and Anicka in the hills, he began to plan his revenge. His weapons were his axe, his knife and his hatred. After a week, he slipped into the village at night. The Red Army, and a few pro-Communists in the village, were holding a New Year's Eve "liberation" party. Labuda waited in the shadows until the party was at its height, until drunken Red soldiers began to reel through the streets. He ambushed them in the shadows, one by one, perhaps a dozen in all, and slit their throats.

There were other daring, lone-wolf acts of revenge in the weeks that followed, acts that made Labuda a local hero. It was his passion that kept him and his daughter alive that first dreadful winter of 1945. Many years later he told one of my couriers what had then gone through his mind. It was a moonlit night, and Labuda and the courier sat together on a moss-covered log in the mountains. The hills fell away in serried rows, soft and misty. Labuda puffed slowly at his pipe, the coals glowing in the silver dark.

"At first I could not sleep at night," he said. "The things that I saw in that cottage on Christmas Eve would not let me. I tried to force them out of my mind. But the day came when I could think of them, when I wanted to think of them. I wanted never to forget, because if I did I might forget that we must always fight the Communists until we destroy them.

"Was I afraid at first? I suppose so. But after a while, I was afraid of only one thing—that I might not live long enough to see them crushed. Crushed like this." Labuda knocked the coals from his pipe and ground them under his foot. "But God has been good to me. He has let me live."

That first winter Labuda and Anicka almost died from the cold and hunger, when they hardly dared light the smallest fire for fear that the Reds would see it; when there was seldom enough to eat, enough clothes to wear, enough covers to warm them at night.

That winter, a guerilla leader was born. Other outlawed, homeless men went into the mountains of Slovakia to meet him and to accept him as their leader. He did not ask to be a leader. Nor did the men put their choice to a vote. They gravitated to Labuda without conscious thought, for the stolid peasant was developing a genius for the irregular guerilla warfare of forests and mountains. Knowledge of the mountains, their trails and gorges, their caves and hiding places, had always been his. Deeper than that was his instinct for the tactics and strategy of this strange shadowy warfare.

Labuda learned how to rally men for a heavy blow against the enemy, and to direct their evaporation before an enemy counter-blow could be assembled. He knew that his force had to be elastic. Its nucleus, its permanent hard core, was limited to a handful of men who stayed with him in the forests, who served as patrols and as liaison with the surrounding villages. Red planes from Prešov and Košice hunted them, flying close to the treetops, but there was no great concentration of men to betray their position.

Labuda's reserve strength lay in the peaceful peasants of the area, men who worked in the fields or villages during the day, who led their cows into the sheds at night, ate dinner with their families and then slipped out in the darkness to join Labuda in some daring raid. The people loved Labuda; more than one wife gave her husband an extra parcel of bacon or bread when he went to join Labuda on a night raid, so that the "mountain lads" might not go hungry.

Never for an instant did Labuda let his men relax their watchfulness. The Soviets parachuted Red partisans into the mountains to fight them. Dogs tracked them down. Micro-phones were hidden in trees and caves where the Reds suspected the guerillas might meet. When Red patrols came too near the camp, they were ambushed and slain with knives. If Labuda wanted the location of his camp kept secret, his band would remove the bodies to a mountainside, ten, twenty, even thirty miles away. Here the guerillas would make discernible tracks away from the new site, but in a different direction from that of their real camp. Later they would double back, leaving the bodies to be found by the Communists.

The natural hazards were as great. The regular soldier on the battlefield has trained medical corpsmen, ambulances and doctors to help him when he is wounded. The guerilla seldom does. If he is lucky, and his companions will carry him away, he can look forward to a muddy hole in the ground, in the heat of summer or the cold of winter, with only the crudest of first aid.

Labuda's band had no organized commissary or kitchens, no regular supply of food. Sometimes they raided Communist stores, and then ate well. At other times, the guerillas ate no more than four or five times a week. Occasionally they found deer or small game. But in most places they could not shoot it, for the noise might have betrayed them to Red patrols. So they learned to trap the wild animals instead.

Labuda discovered how to take what he and the people needed from the Communists. One of the earliest of his exploits was the salt raid. The year 1945 had been a hard one. Crops had been destroyed in the fighting between Nazis and Soviets in Eastern Slovakia and hunger stalked many villages. Worst of all, there was no salt for preserving meat. Here and there UNRRA had started its operations, but the Communists took control of the distribution of UNRRA's food. They set high prices, demanding chickens, eggs and other produce for soap, sugar, textiles and salt. Only the few who had embraced communism could afford UNRRA goods in satisfactory quantity.

Where could the people get the things they needed? Labuda had the answer—from the Soviets. Through his scouts he learned that a Red Army truck convoy, loaded with food and salt, would pass through the Dargov Mountains from Secovce to Košice in the late spring.

Labuda and his men met that convoy. They felled trees to block its path over a narrow curved section of the forest road cut through the low hills. When the trucks stopped, guerillas swung out of trees, leaped from behind the hills and disarmed the Red soldiers before they knew what was happening. The supplies from the trucks were spirited away into the mountains and later distributed to the villagers at secret places in the woods.

The raid brought Red police and troops swarming into the region. But there was no trace of Labuda or his men. They had vanished. And while the Reds combed the mountains, Labuda added a personal touch that endeared him to his followers. He drove a peasant's cart down a dusty road toward Košice, with false papers to show that he was Jan Sobej, from the village of Slavkov, on his way to the Košice fair with a load of pots to sell. He showed his papers to Red policemen who stopped him on the road. He chatted with them. He was indignant at the news of the salt raid.

"Those devils of the mountains!" he shouted. "It is time they were taught a lesson. To think they would do that to the good Communists who protect us. But they will learn. Mark my word, you will live to see them all strung from the trees."

The police nodded, and waved Labuda on.

As the months and years passed, Labuda began gradually to realize that his task was far greater than the mere harassment of the Communists in a small section of Slovakia. This peasant whose horizon had once been confined to the mountains that circled his farm slowly began to grasp the vision of the fight on a national, even an international scale. He met other guerilla groups that were operating in Slovakia, and step by step the diverse groups formed a coalition, loose at first, but ever tightening. The first links were forged with guerilla organizations in Poland, Hungary and the Ukraine.

38

By the late 1940s the Underground was sure of itself. Its general staff decided the time had come for the greatest test of all: a major, full-dress operation against the Red Army. Jan Labuda was selected to conduct it. The idea was brought to Labuda by Jozef Maryan, a leader of the Underground's central organization. Maryan was a six-footer, a striking figure in his early thirties with tossing black hair and a classic Roman nose.

"Jan," he said, "we want to make a full-scale trial of strength. We want to prove that we can meet the Red Army head-on, that we can seize towns and hold them for a day, perhaps for two or three days. We want to throw the Reds off balance. And we want to show not only the Reds, but the outside world what we could do if a war should come. Do you have any suggestions?"

Labuda didn't hesitate for a moment. "Yes, I have. Let me read you a bulletin that came in a few days ago. It says: 'Two hundred guerillas struck at the rail communication system at Humenne in Zemplin District. Soviet trains were wrecked, rails were torn up and the guerillas escaped before the surprised Red troops could rally. Soviet authorities have made violent protests that local security police failed to provide protection.' "

"That's marvelous, Jan," Maryan commented, "but we have in mind something that would be even bigger than that."

"I know," Labuda answered. "I'm leading up to something. That was a good raid. But there is another bulletin here that may give you the same thought I have."

He read the second bulletin: " 'On the heels of the raid at Humenne, SNB forces and reinforced Soviet NKVD agents carried out the cruelest retribution. At Humenne High School, the Communists arrested sixty students on the charge, patently false, that they had blown up the train. The students were taken to jail at Košice, where they were tortured in an effort to make them confess they were paid by American agents. Several were beaten about the head with iron bars. As a result, four are blind.' "

39

"And what is your idea?" asked Maryan, his face white with anger.

"I plan to teach the Reds a lesson," Labuda said. "I plan to take revenge for the abuse of those school boys. You can have your demonstration, Jozef. We'll organize a raid such as the Reds have never seen!"

The two men planned together. The raid was to utilize the guerillas' strength to the fullest. Couriers brought news of the exact disposition of Red forces in the Humenne-Košice area. The plans were submitted to the general staff of the Underground. Guerilla bands from all over Eastern Slovakia were invited to join. Couriers were sent to the Ukrainians across the Carpathian Mountains, asking their participation.

Early on the morning of March 13 the battle was to begin. The men assembled at 3 A.M. A green rocket burst over the mountain, the signal that the Ukrainians were in position. A trumpet sounded and the guerillas plunged down the rugged slope.

For three days the guerillas rolled on through Zemplin District, smashing the Reds in their path, killing, burning, destroying every Communist life and belonging they could. The savageness of the raid set loose the bottled up anger and frustration, yes, even the cruelty, of the peasants and workers who had been stamped down by the Communist boot. In one village a woman whose husband had been hanged by the Communists poured oil on the Red headquarters, set it afire—and danced a mad dance in the shadows cast by the flickering flames.

But the guerillas brought more than violence and bloodshed to Zemplin. With them came priests who had escaped the first Soviet attempt to shut down the churches of Eastern Slovakia. There were men such as Father Theodore, a Catholic of the Greek Rite. He was dressed like the guerillas as he came down the mountain, but his black priestly robe was in a bag he carried over his shoulder. When the first village was taken by the guerillas, he opened the church that had been shut by the Communists and donned his robes. He administered the sacraments to scores of villagers who had waited for them for months. He performed marriages, baptized babies and heard the confessions of their parents.

On the second day of the assault, as the developing battle showed clearly that Humenne and Secovce were the targets of the guerillas, all Red forces in the area were mobilized. Eighteen Red tanks joined the fight. But nothing could stop the fury of the Slovaks and Ukrainians.

On the third day, Labuda passed through the rebuilt village of Solna Bana, where his family had lived for generations. That day the guerillas stormed their final objectives. Food, military stores and other supplies were taken. Rails were ripped up, telephone wires cut, the towns and cities were turned into chaos and Red Army installations razed.

Then, and only then, Labuda gave the order to withdraw. They had achieved their purpose. The students were avenged; the guerillas had captured supplies that would last for months; they had proved they could meet Red Army troops in open battle and smash them; and they had given new proof that guerillas from more than one country could work in complete harmony.

There was one final Labuda touch. A Red column, marching back toward Humenne as the guerillas withdrew, saw a horse and driverless cart speeding along the road. The Communist troops stopped the cart and one Red pulled at the ropes that held the cart's canvas cover, perhaps to see what loot might be found. The first tug at the rope set off the cart's booby-trap charge of explosives, and many of the Red soldiers were killed.

Of all the deeds of violence he had performed the exploit that engraved Labuda's name on the consciousness of his countrymen was one in which few shots were fired and no blood was spilled. It took place during Indian summer, when the sun is soft and warm and the nights cool, when there is a haze over the mountains and long threads of clouds drift slowly through the lazy air. The valleys were rich with the scent of plum marmalade housewives make in ovens in the orchards. In Slovakia it is often said that October, not June, is the month of romance.

A campfire blazed brightly, casting flickering shadows against the darkened entrance to a natural cave in the side of a mountain. Great casks of water stood near the fire, ready to douse the flames quickly at the first hint of enemy reconnaissance. At the crest of the mountain above the cave's entrance, sentries mounted machine guns. Any Red patrol attempting a frontal assault on Labuda's hideout would be cut to ribbons— the terrain made a flank attack next to impossible. Inside the cave Labuda had stored food, supplies and ammunition enough to withstand a siege of several weeks.

At a table near the fire, Labuda sat poring over a map. The man sitting next to him was short, wiry Leon Opalov, one of the leaders of the UPA, the Underground army of the Ukraine.

With an enigmatic smile on his face, Labuda called Martin Hatala, his young chief lieutenant, to his side. "Martin, we are going to undertake a joint operation with our Ukrainian friends. As a matter of fact, we are going to hit the Communists where it hurts most—right in their dignity." Labuda roared with laughter.

Hatala found himself laughing, though he did not yet know what the plan entailed. Opalov contented himself with a wry grin.

Labuda motioned to the map. "Here, Martin. Here's where we are. There is Javorina, and over there Tatranska Lomnica. Those will be our targets."

"Javorina? Tatranska Lomnica?" Hatala's face wore a puzzled frown. "Those are resorts. There's nothing of value there."

"No?" said Labuda. "I think we will find much of value. The fattest commissars and Red Army officers. Opalov tells me the UPA knows of at least a dozen Russian officials vacationing at the Grand Hotel in Tatranska Lomnica and the wooden castle at Javorina. He understands our old friend Bolnikov of the MVD is at Javorina."

"Ah, that's more like it," Hatala beamed. "Disposing of Bolnikov and his kind is the sort of job I like."

"Who said anything about disposing of them? No, my bloodthirsty young friend, we are not out to kill this time, we are out to make them look silly."

Labuda went on: "Now here is the plan. The UPA will cut off Tatranska Lomnica from all communication, except from Javorina. Then, while we are getting into position before Javorina, we will cut the town off from all outside help, except Tatranska Lomnica. Then we will attack in force."

The look of bewilderment returned to Hatala's face. "And then what will we do?"

Big and hulking as he was, Labuda managed to put on a pixie-ish expression. "You will see, Martin Hatala, you will see. And now, you had better get to bed. Tomorrow I want you to go to Matisova and round up our peaceful peasants. We have not called on our allies in Matisova for help in a long time and I think they will enjoy this little outing."

Hatala grunted "Good night" and left the cave. He could see that Labuda was enjoying himself too much to reveal his plans any further.

Hatala looked down on Matisova from the crest of the hill. It had been two years since he saw it last, and nothing had changed. A stream sliced through the valley and along the stream stood rows of old but clean-looking houses. Surrounding the houses were small strips of land and beyond the town were the woods and forests that slanted gradually up the Carpathian Mountains.

The village looked peaceful in the hazy sunset. From his vantage point there was no sign of the Communists' imprint on Matisova. In the oblong fields Hatala saw farmers busily working singly or in small groups. There was no trace of any collective farm as existed in most Slovakian villages. Here the soil was thin, suitable only for potatoes or hay or barley, and the Communists had not seen fit to merge the little individual landholdings as yet.

Hatala filled his lungs with fresh air, shook the dust off his boots and began walking downhill toward the village.

On the outskirts he was surrounded by road workers. They stopped digging when they saw him approaching. Whether they were suspicious or curious at seeing a stranger or simply welcoming the chance to stop working, Hatala could not tell. The men eyed him cautiously and as he came nearer, he could see fear in their faces. Hatala assumed the villagers were afraid he was a messenger of the ruling Communist regime, come with tidings that would somehow depress their already marginal existence.

But the alarm that ran through the crowd of workers was of short duration. "That's my nephew," exclaimed an elderly member of the group. He spoke hurriedly in low tones to his fellow workers and their faces lit up in relief. The old man who had spoken was Tomas Horak, always referred to in the village of Matisova as "the good one." Anyone who was accepted by Horak was automatically accepted by his friends.

For two days now, Hatala was told as he walked back with his uncle to Matisova, Red planes from the air fields at Spišska Nová Ves, Prešov and Košice had been circling low over the forests. The villagers had grinned knowingly at each other as they dug with their shovels, for the planes meant that the guerillas had left their hideouts and were on the move out of the hills. The continued circling indicated, too, that the guerillas were still at large. And the sympathies of the people of Matisova were with the hunted, not the hunters.

When Hatala suddenly appeared, the road workers suspected him of being a Communist spy seeking information about the guerillas. Ever since the Communist coup that took over Czechoslovakia in 1948, agents of the State Secret Police, the STB, and the Army came to their village from time to time,

44

dressed in workaday garb that protected their identity until they began asking questions about this person and that.

The workers milled around Hatala as they proceeded. They were flattered and pleased that he had come to their little village nestled in the Carpathians and they asked him question after question about what was happening in the outside world. His recounting of the steady spread of communism throughout East Europe they could not truly comprehend, but they nodded in solemn satisfaction when he told them, "Nothing lasts forever." They were poor as ever and their stomachs were no fuller, but the presence of a newcomer with sympathies like their own and the knowledge that guerillas still roamed the hills made their burdens easier to bear.

The bell of the church interrupted their questioning. Though the people of Matisova had lost their priest when the Communists came, they still maintained their church and congregated in it on holidays and Sundays to pray their rosaries and sing together. At dusk the bell of the church reminded them of the "Angelus," a traditional prayer they faithfully observed whether they were in their homes or in their fields. They worshiped as their fathers and forefathers had worshiped and not even the absence of a priest would stop them. So they crossed themselves silently as they went, each saying his prayer to himself.

The day's work for the Communist regime was over, and now the night would belong to them. Farmers from the field, lumberjacks from the hills, workers from the sawmill, all were returning to their homes. Tomas Horak darted among them, whispering first to one, then another. He rejoined Hatala just before the workers entered the village, where a pair of uniformed SNB men spotted the stranger in their midst. To their questions, Hatala spouted a long litany of names that seemed to connect the Hatala family with the Horaks and the police let him pass.

Hatala ate a simple dinner with the Horaks. After it was over the sound of music broke the stillness of the night, as the young men of the village brought their fiddles into the street and broke into song, marching in groups of threes and fours, here and there mingling with the young ladies of the village. Singing, dancing, story-telling, drinking when there was something to drink—these were the ways the people of Matisova sought relief on Saturday nights from the drabness of their plight under the Communists. While the merry-making in the streets drew the attention of the handful of SNB troopers on duty that night, other villagers, mostly men in their middle age, filtered out of Matisova under cover of the enveloping darkness. Hatala quietly left his uncle's house to join them as they made their way into the mountains.

They gathered at a pre-arranged point, several score strong. The townspeople were all armed. Most of them had fought in the war and many had taken part in the Underground resistance to the Nazis that started in 1944. Joining the hunted came naturally to them. Like professional soldiers they were almost totally incurious about the details of the raid they would carry out. When the time came, each would be told what to do. The farmers and workers took one last look back at Matisova, heard the sad, haunting strains of "Gorali," the song of the wandering mountaineer, rise from the town, then started their march through the mountain pass to rendezvous with Jan Labuda.

Hatala and his group reached the meeting point, a sheltered hollow on the mountainside overlooking Javorina, at six o'clock the next morning. Other groups arrived in twos and threes until there were well over one hundred men assembled. After walking all night it was sheer luxury for Hatala and his crew just to sit down.

Labuda was giving instructions to his lieutenants. "Rudolf, take three men and cut the telephone and telegraph wires. Leave only those that connect Javorina with Tatranska Lomnica. Will that be enough men?"

The tall bearded one named Rudolf nodded. "One of our

46

men works in the telephone exchange. He will know which wires must be cut."

"Excellent. Now, there are three roads leading out of Javorina. I want them all blocked. Nothing is to leave Javorina, not even a bicycle. Ivan, what is the condition of these roads?"

An elderly man sprang forward. "There have been some strange accidents, Jan Labuda. A funny thing, lightning. You never know where it will strike next. Last night three gigantic trees fell across the roads leading out of Javorina, and just half an hour ago a Red Army lorry came hurtling around a bend in the road and crashed right into one of the trees. It was a shame. Three of our glorious liberators died in the wreckage and I would be surprised if the road could be cleared before several hours."

Labuda grinned. "Yes, Ivan, lightning is so unpredictable. I believe, though, that more trees had better be struck by lightning. I want two or three barriers on each of those roads. Take the men you need, woodcutters preferably."

The old man and several of his companions left at once.

"Now," said Labuda, "we move in a body. The object is to sound like a thousand men instead of a hundred. We will rest an hour until the wires are down and the roads are blocked. Then we will break out of the forest and head straight across the fields for the wooden castle.

"Pay no attention to the villagers. They have all been warned to stay out of the way. We are to make a lot of noise as we go in. Shoot off as many rounds of ammunition as you like, but do not try to kill anyone. If Opalov and the UPA have done their job well, we will take the castle without killing anyone."

An hour later Labuda roused his band and waved half of them forward, keeping the rest with him. As Hatala rose and started to follow, Labuda held him back. "Wait, Martin, stay here with me. I want you to see the fun."

Labuda trained his binoculars on the castle, a quarter of a mile away. The binoculars were of a superior German make and he could clearly distinguish some extremely perplexed

47

Communists on the veranda that adjoined the old castle. He handed the binoculars to his curious lieutenant.

"Notice, Martin, that although our forces have opened fire, they are not hitting the castle or any of the people in it?"

"Yes," Hatala replied.

"Now look on the veranda directly ahead of you. Do you see the fat one?"

Hatala adjusted his glasses. "Yes, I see him."

"That is General Bolnikov of the MVD. If you watch carefully I think you will see him pick up the telephone nearby."

Hatala's eyes strained through the binoculars. Sure enough, Bolnikov picked up a phone on the veranda. He spoke into the mouthpiece excitedly.

Labuda laughed. "Just about now, he is finding out that the only telephone line open is to Tatranska Lomnica."

Hatala sighed. "Jan, you must possess a degree in black magic. How do you know what he will do, even before he does it?"

A sly grin on his face, Labuda answered, "Because we planned it that way."

"Now look," he continued. "Our first line has surrounded the hotel. And the Reds are starting to return the fire with the few arms they have."

Suddenly, Bolnikov dropped the phone and began shouting instructions to his men. Soon all firing from the hotel ceased and the Reds drew back inside the windows of the castle hotel.

"What happens next?" Hatala asked.

Labuda motioned the rest of his men to attack the castle. "Our second wave now goes in, but without danger, since the Reds will not fire into them."

"How on earth can you be so sure of that?"

Labuda pretended to be stern. "I have already explained, Martin, that we planned it that way."

Hatala was flabbergasted when the second line of guerillas overran the first line and entered the castle without being fired on. Labuda finally took pity on his aide's bewilderment. "You

48

see, Martin, we arranged it so that the only telephone line from Javorina went to Tatranska Lomnica. Now the Reds here in Javorina knew that the only other Communists at Tatranska Lomnica are staying at the Grand Hotel there, for that is also the headquarters of the Secret Police. So I knew Bolnikov would call the Grand Hotel when trouble began."

"Yes, but . . ."

Labuda cut him off. "The rest is simple. By the time our fat friend was able to reach the Grand Hotel and ask for help, we were prepared for him at that end. The man at the switchboard at the Grand Hotel was our friend Opalov. Simple, no?"

"Magnificent," agreed Hatala.

"Opalov and the UPA forces had already captured the switchboard at the hotel. They were waiting for the cry for help from Javorina."

"But how could he convince them to hold their fire?"

"Also very simple," Labuda replied. "He told Bolnikov that they already knew about the raid and had sent reinforcements. Only he told them they must not fire at the guerillas because the reinforcements would be disguised as guerillas in order to infiltrate our lines."

Hatala shook his head in wonder.

"And now, look," Labuda said, pointing to the castle and choking with laughter.

A line of prisoners was leaving the hotel. They were one of the sorriest-looking groups of prisoners Hatala had ever seen. All were stark naked!

Not a single head was raised among the captives. Each hung down, looking at the ground sheepishly, as they were marched through the village.

"We will let the people of Javorina see their Red masters in the flesh," Labuda said, "then we will take them into the woods for a long walk."

"And there you will kill them." Hatala interjected.

"Not at all. We will let them make their way back to the castle unharmed. There is no one left in the castle now but their wives and children, who will remember for a long time how their husbands and fathers were marched before the people without a stitch of clothes. To shatter the dignity of a Communist can sometimes hurt the Reds more than physical torture or death.

"We have taught the Reds a lesson in humility, Martin," Labuda concluded, the laughter disappearing from his face, as he stood erect. "All that remains is to make certain the story is told to the people."

Labuda need not have worried. Almost before his guerillas had been swallowed up by the virgin forests of the High Tatras and the villagers of Matisova had filtered back to their homes, the people of Slovakia were laughing uproariously at the high and mighty Communists who had been trapped by a handful of guerillas and marched off in disgrace into the woods. Besides Bolnikov and his Soviet cohorts, two members of the Czechoslovakian Politburo had been among the prisoners forced to disrobe.

The Underground's secret radio transmitters blared out the news, and by word of mouth and other means, the story went past the borders of Slovakia into Poland, Hungary, Romania, Bulgaria, Austria, and even into Russia itself. Hatala heard the story retold many times, and it was good to see the laughter the tale never failed to evoke. Ridicule, he realized, is dangerous to the Communists. Resistance, insurrections, they can put down by force of arms. But how can they cope with laughter?

3. Mission to Svaty Martin

THROUGH the train window, Peter Dub watched the scenery flow past. His mind, however, was elsewhere. He was thinking of Katka, dark and sad-eyed Katka, to whom he would be married, God granting, in three months. The date had been set a week before and Dub had been looking forward to the planning and shopping and all the other big and little things that occupy couples about to be married in the free world—and trusted Communists behind the Iron Curtain. Dub and Katka were trusted Communists.

Then, just two days after the wedding date was set, Jozef Maryan of the Slovak Underground paid a visit to Dub with an assignment of the utmost importance. It would take Dub away from Katka for two months or more. The only consolation was Maryan's guarantee that the task would be completed in time for him to return to Katka before the wedding day. Though Maryan was vague, Dub got the distinct impression that the timing of the assignment was as important as the job itself.

Well, Dub thought, he would find out more about that when he arrived at his destination, Svaty Martin. But for the enforced parting from Katka, Dub would have enjoyed the ride on the train. He had never ridden on one in his youth and though he had done so many times in the past few years, each trip retained some of the excitement of the first one.

The land blazed with the bright colors of September, for fall comes early to the mountainous areas of Slovakia. The train rattled along through the picturesque valleys, following the contours of the banks of the Hron River and its tributaries, which are hemmed in by the majestic Low Tatra Mountains. The foliage ran up from the riverbank in a swirling kaleidoscope of reds, oranges, browns and greens, thinning out to whiteness where the ever-present snow already lay on the bald mountain peaks.

Every so often, however, deep ugly scars gashed the pastoral canvas. As the train came round a bend in the river's course, Dub saw a huge factory belching clouds of black, odorous smoke. It was one of the dozens of war plants the Communists had superimposed on the picture-postcard loveliness of Slovakia. A new factory here, a new power plant there, new railroad track somewhere else. And as the years passed, the face of the land was changing irrevocably into yet another arsenal of the Soviet war machine.

Smiling inwardly, Dub took solace in the knowledge that the Underground was well organized at many of the plants. Secret labor cells had been set up, and slowed down work, at the steel mills of Podbrezova; at a poison-gas plant at Novaky; a new oil refinery at Istebnik; an aircraft factory at Biskupice, ammunition works at Trnava, Dubnica and Habura, and plants that turned out explosives, chemicals and synthetics at Bratislava.

The Reds might control the factories themselves, Dub mused, but the machinery inside them was, in many cases, under the supervision of dedicated members of the Underground. When the proper day came, there would be explosions throughout Slovakia and the Communist war machine would grind to a halt.

With such pleasant visions of the future, Dub swung off the train as it huffed to a stop in Svaty Martin. He felt so good that he even smiled at a Communist policeman in the depot. The policeman, spotting the Communist emblem that Dub wore, smiled back.

Peter Dub was sixteen years old when the Red Army came to Slovakia. He was the only son of a coal miner in the town of Dolna Zdana, on the Hron River in south central Slovakia, and when he finished school he went to work in the mines beside his father. The coal was low-grade but it was needed in the fuel-poor country and helping get it out of the ground provided a living for the Dubs. Not a sumptuous living, of course, but there was time for a little joy and relaxation, a glass of beer in an inn, a dance or a quiet evening with the family.

Dolna Zdana had been a happy mining town; there was light and laughter in the streets in the evening. Then the Communists took over. People found themselves with little money or time for amusement. Everyone was deadly tired at the end of the day. There was never enough food and the citizens had only enough energy to work and sleep. At night the only sound outdoors was the cursing of a policeman. Men passed each other on the streets with stolid faces and downcast eyes; the police and their informers were everywhere. A man hardly dared trust his family, much less his neighbor. Several miners had been arrested and taken away in the night. Two had been hanged in the town square for all to see as "enemies of the people."

Young Dub witnessed one of the hangings. He was walking through the square when a young man was dragged through by the State police, his hands tied behind his back and his eyes looking up at the grey sky as if he must see enough of it those last few minutes to last him for all eternity. Peter knew the condemned man. He had played soccer with him at school.

The young man had been caught trying to smuggle guns to the slave workers in one of the mining compounds. It was a mad, gallant, daring act that had been doomed to failure from the first. Peter did not know much about the plot, but like many others in Dolna Zdana he had heard rumors of plans and conspiracies against the Reds, most of them sporadic, ill-organized efforts.

Peter found himself in a little knot of workers as his friend was hanged to a lamppost. Anger rose in him and his fists clenched. His eyes, more than anything else, might have betrayed him. He had a wild desire to burst into the streets, to throw himself on the Red soldiers, to do something, anything.

Suddenly he felt a hand on his arm. An old miner, Anton Velaty, was standing beside him, a man grown grey in the mines who had known Peter since he was a boy. He had seen the flush of anger on Peter's face, the tremor in his hands.

"Steady," he whispered. "Steady, before someone else sees you. This is not the time to start anything."

With an effort, Dub brought himself under control and looked nervously about to see if anyone else had noticed him. No one, it seemed, had and after a few minutes he slipped away and went home.

A few days later, the old miner Velaty took him to one side in a dark mine shaft and said: "Peter, I know how you feel about the Communists. Would you like to do something about it?"

Dub hesitated. He knew Anton well and certainly the old man did not betray him in the square. And yet, how could he be sure of anyone? Anton pressed his hand and comforted him. "I know. You are afraid. But you do not need to be. I would not have spoken to you if I hadn't seen for sure how you felt. Come to my house tonight. Some friends will be there and we can talk."

Anton walked away. Throughout the afternoon Dub was torn by doubt. He was sure Anton was not a Communist. But even if Anton could be trusted, the idea of a meeting was itself dangerous. The police might learn of it and arrest those attending.

He was preoccupied at dinner that night and his parents watched him anxiously. But as he thought of all the Communists had done, of his friend hanging from the lamppost, anger flooded through him again and he knew he had to go.

He walked through a dark street to Anton's house and rapped softly at the door. Anton let him in and took him into a basement room. There were half a dozen men there, some

54

older than Dub, some his own age. They greeted him quietly and Anton said:

"I'm glad you came, Peter. We need you."

"For what?"

"I think you know, Peter. To help us fight the Communists. Come, Peter, what do you think of the Reds?"

Dub looked at the faces, gathered at a table over a dim oil lamp, faces of men he had known all his life. He could trust them. He said:

"I hate them."

"How much, Peter?" Anton shot back. "How much do you hate them? Enough to risk your life to fight them?"

Dub's answer came back as quickly: "Yes, enough for that."

"Good," Anton said. "It is not going to be an easy fight, or a short one. Old men like me may not live to see the end of it. That is why we need young men like you."

It would not be a fight with guns and bullets, Anton told him. "We must fight another way. We must get the confidence of the Communists. We workers must organize. We must have our labor unions, secret unions. We must place our men in responsible positions in the mines. We must grow in strength and size until the time comes when we can strike at the Communists from within."

"What do I have to do?" Dub asked.

"Become a Communist!" was Anton's answer.

For a moment, Dub wondered if this were a trap. "No, do not be afraid," Anton soothed him. "Not a Communist at heart, but a Communist in name and words and appearance. It will not be easy. You must go to the Communists' Workers' Academy. You must learn to be a good Communist. You are a good worker and you and your parents have guarded your words in the past. The Reds don't know how you feel about them and if you are a good pupil, they will trust you. You will get better and more responsible positions in the mines. And then, some day . . ."

55

Peter took the assignment. He became one of the Academy's star pupils and convinced the Reds that his heart and soul lay in communism. He was given promotions, he became a supervisor, and his pay increased. Life became more comfortable, at least from a financial point of view, though it was far from comfortable in other ways. Because he was not allowed to tell his parents that he was working for the Underground, he earned their increasing contempt. "How," his mother would ask him, "can you sacrifice the men you work with for a larger slice of bread?"

As the Communists' confidence in him grew, Dub was made an "informer" for the Red-ruled "Workers' Militia," which helped to maintain the Communists' authority and to administer the mines. He was sent on occasional trips to Prague with reports to the Central Mining Administration, to Bratislava and even to Budapest, the headquarters of the Soviet director of all coal mining in Central Europe.

Peter's reputation within the Underground was growing, too. One day a man came to see him from Bratislava, a man with flowing black hair and penetrating eyes: Jozef Maryan, one of the coordinators of the growing Underground. Maryan looked carefully at Dub. He saw a young man of moderate height, with brown hair and blue eyes, a man of quiet, gentle manner. Dub's face, in repose, looked innocuous. But as Maryan talked with Dub, he could see the determination, the controlled passion, the quick intelligence that lay behind the mild appearance. Maryan was satisfied.

"We will have work to do together, you and I," he told Dub. "There are many men like you, in the mines and factories. But you must know each other, you must work together. When you learn to work as a team, not only in Slovakia but in every country in the hands of the Soviets, not all the power of communism can stop you. You are the workers, and yours will be the greatest strength of all.

"But, we have to build slowly," he added, "and everything

56

will take time. Meanwhile, I understand that you travel from time to time for the mines' administrators?"

Dub nodded.

"Good," said Maryan. "Then when you do, you may find occasion to slip through to Vienna, to Salzburg or Munich to give information to our people there. I will tell you how and when to do it."

So Dub broadened the scope of his work. Several times, he crossed the Iron Curtain to the West to bring word of the Communists' increasing concern over the rising rate of sabotage and the slowdown of production in the mines.

One day Dub was called to the office of the commissar of the Dolna Zdana mines. He was told to go to Bratislava to ask for better safety devices. "Comrade Dub," the Commissar instructed, "here are the descriptions, charts and maps of the mines at Dolna Zdana and Handlová that you will use in explaining our needs at Bratislava. And here are your credentials for the trip."

It was difficult for Dub to conceal his elation. He could not have hoped for such a windfall: complete details of the mines and their equipment were in his hands. Dub left on his mission to Bratislava. But he did not go directly. He managed to slip across the Iron Curtain to turn over the details of the mines to Underground members in Vienna for use in future attempts at sabotage.

From there he went to Bratislava and called on Feodor Gondurov, one of the top Soviet mining officials. Gondurov greeted him cordially and cried, "What have you brought me, Comrade Peter? I am glad to see you in such good health." Gondurov was obviously taken with young Dub.

Peter turned over his documents and sat for more than an hour, outlining the needs of the Dolna Zdana mines while the rangy Gondurov slumped in his chair. At the end Gondurov summoned his secretary, a pretty dark-haired girl barely out of her teens named Katarina Novotna. Gondurov was unaware that Katarina had ever seen Dub outside his office or that she had given him important information about coal mining production in the past.

"See," Gondurov told her, "here is Peter Dub from Dolna Zdana. He has brought important reports. Show them to those who should see them and return them to me. And," he added with a wink, "if Comrade Peter should try to flirt with you, watch out! He's a sly dog, this Peter."

The girl gave no sign she knew Peter but left with the documents. When she was gone, Gondurov promised Peter answers to his request the following day. Peter left the office. There standing in the hall was Katarina.

"Peter," she whispered, "I must see you tonight. It is a matter of life and death for you."

That evening he met Katarina at her one-room apartment. She handed him a confidential letter from the Department of the Interior, Internal Security Division, in Prague. It was signed by Ivan Volkov, and addressed to Gondurov. It said someone answering Peter Dub's description had been seen twice in the American zone of Vienna, that he had been in communication with the "traitorous Slovak exiles" and that he was presumably selling secret information to them and to the "American imperialists." It asked Gondurov what information he had on Dub, who his closest associates were, and what, in his opinion, should be done with him.

"Has Gondurov seen this?" Peter asked worriedly.

"No," Katarina told him. "It arrived yesterday and I withheld it. I knew you were on your way to Bratislava. Oh Peter, what can we do?"

Dub hesitated. He knew that sooner or later Katarina would have to turn the letter over to Gondurov. He needed time, time to warn his associates of their danger. "Katarina," he said, "you have saved not only my life, but the lives of others. I know it will be a great risk for you, but can you keep this file from Gondurov until I can get home and warn the others?"

Katarina did not answer immediately. She pointed to a picture on the wall, the picture of a man, a woman and two

58

children. "That is a picture of my mother, my father, my brother Stefan and me. I was eight when it was taken and Stefan was eleven."

Tears welled up in Katarina's eyes. As she told of her family, Dub came to realize the depths of feeling and maturity that lay beneath the lovely young face. He had never noticed before the plaintive softness of her eyes. Katarina told how her father, shamed by the bloodless Nazi conquest of Czechoslovakia in 1939, fled with his family to Russia. He was certain the Russians would fight the Nazis and he wanted to take part. But five months later the Nazis and Soviets signed their peace pact and Novotny was disillusioned. He was careless with his words and soon he and his wife were shipped off to Siberia and never heard from again. Katarina and Stefan were separated. Katarina was brought up in a Communist school and was allowed to go back to her home when the war was over to live with relatives.

Katarina looked off into space as she recounted her story. When it was over, she turned to Dub and held up the letter to Gondurov. "Yes, Peter, I will keep the letter from Gondurov as long as you want me to."

Her voice was rising, her face flushed. Peter put his hand on her shoulder to quiet her. But Katarina leaped to her feet. "I will do more than that, Peter," she cried. "I will answer the letter myself, and send the answer back to Volkov saying that so far as we know you are loyal to the People's Democracy. I will forge Gondurov's signature, so that he does not need to know anything about it."

Her eyes were shining. She took Peter's face in her hands and she kissed him. He looked at her in wonder, in pity and then in love, clasping her to his chest and kissing her, first gently and then with ardor.

Peter kept his appointment with Gondurov the next morning. He did not want to arouse Gondurov's suspicions by failing to appear, but all went well. That evening he returned to

Dolna Zdana and told Anton and several other associates of the danger.

"Who could have betrayed us?" he asked over and over. "It must have been someone who knows us. Seeing me in Salzburg was not an accident. Someone was told to look for me. There is a traitor in our own ranks."

They thought for a moment. Then a short, swarthy young man named Milan cried, "I know who. Rudolf Uhorsky. He is always flattering me and asking where you go on your trips. He asks if you go to Vienna and says that he has a brother, Pavel, who works there as an informer for the Americans. He says that you should get in touch with Pavel. I have never told him anything, but he could have learned from others. It must be Rudolf. He is too curious."

The members of the labor cell deliberated and decided that Rudolf was the guilty party. Against the chance he was innocent they measured the risks to their cell and to other labor cells with which they were in contact. The next day Rudolf Uhorsky was killed in an accident in the mines and at his funeral the Communist commissar of the mines praised him as a staunch pillar of the Party and as an example to other workers.

One traitor to the Underground had been liquidated. But there remained another, Pavel, in Austria. He was the one who had reported Dub's visits. A courier was sent to Austria who spoke to Slovak exiles, who in turn brought charges against Pavel before the American authorities. He was discharged from his job. But the Underground went even further, for it wanted to destroy Pavel's position with the Reds as well. Slovaks in Austria raided Pavel's rooms and found documents showing he was playing the game of espionage both ways; he was selling information to the highest bidder. The documents completely discredited Pavel. The courier brought them back to Dolna Zdana and gave them to Peter Dub, who arranged to have them placed on the desk of Volkov in Prague by an agent of the STB, the State Secret Police. The agent was also an Underground member.

"This man Pavel Uhorsky," the agent reported to Volkov, "is a complete double-crosser, utterly unreliable. He should be liquidated. We cannot trust any of his reports. And we know that he accused our Comrade Peter Dub for his own traitorous purposes. Peter Dub is a loyal man."

The agent's report, following the forged letter endorsing Dub that was prepared by Katarina, convinced Volkov of Dub's innocence. He wrote to Gondurov, telling him there was no reason to suspect Peter, that he was a trusted Communist who "could never betray the People's Democracy." Katarina received this letter and gave it to Gondurov, who of course was puzzled since he had never received the first letter denouncing Dub. But Katarina concocted a story about a mix-up in the office that satisfied Gondurov, who was genuinely fond of Dub and Katarina anyhow.

Caution dictated that Dub not draw any more Underground assignments for a spell. He made several trips to Bratislava on business, seeing Katarina each time, until finally they decided to get married. Gondurov gave his blessing and promised to try to get Dub transferred to a better-paying job in his own office. "These things are not easy," he told the betrothed pair with a smile, "but I cannot afford to lose Katarina. This office would be lost without her."

Shortly afterwards, Jozef Maryan paid a second visit to Dub in Dolna Zdana. He did not go directly to Dub's house, but stopped first at an inn and ordered a beer. He drank one glass, two, three and more. When he left anyone watching him would have sworn he was roaring drunk. He stumbled through the streets to Dub's house, and pounded on the door, shouting so loud that the neighbors opened their windows to ask him to be quiet. A policeman came running up and said, "Quiet, there! Do you want me to arrest you!"

"Jusht try'n shee m'frien," Maryan said thickly.

"All right, but take it easy or I'll have to run you in."

61

Dub opened the door and took in the situation quickly. "It's all right," he reassured the policeman, "I'll quiet him down."

"See that you do," the officer said gruffly and left.

When the door closed, Maryan was instantly sober. "Where can we talk?"

Dub's mother came into the room, and Maryan seemed drunk again. Dub said to his mother, "Don't mind him. I'll fix him up." He took Maryan to a room in the basement where Maryan spoke between bursts of shouts and drunken laughter.

"We've got more work for you, Peter. They need some help at Svaty Martin. There is a cell of our workers in the Stalin Enterprises. I think you know about the factory."

Dub had heard of it. Svaty Martin, on the Turiec River some fifty miles north of Dolna Zdana, was called "the Athens of Slovakia." It was a lovely center of museums, schools and publishing houses surrounded by towering mountains. The Communists had chosen the city for the construction of the Stalin Enterprises, which produced steel parts for Soviet armored cars and tanks. Those parts were sent to other new factories in Central Slovakia for assembly into finished products.

"What do you know about heavy machinery?" Maryan asked.

The question took Dub off balance. "A little. Why?"

"Do you know how to run a metal stamping machine?"

Dub thought back to his days as a teen-age mechanic and machinist, before he went into the coal mines, when he had worked part-time in small machine shops to supplement the family income. He had learned a considerable amount of mechanical lore during that time, and could even now find his way around a factory without looking awkward.

"I never worked a metal stamping machine," he finally said, "but in theory I know how they operate. With some practice, I think I could run one."

"Good," said Maryan. "You will have an opportunity to practice." Filling his pipe, he continued: "What do you suppose would happen if the Russians were unable to get the most important parts for their tanks and armored cars? The assembly plants would have to close down."

"I think I begin to understand," Dub said. "You want the Stalin Enterprises sabotaged."

"Exactly so."

"But why have I been chosen for this?"

Maryan smiled beatifically. "Because no one at the Stalin Enterprises knows you, and when the sabotage is discovered, suspicion will naturally fall on you as the newest worker."

Dub's eyebrows rose perceptibly. "This is a signal honor," he said, not without a touch of sarcasm.

"It is," Maryan agreed evenly, ignoring the gibe. "You see, Peter, we have a trained cadre of saboteurs inside the Stalin Enterprises, but we don't want them anywhere nearby when you put the plant's stamping machine out of commission. That way, we will be able to use our inside men again and again for the little acts of sabotage, sand in the bearings, overheated machines, the things that look like accidents and don't endanger our workers there."

The idea seemed sound to Dub, but now that he was going to marry Katarina the prospect of a dangerous assignment seemed to have lost some of the old excitement. "And what am I supposed to do when, as you put it, suspicion naturally falls on me?"

Maryan smiled good naturedly. "I think we can manage to get you out of the plant before harm befalls you."

"I think I like the plan better now," Dub said. "But if I am to bear the blame, then I will have to assume another identity."

"Papers will be drawn for you."

"And how will my absence from the mines be explained?"

Maryan grinned. "Two days from now your boss will get a letter from a highly placed official in the coal mining administration telling him that you are to be detached for a trip of two months or more to see the new mining methods being used elsewhere in Czechoslovakia, Poland and Hungary. The high official is one of us, so you are safe even if your boss checks back and asks questions."

The last few words were lost on Dub. All he could think of was "two months or more." What of his forthcoming marriage to Katarina? He said nothing of that to Maryan. "Why two months or more?" he asked.

"Stalin Enterprises is a 'high security' factory. The experts there are for the most part trained in Moscow. The workers are also carefully screened and it will take awhile to get you into the factory."

"What if it takes much longer?" Dub demanded, the concern in his voice puzzling Maryan.

"The job must be done in late November for reasons that I cannot now tell you." Maryan strode around the room. "We are aware you might not be able to work your way into the plant in time. If you cannot do it, then we will have to let the labor cells inside the plant do it. It may end the usefulness of our workers there, but that cannot be helped. The job must be done at a certain time. It is of the utmost importance."

The Underground leader said impatiently, "I have been here long enough, Peter. Will you do it?"

Dub hesitated only an instant before answering, but the brief faltering did not escape Maryan. "Yes, of course," said Dub.

"Good." Maryan snapped out instructions. "You will go to Svaty Martin as soon as possible. You will get further instructions there. The job will have to be done, I think, by December 1st at the latest, but you will be told the exact date later on. Here is the address of your contact in Svaty Martin."

With that, Maryan wheeled, left the basement and once again broke into loud and raucous song.

After an apparently aimless stroll through the town of Svaty Martin, Dub reached the address he had been given, knocked

64

twice, and was admitted quickly after a brief exchange of words. He was led to a house where another young man, several years older than Dub, was waiting. Dub took an instant liking to his contact, who in fact resembled him in his medium height, pleasant though not handsome face, athletic build and calm but forceful way of speaking. Dub's hair, normally brown, had been dyed black, the color of his contact's hair.

The contact introduced himself: "I am Filip Polhora."

After a brief exchange of pleasantries, Filip got down to the business at hand. "Starting tomorrow, you will begin work at a small machine shop here. Everyone who works in the shop is a member of the Underground, but of course it is under the supervision of the Communists. Therefore, I hardly need tell you to be careful. While you are learning the latest techniques of metal stamping, our people will furnish you detailed drawings of the big machine at the Stalin Enterprises. When you know that machine by heart, something will have to be done about transferring you to the factory."

"Will you be working with me?"

"Oh, no," Filip said. "I am a courier. I will be leaving here tomorrow. However, either I or another courier will return with the explosives you will need a few days before the stamping machine is to be blown up. We will tell you the exact date the job is to be done when you get the explosives.

"Whoever does come back with the final instructions," Filip went on, "will wait for you and help you escape from this city. The usual methods of leaving will be blocked by the Communists, no doubt. We can't plan an escape this far ahead. In fact, we may even have to improvise a bit," he added with a knowing smile.

Once the instructions were concluded, Peter and Filip got up to leave. But Peter seized Filip's arm and held him back. He had felt a rapport with Filip and thought his words would be received with understanding. "Have you ever been in love?"

Filip immediately sensed the deep emotional currents beneath the quick, brief question. "One meets attractive girls now and then," he said non-committally.

"I am in love," Peter said, surprised at his sudden eagerness to talk of Katarina to a man he hardly knew. As Filip nodded sympathetically, Peter told of Katarina and of his wedding plans and of the chance that his assignment would delay the marriage.

Filip said, not unkindly, "You must have been told there can be no time for your personal life in the Underground. If you choose to fall in love, then you must be ready to pay the consequences."

"I did not choose to fall in love. It just happened."

"My friend," Filip said, clasping Peter, "you must keep your mind on your work. The lives and future of many people depend on you, not just your Katarina's. Everything will work out for the best and I am sure you will see her again soon."

Late that night Peter was established at a worker's cottage on the outskirts of the city. He was there as a lodger and he began immediately to familiarize himself with his new identity. He was now Peter Slezak, machinist. He spent several hours dipping his hands into a can of thick black grease, wiping them, then immersing them over again. When he finally retired for the night, his hands had the proper patina of embedded grease. The mirror over his washstand satisfied him that the mustache he had been growing for the past few days, the dark black hair color and the glasses he had begun to wear might not fool close friends but should do in Svaty Martin.

In the days that followed, Peter laboriously studied everything about machinery he could get his hands on. Manuals from the machine shop he worked in, books from the public library. In two weeks he had caught up with the techniques that had been developed since his first try at machining and metalworking and he became proficient enough to hold his own at the small machine shop. For the first few days, his co-workers had covered up for him every time a Communist inspector came near his workbench, but soon this was no longer necessary.

Peter applied for membership in the Communist Party and he spent much of his spare time at Party headquarters. He volunteered for the menial tasks that other workers shunned and even helped the farmers nearby harvest their crops. He made sure to work for the Party on Sunday, convincing the local Communist leaders he was an atheist, for most Catholics in Slovakia attended church on Sunday if their church was still open. And if the church was shut down, they stayed home and rested.

One evening Peter met Boris Kosmolov, the foreman in charge of Hall A of the Stalin Enterprises, at Party headquarters. Kosmolov, Peter had been told, was a Russian citizen, an important cog in the chain of command that went from Moscow to Prague and to the Stalin Enterprises. He was also reputed to be a member of the Soviet secret police. All in all, thought Peter, a man worth cultivating with the care one porcupine would use in making love to another.

Peter acted deferentially toward Kosmolov and asked him question after question about obscure points of Communist theology. The questions assumed Kosmolov was steeped in Communist theory and Kosmolov was quite flattered. He was delighted to have such a willing and eager young pupil come to him for advice and counsel and took pains to answer Peter's questions at length.

Peter managed to meet Kosmolov frequently at Party headquarters and they became good friends within a short time. Kosmolov sometimes took Peter to a café after the Party's work for the evening was over and bought him wine. Peter offered to buy the drinks once in a while, too, but he pointed out that he could afford to stand treat only rarely, since his wages were small.

Kosmolov looked at Peter's hands, which lay palms down

on the table in the café, straddling the wine glass. The ever-present grease had worked its way into the fingernails and the hands showed evidence of hard work. "What do you do for a living, young Slezak?" Kosmolov asked.

"I am a machinist, Comrade Kosmolov," Peter said. His expression told Kosmolov he was flattered to have the older man take such an interest in him.

"Is that so? Where?"

Peter named the small machine shop.

"How much do they pay you?"

Peter told the truth. Kosmolov, he knew, would probably follow up his questioning by checking at the source. Silently, he prayed that the Underground would do a thorough job of backing up his cover story as Peter Slezak.

Apparently the Underground had. Several nights later, Kosmolov confided to Peter that he had been making "a few discreet inquiries" about him.

Peter assumed an air of bland innocence as Kosmolov continued, "I think it's high time you made more money, Slezak. How would you like to work at the Stalin Enterprises as a machinist? You would be working directly under my personal supervision."

"Comrade Kosmolov, I have no words to tell you how happy that would make me. I would be proud to work for you and the Stalin Enterprises and the Union of Soviet Socialist Republics. If only I get the opportunity, I will double whatever work quota is given to me. How good you are!"

Kosmolov smiled with becoming modesty. "It will be hard work, Peter, but I think you are ready for hard work."

"Oh, yes, Comrade Kosmolov," said Peter, trying to keep from gushing too much.

Early on the morning of the day Peter Slezak started to work for the Stalin Enterprises, he boarded the special worker's train at Vrutky, a suburb of Svaty Martin to which he had moved at the suggestion of Kosmolov. The train was heated that cold November morning, a rare luxury in Slovakia, but this was a special train for the elite class of workers at the Stalin Enterprises. Also, Peter discovered, the train was closely guarded at the Vrutky Station by members of the Workers' Militia. As each worker boarded the train, his identity card was inspected and stamped by security guards.

During the short ride to town, Peter listened intently to the talk of the factory workers. It concerned mostly sports, food and women. Apparently, thought Peter, the train was unsafe for anything other than general conversation. That could only mean there were informers aboard.

Peter unconsciously put his hand to his neck. He felt hopelessly trapped, surrounded as he was by dedicated Communist workers, by special Workers' Militia and by the secret police. How could he dream of sabotaging the Stalin Enterprises?

At the depot at Svaty Martin, identity cards were once again punched and the trainload of workmen boarded special buses under guard. Once aboard the buses, a roll call was taken. At the gates of the factory, still another inspection took place. Finally, Peter reported to Kosmolov, ready to work for the glory of Communist defense against the warmongers of the West.

As befitted a man of his station, Kosmolov maintained a private office in the plant. The office, however, was sparsely furnished, its sole decorative note a reproduction of a painting showing Stalin looking benignly over a group of starry-eyed workers and peasants.

The interview with Kosmolov was brief and businesslike. Peter's duties were explained to him and Kosmolov led him to the machine he was to work. There was no camaraderie between them this morning, but as Kosmolov introduced Peter to his co-workers he slapped the newcomer on the back.

This seemingly insignificant gesture proved enough to make Peter a pariah. Newcomers are always suspect in a factory, especially behind the Iron Curtain, but Peter Slezak had the extra disadvantage of seeming to be a pet of Kosmolov. The workmen at the benches near Peter's machine studiously avoided him in their conversations and talked across him as if he were not there.

The surliest treatment Peter received came from Jakub, a wizened old man whose job it was to stack up finished pieces from Peter's machine on a dolly, then wheel them on to another part of the factory, where they would be assembled. Jakub grumbled at Peter for being too slow, then for being too fast, then for being too careful in his machining, then for being too careless.

Peter was fearful that the old man might be trying to trick him in some way, but he decided to call a halt at the point where he knew any other man would rebel. He turned off the switch of his machine and faced the old man. "Listen here, old-timer," he snapped, "your job is to cart away what I turn out, not to tell me how to do my job. Now be quiet when you're around this machine or I'll have to report you as unsatisfactory."

Jakub turned away without a word. A while later, after Peter returned to his machine from lunch, he found a slip of paper wedged inconspicuously into a corner of the control panel. He slipped it into his coveralls and went back to work.

The next time he left the machine to wash up after work, he managed to find enough privacy to inspect the paper. It said: "Meet me at ten o'clock at the Café Metropol." It was signed with the initial J.

Obviously J stood for Jakub. But what was the old man up to? Was he a Communist? A member of the Underground? Or was he seeking satisfaction for the humiliation he had undergone at Peter's hands that day? The only way to find out, of course, was to go to the Metropol and meet Jakub. Still, the mission of sabotaging the Stalin Enterprises was hazardous enough without any new complications.

Peter decided to brazen it out. At nine-thirty he entered the Metropol café, seated himself at a table in an obscure corner

70

and waited. No one paid particular attention to him and his careful scrutiny of the room failed to disclose any faces that spelled danger, at least obviously. Yet he knew instinctively that danger lurked in the café.

At ten o'clock Jakub shuffled into the café, making his way unerringly to Peter's table. "May I sit down?" he asked Peter. Peter nodded, and Jakub lowered himself warily into the chair facing Peter.

Under the table, Peter's hand stealthily found the handle of his knife and slid it out of its sheath. It made him feel better prepared to cope with whatever might come. The old man called for wine.

Once the wine was poured, and the waiter left, the old man lifted his glass. Gesturing with it toward Peter, he toasted: "To Jozef Maryan."

"Who is Jozef Maryan?" Peter asked innocently.

Jakub smiled. "It's all right, Peter Dub. You can relax." He whispered a few words, a slogan known only among leaders of the secret labor cells.

Now it was Peter's turn to smile. Without any attempt at concealment he slipped the knife back into its leather case. "All right, I shall relax. Who are you?"

"I work with Maryan," Jakub said. "He is pleased that you managed to get inside the plant so quickly without any help from the Underground. It looks even less suspicious that Kosmolov himself brought you in. Your job now is to find a way of working the giant stamping machine in Hall A. I think I can help you."

"How?"

"Let us have some more wine," said Jakub, beckoning to the waiter and pointing to their empty glasses. When their glasses had been filled, Jakub resumed. "All that is necessary is that the man who runs the machine now be replaced. He is a member of the Underground and I think he can be persuaded to become ill at the proper time."

Peter gestured approval. "And when he is sick?"

71

"That is when you will volunteer to help out your great friend, Comrade Kosmolov."

The pair finished their wine and parted.

Two weeks later Peter was walking home from the depot at Vrutky one evening when an SNB trooper fell in step beside him. "Ah, my old friend Slezak, how are you?"

Peter turned around quickly, saw the green uniform and suppressed a gasp of fear. But he soon breathed a sigh of relief. The hair was blond and cut short, but it was obviously Filip Polhora. Peter followed his lead. "It's good to see you again," he said, and invited Filip to his one-room apartment for a drink.

With the radio turned up loud, Peter filled Filip in on his progress. After he finished, he asked, "And now what are the orders?"

Filip patted the lunchbox he had been carrying. "In here you will find two sandwiches and a loaf of bread wrapped in napkins. At least they look like sandwiches and bread from the outside. They are really plastic bombs molded to shape. It's up to you to figure out where to place them so they will do the most damage."

Peter opened the lunchbox, took off the napkins and examined the pale-colored doughy mass. He put the napkins back on and transferred the explosives to his own lunchbox. Turning to Filip, he said, "When is the machine supposed to be exploded?"

"The day after tomorrow."

Peter's eyes lit up. "Wonderful! That will give me ten days to get back to Katarina in time for our wedding. This is good news, Filip."

"You have only yourself to thank for it," Filip noted. "If you hadn't been able to get into the plant so quickly it might have been later."

The glad tidings did not dim Peter's curiosity, however. "Have you found out why the date is so important?"

"I have not been told the reason officially, but from what I can piece together the Underground leaders want to show military people in the United States how well-organized we are. As I understand it, the Americans feel our claims of strength are exaggerated. Whenever our people take credit for an act of sabotage, the Americans scoff and say that doesn't prove anything except that there might be some guerillas here and there acting independently of each other. The idea is if we tell them in advance that we are going to sabotage a specific plant on a specific day, they will believe us when we say we have an organization they can work with if war ever starts in Europe. Meanwhile, they may send more money and arms to keep us going."

"My God, Filip, haven't we already done enough to prove how strong we are?"

Filip shrugged, and gave the usual answer, "I am only a courier."

He reached into his lunchbox and pulled out a small white handkerchief. "I have something else for you, Peter. Someone gave it to me for you when I was in Bratislava."

Peter accepted it gingerly, and examined it. It was a common everyday white handkerchief, except that in one corner a single word had been painstakingly embroidered.

It said: "Forever."

His eyes suddenly moistening, Peter grasped Filip with both hands. "It was good of you to see Katarina for me," he said, his voice close to breaking.

"I think I know how lonesome you must be for her," Filip said. "Since I saw you last, I too have met a wonderful girl. Some day, when all this is over . . ."

"Tell me about her, Filip," Peter urged.

Filip arose. "There is no time. We must arrange where I shall meet you after the job is finished and we can talk about our women on the way home."

The arrangements for the rendezvous were made and Filip walked to the door. He stopped with his hand on the knob and turned back to Peter. "She gave me a message to give to you, too."

Peter's eyes sparkled eagerly. "Yes, what did she say?"

"She said, 'Tell him not to blow his nose on the handkerchief.'"

Two days later Peter was working furiously on his own machine and by three-thirty in the afternoon he had already surpassed his work quota for the day. He stood idly by until such time as a new supply of unfinished parts should arrive for machining. He could feel the blobs of explosive he had planted all over his clothes and body, pieces that would not bulge or stick out. Lumps in each of his pockets, pancakes taped to different parts of his body.

As he was taking mental inventory, he heard a commotion raised in Hall A nearby. The disturbance brought work in Peter's sector of the factory to a halt. Along with the others, he hurried toward the giant stamping press to see what had happened. A crowd had gathered around a prostrate figure on the floor. It was the press operator. Kosmolov, his face grave, appealed to the crowd: "Does anyone here know how to work this press? We are already behind our quota for the month and the next shift won't be on till six."

Peter recognized his cue. "I believe I know how to work it," he volunteered. Kosmolov looked doubtful. "But what of your own work quota, Slezak?"

Peter looked down modestly. "I have already exceeded my quota for the day."

Kosmolov slapped him on the back heartily, to the apparent disgust of the other factory hands. The stricken operator was carried off and Kosmolov took Peter by the arm to the press.

For half an hour, Peter operated the press as Kosmolov watched, first haltingly as he tried to remember the plans he had read, then with increasing assurance. Kosmolov grinned broadly, patted his protégé on the back again and left.

Peter looked at his watch. He had less than two hours before the shifts changed. Just before the change would be the best time to do the job, for there would be the fewest workers around. As he worked, he studied the machine carefully. It was just as his predecessor at the press had told him one night.

The stamping press, roughly comparable to a hammer and anvil, was braced on its left side, which faced the door to Hall A, with an intricate labyrinth of bolted and welded steel beams. At the upper part of the machine, the hammer was lowered electrically toward the lower part, the anvil. The network of bracings guided it safely and surely. Metal pressed between the shaping tool and anvil would be tortured into whatever shape the dies were arranged to produce.

On the right side, however, the stamping press was fastened to the concrete block wall. Instead of building a network of braces to the right to equalize the pressure exerted on the left, the Reds had decided to let the wall do the job. On this side the hammer rode up and down on a single tube which was fastened to the wall at the top with bolts. The bolts, no more than six inches deep, were fastened to the mortar between two concrete blocks.

If Peter could explode a small charge at the joint where the bolts were fastened just as the huge hammer was beginning its slow descent, the steel tube on which the hammer rode would tear loose and the hammer would fall on the anvil with shattering force. If the rest of his plastic charge were placed on the anvil, the explosion should blast the machine into a shambles.

At five minutes of six, the other workers left their machines and walked out of the hall toward the locker rooms to change their clothes and go home. All except old Jakub, who walked unobtrusively to the entrance of the room where Peter was working the stamping press. In the semi-deserted hall the chances were excellent that no one would pay attention to the crusty old menial as he stood guard.

His face thoughtful, Jakub read the posters stuck up on the

walls nearby. "American dollars are bloody—don't be fooled by them!" one sign said, warning of American attempts to bribe workers to sabotage the plants. "The factory is yours, work for yourselves!" said another.

Jakub caught Peter's eye. The latter nodded, then quickly climbed a ladder set against the wall on the right side of the stamping machine for use in repairing the press. He took several balls of the plastic, molding them together and fitted as much of the charge into the mortar joint as he could, flattening the rest out against the wall. He inserted a fuse that should take forty-five seconds to burn, then lit it.

Racing back down the ladder, he tore open his shirt and ripped the plastic pancakes off his body. He rolled them into one ball, adding some other chunks from his pockets that he had not used for the first charge, and stuck a blasting cap into the mixture. Placing it in the middle of the anvil, he looked at his watch. Fifteen more seconds and the charge would blow the bolts loose.

Concentrating intensely on the job at hand, Peter was barely aware of the sound of scuffling behind him. There was no time to lose, no time even to look back just yet. He pulled the lever that started the hammer on its slow inexorable descent, then turned to run out of the room.

"What are you doing, Slezak?"

Kosmolov had just entered. In the distance Peter could hear feet running, obviously Jakub's.

"I am sabotaging your machine, Comrade Kosmolov," he bit out past clenched teeth. "What do you think of that?" He whipped out a pocket knife and lunged for the foreman.

Kosmolov stepped aside and grabbed Peter's striking arm. He whirled Peter around and smashed him across the nose with his right fist. Blood spurted out. Peter turned for the door and tried to run, but the big burly Kosmolov tackled him before he could move more than two steps. Peter was slammed to the ground. He twisted out of Kosmolov's grasp and turned toward the stamping machine. The fuse had burned down to the end.

"Katarina!" The shriek of her name echoed in the halls just before two successive explosions, one small, one huge, shattered the machine and rocketed huge pieces of metal in all directions. Peter and Kosmolov were killed instantly.

On the day on which the wedding was to have taken place, Katarina Novotna walked the streets of Bratislava tearless. Only in the sadness of her eyes, the brown haunted eyes, did she show what she suffered.

4. The Hunt

FILIP POLHORA decided he could delay no longer. He had waited for Peter Dub in a dense wood near Svaty Martin for twenty-four hours, until the evening after the explosion at Stalin Enterprises. Dub had either met with an accident or had been captured, Filip reasoned. In either case, Filip had to push on, for the plan of escape did not allow any more time.

Following a subtly marked trail, Filip came to a cottage on the edge of the woods that adjoined the city. Hanging from the window facing the forest was a white towel.

This was the signal Filip feared. It meant danger.

Filip and Peter were to have changed out of their clothes at the cottage, then make their way to the railway station.

But the white towel spelled "stay away—danger" in the language of the Underground. Had Peter revealed their meeting place? Filip could not believe Peter would give him away, even under torture. Drawing back to a vantage point in the woods where he could keep an eye on the cottage, he drew out his revolver and waited.

The sound of a door creaking open brought Filip swiftly alert.

A buxom blonde girl with her arms full of wood came out the rear door of the cottage and started toward the woods. She was followed closely by two members of the SNB.

"Where are you going?" one of the police demanded.

The girl turned. "I have to burn the rubbish."

Arms akimbo, the SNB watched as she started a small fire in the clearing between the cottage and the forest. Over her shoulder, the girl smiled at the troopers. "Why are you two officers here at my house? Surely you don't believe my old uncle or I are criminals?"

The taller SNB man stroked his thick black mustache. "No, my dear," he said. "We don't think you or your uncle are criminals. But we are looking for a man who might be coming this way."

"Oh?" she said in surprise. "What sort of man? A criminal?"

"Yes, a saboteur. He may be wearing a uniform like ours and we think he might try to hide out in this neighborhood."

The girl looked up and scanned the woods. To Filip it seemed that her eyes paused for an instant as they swept past the spot on which he stood. But could she see him at such a distance? "You can search wherever you like," the girl said indifferently.

Once the fire was burning briskly, the girl rose. "Now to get the rubbish," she said and turned toward the house.

"Stefan," the taller officer said, "why don't you see if anyone is hiding in the house. Make a good thorough search," he added with a wink.

Moments later, the girl returned with an assortment of garbage and trash and started heaping it on the fire. The wind blew the smoke toward Filip and he was forced to stifle a sneeze.

The girl made a second trip to the cottage and returned with a bundle of rags. The SNB man regarded her with suspicion. "What are you burning now?"

"These are some castoff clothes of my uncle's. The doctor said we should burn them. They are the ones he wore when he got sick."

"Sick. What was wrong with him?"

"Scarlet fever."

The SNB trooper backed off a few feet. "By all means, burn them then."

Taking care to stand between the officer and the fire, the girl threw the bundle just a few feet beyond the flames. She

79

then turned toward the officer and smiled. "You are a handsome man," she told him. Coyly she asked, "Where is your friend? Is he looking this way?"

The officer assured her his colleague would be busy for a long while, then took her in his arms. She twisted him around and backed away from the fire, so he would be facing away from the flames. While he was thus occupied, Filip stealthily crept closer to the fire and snatched the bundle of rags back into the woods. He unwrapped the bundle hurriedly, tore off the SNB uniform, then put on a suit and cap that was mixed in with the rags and stuffed the guard's uniform back inside the bundle.

By the time Filip had crept closer to the fire and deposited the rags in it, the girl's sweater was ripped open and she was struggling against the trooper's advances.

Preoccupied with his wild gropings, the trooper did not hear Filip sneak up behind him. Filip wrapped his left arm around the officer's throat, applying pressure so that all that came from the SNB man's throat was a low choking sound. Filip pulled him away from the girl, brought his right arm around and plunged the knife carefully into a spot below the trooper's intestines, a spot that Filip knew from practice would kill his victim quickly and silently. He let go the officer's throat and watched him crumple to the ground, his mouth moving open and shut like a ventriloquist's dummy.

The girl simply stood there, whimpering quietly. Filip handed her the knife. "God bless you," he said.

"I wasn't sure," she sobbed. "I couldn't be sure you were there. There's another one inside. What should I do now?" Her words came out in a rush.

"Give me two minutes to get clear, then start screaming rape. When he comes out, you will be holding the knife and your friend here will be dead. Your honor will be saved. I think that's the best thing to do under the circumstances."

She nodded dumbly. "If you hadn't come when you did, I don't know if I could have held him off. Thank you for that."

Filip smiled down at her. "Thank you for saving my life."

"It's all for the Underground."

Filip gestured. "Wait a minute. Let's make you a little more believable." He gently mussed up her hair, tore her sweater further until a well-filled bra showed, and ripped her skirt. Then, on an impulse, he kissed her. "Goodbye," he called, and he darted across the yard to the field behind the next cottage.

He had reached the street five cottages away when he heard the girl start screaming. Tugging his cap low on his forehead, he pulled up the lapels of his suit against the wind and walked away from the sound. Everyone he passed was headed toward the disturbance.

The first snow of the season began falling when Filip was halfway across Svaty Martin. In the suit pocket was money and a train ticket to Bratislava. Filip headed toward the depot. The snow had started with a deceptive gentleness, but by the time Filip could see the railway station the streets were already covered and the trees and houses wore a mantle of white.

The few pedestrians who remained on the street walked briskly, intent on completing their errands before the full fury of the storm could catch them outside. Filip stepped up his pace. It would not do to walk slowly in such a snowstorm.

Across the square from the station, Filip sought temporary shelter under a shop awning already sagging with the weight of the snow and peered intently at the depot. The square, ordinarily bustling with people, was now deserted. The distance between the shop where Filip stood and the railway station took on the aspect of a yawning chasm. "I would make an excellent target crossing there," Filip muttered to himself.

The storm had chilled him through and snow had worked its way into his shoes. I would give fifty crowns for a glass of brandy in a warm café, he thought. But his orders were to board the train for Bratislava.

Out of the corner of his eye, Filip caught sight of something moving. He pivoted his head to look at the shop. A cat in the window was swishing its tail and purring warmly behind the frosted glass. Above the cat, Filip made out the sign, CAFÉ.

The train to Bratislava could wait. After all, when a man has killed another, skipped four meals and walked across the city in a snowstorm, he deserves a brandy. Filip walked into the café.

Five old men, who looked as if they were permanent fixtures in the place, sat sipping their beers with an air of ultimate boredom at the table nearest the stove. Except for the bartender and a waiter, who looked even more ancient than the five beer drinkers, the café was empty.

Spotting a rear exit, Filip selected a table near it, sat down, took off his cap and slapped it against his thigh, sending a shower of snow onto the floor. The old waiter shambled resentfully over to Filip's table and sighed at him.

"Brandy," said Filip.

"Brandy?" repeated the waiter.

"Brandy."

The waiter nodded. "Brandy," he said reluctantly and shuffled off.

The beer drinkers eyed Filip warily, as if he were trespassing on their property. Although caution warned him to pay no attention, he was wet, cold and miserable enough to glower back at them.

Filip's stare was successful. Each of the five, in turn, lowered his eyes.

The old-fashioned clock on the wall ticked laboriously. Across the room, the portly bartender was attempting to transfer the brandy from the bottle into a glass without spilling any, but it was a losing battle, since both hands were shaking.

Filip's nerves themselves were near the breaking point. He was about to shout for service, but he changed his mind quickly. Two uniformed men could be seen through the window, crossing the square from the general direction of the railroad station. Their dim figures, distorted by the moisture of the café window, loomed larger and larger. Filip watched them intently. Please, God, he prayed to himself, don't let them come in here.

The waiter slowly lowered the brandy glass and set it on the table before Filip.

By now, there was no doubt. The two men in green were obviously about to join the gay party in the café.

Filip quickly studied the rear exit, the front door, the five beer drinkers, the waiter and the bartender. If he bolted out the rear door, pursuit would be inevitable. The door to the washroom was closer. He stuffed his cap into his pocket and arose as casually as possible.

He was inside the washroom seconds before the police entered.

By breathing very slowly and pressing his ear tightly against the thin wooden door, Filip could make out what was said in the café. There was a great swirling noise as the outer door of the café opened, then a grunt as one of the policemen shoved it closed. Then the tread of boots and the thud of two heavy men sinking wearily into chairs.

Next came the old waiter's voice. "Good evening, Michal. Good evening, Jan. Is it still snowing?"

A new voice sighed, "Yes, Martin, it is still snowing. Why don't you ever look out the window."

"My eyes aren't so good," the old waiter said. "Beer as usual for you two?"

"Not tonight, Martin," another voice said, "we're still on duty. Bring us some coffee. Nice and hot."

Although he had been shivering with the cold only minutes before, Filip was now sweating profusely. Of all the luck, he thought, I have to pick out the one café in town that caters to the police. He recalled the unfriendly faces of the waiter, the bartender and the five beer drinkers, then peered down at his revolver. It held six cartridges. Not nearly enough to kill

83

nine people, even if the nine were cooperative enough to line up quietly to be shot.

Oh God! Filip suddenly thought, the brandy on the table!

The incredibly slow shuffling noise indicated that the old waiter was bringing the coffee to the SNB men. Then a rattling as the cups and saucers were put on the table. The waiter's voice said, "Keeping you busy tonight?"

"Mm-hmm" came a mumble. "We're manning the depot around the clock."

"Somebody steal a locomotive?" asked the waiter.

"Very funny!" snapped a policeman.

"We're looking for a man," said the other.

"What sort of a man?"

"A saboteur. He is an accomplice of the man who wrecked an important machine at the Stalin Enterprises yesterday and killed the factory manager."

"What did he look like?"

"A little hard to describe. A young man, about average height, no distinguishing features. Light hair, dark eyes. He was wearing a Security Police uniform the last time anyone saw him, but he's probably changed clothes by now. Anyone like that been in here tonight?"

Filip held his breath. Someone must have seen him in Vrutky when he approached Peter Dub on the street. There was a long silence on the other side of the door. Then the old waiter broke it. "No, no one I can recall."

The other policeman's voice had an edge of suspicion. "Who's the brandy for?"

Filip pointed the revolver at the middle of the washroom door.

A voice he had not heard before answered. "That's for me." It must be the old bartender, Filip speculated.

"Then why don't you drink it at the bar?"

"Policy of the house. Mr. Hlatka, the owner, lets me have one brandy every evening, provided I sit down and drink it like a gentleman."

84

A whoop of laughter. "That's a good one. I suppose Martin has to bring it to you?"

The reply was dead serious. "Yes, of course. Then, when it is Martin's turn to have his brandy, I bring it to his table."

From further across the room, Filip heard one of the beer drinkers assent. "That's the way it happens every night, Michal. Every night the old fools go through the same routine."

Filip heard the cups banging onto saucers and again the the scraping of chairs against the floor. "Well, back to the station," said one of the policemen.

"I hope you catch your man," said the waiter.

"We will if he comes near the station. It's swarming with police. We have all the roads out of town covered, too. I've seen troopers today I haven't laid eyes on for years. They've cancelled all leaves. Every officer in the city is looking for this fellow. If he's still in the city, we'll catch him."

"We certainly hope so," said a voice from the beer drinkers' table. "It's terrible what the younger generation thinks it can get away with these days."

A muffled "good night" was followed by the opening and closing of the outer door.

Then there was prolonged silence. Filip strained his ear against the door, but he could hear nothing further.

The door was pulled open so swiftly that Filip almost fell out of the washroom.

The waiter, his face betraying no emotion whatever, said, "You can come out now. And if you will sit down again, I will bring you another brandy."

Shamefacedly, Filip remembered he was still holding his revolver and quickly tucked it back under his belt.

"My friends," he said in a voice hoarse with emotion, "if you will permit me, I would like to buy brandy for everyone in the house."

Suddenly, everyone was smiling at him. "It's all right," said one of the beer drinkers. "Anyone who is running away from the SNB must be a patriot. The police get no information from us."

The others nodded agreement.

"However," said the bartender, "the danger is not yet past. I think it may prove very difficult for you to leave this city. You heard those two who came in. The whole police force is searching for you."

"On the other hand," the waiter interjected, "you certainly can't stay in Svaty Martin, either. It is only a matter of time, hours probably, before they organize a house-to-house search. They would surely catch you if you stay."

Filip sat down at the beer drinker's table, in response to a beckoning gesture from one of them. The irony of the situation struck him. Here were seven men, unknown to him, whose lives he was ready to take a few minutes ago, now planning ways and means of saving his life. They did this without being asked, because they believed in the Underground and what it stood for. Once more, the struggles and sacrifices seemed worthwhile to Filip.

"The snow," one of the beer drinkers interrupted Filip's reverie, "is both a help and a hindrance. On the one hand, it will slow down pursuit, but on the other, it will slow you down, too. And then there is the business of tracks in the snow.

Another of the old men snapped his fingers. "I think that is the answer. The tracks in the snow. Now the police would surely be able to follow the tracks of a lone man walking through the snow. But if there were a group of men, say six, the footprints would be impossible to distinguish. Let us all leave here together with our friend."

The idea was quickly agreed to. "But surely," Filip broke in, "there is no reason for you to involve yourselves in danger. This is my affair, this is between me and the police."

"No, you are wrong, young man," retorted the old man who had made the suggestion. "This fight is not between you and the Communists. It involves every one of us. We are old men, and we will probably never see our country free. But it is up to us to do what we can to see that you young people who can fight live to do the job. Am I right, my friends?"

They all nodded vigorously.

Filip realized he was outvoted and smiled his thanks. "Very well," he said. "Now the details. Obviously I cannot take the train. My only chance is to reach the guerillas. I have been in the mountains near here before, and perhaps I can make contact with one of the groups. If you gentlemen can accompany me to the edge of the city, I can make my way into the mountains. But how do we get away from here?"

"Perhaps," suggested the waiter, "if you were to buy a few more bottles of brandy, you might leave through the front door as if you were celebrating something. Perhaps you can even sing."

"I like the idea," said Filip. He called for six bottles of brandy. The bartender not only refused payment for them, put pressed an overcoat on Filip as well. "You'll need this in the mountains," he insisted.

Minutes later, Filip Polhora, in his outsize overcoat, encircled by the five old men, walked boldly out of the café and started boisterously down the street. To the occasional passers-by, they tipsily brandished bottles of liquor as they sang off key. The curious procession evoked a few laughs, but no curiosity. Twice they passed police patrols, waved gaily at them, and stumbled along through the snow.

One by one, as the brandy bottles were emptied, they were tossed into the snow. Filip was concerned at the trail of bottles they left behind, particularly in case the police decided to investigate the party of tipsy old men who wandered unevenly across town. Still, he decided against mentioning his fears to them. Theirs was a very brave act, and he would not do anything which might humiliate them.

The houses were now farther apart and Filip realized he must soon leave his new-found friends. The Fatra mountains loomed beyond the last lights of the town and Filip had never been happier to see them. The time had come to say goodbye, for Security Police would be stationed further along the road at the edge of town. He had better cut across the fields and through the woods into the mountains.

Filip halted the party and peeled several bills from the wallet that came with the suit. "Gentlemen, I do not know how to thank you properly for your bravery, but I can at least do this. Take this money into the café and drink to the Underground. When all the money is spent, I shall be far away and no longer a danger to you."

One of the old men, who had begun the long trek feigning drunkenness but by now was no longer playing a role, wept. "Goodbye, young man, and God go with you."

Quickly Filip left the road and plunged into the wilderness of the foothills leading to the sanctuary of the mountains. At least, he thought, the Stalin Enterprises will be out of commission for awhile until they could build a new stamping press. His hopes, almost dashed a few hours before, now rose as he climbed higher into the mountains. The snow had stopped and before too long, he convinced himself, he would probably be challenged by a sentry from one of the guerilla outposts.

By morning, Filip was deep into the mountain fastness northeast of Svaty Martin. The air in the mountains was cold in his lungs, but the wind of the night before had died down and the going was a little easier.

Making his way slowly but steadily through the snow, Filip was struck by the fact that he had not yet seen a single sign of the guerillas. Though the white blanket of snow covered any landmarks he might have remembered from past trips to the area, he was sure he should have come across one group of his compatriots by now. He kept walking, in order to keep warm. By noon, however, he realized he had no idea of where he was. He thought he might be somewhere near the River Vah, and he knew instinctively his best hope lay in continuing eastward. Eastern Slovakia had always been the home of the fiercest partisans of freedom.

But Filip was now aware, once the optimism of last night's escape from the city had faded, that he might walk for weeks in these vast mountains without meeting another human being. He was poorly equipped for a trek through the mountains, clad as he was in an old suit, an overcoat that was far too large for him, and a shapeless old cap. His shoes were equally unsuited to their present task.

Filip stopped a few yards from the crest of a high ridge to rest. He reached into the pocket of the overcoat and pulled out the last of the *klobasa,* the smoked pork sausage the bartender had stuffed into the coat before he left the café. Food would be hard to come by from now on, he knew. He still had a revolver and a few cartridges, but his knife had been left behind with the girl at the workman's cottage. Killing game with a revolver is not the safest or easiest way to obtain food. And in the snow-laden mountains, game can be scarce.

After his little repast, Filip sat down against a tree. Falling asleep in the cold was dangerous, he knew, but he could not fight exhaustion any longer. He fell asleep instantly.

It was still light when he awoke. Far off to the east, a thin plume of smoke rose slowly into the leaden sky. Smoke meant fire, and fire meant human companionship, possibly even food. Filip rose slowly, stretched his arms, and started over the crest of the ridge. Down he plunged into a depression, then up the next hill. He skirted two other ridges, following a tortuous path, always keeping his eyes trained on the spot where the smoke spiraled upward. For what seemed like hours, Filip made his way through the snow, no longer making any effort to cover his tracks.

The sun had almost set behind him when he came in sight of the fire. There was enough light, however, to throw his shadow, elongated almost out of recognition, across the snow ahead of him. Instinctively cautious, he slipped behind a large boulder as he drew near the fire. He waited patiently for some sign of life.

Something, obviously, was wrong. The fire had plainly

been set by a man, or a group of men. It had been used for cooking. It had been burning for hours, yet there was enough wood left for it to burn several hours more.

What troubled Filip was the fact the fire was deserted. It warmed no one. Filip studied the ground around the fire carefully, but could not tell whether the tracks had been made by one man or many. He also had no way of knowing when the man or men whose fire this was would return to its warmth.

Who had lit the fire? It could be guerillas, or trappers. Or could it be a Red patrol? Filip waited another fifteen minutes until the last light of day disappeared. The wind sharpened and Filip shivered. The fire began to look more inviting. It was then that Filip realized his ears were numb.

The threat of frostbite overcame his natural caution. He checked his revolver, and holding it carefully in front of him, walked out of hiding toward the welcoming warmth of the fire.

No one shot at him.

After a moment, Filip smiled sheepishly to himself, pocketed the revolver, and rubbed his hands near the flames. It felt good. Slowly circling the fire, he found a bone with some meat left on it. He skewered it on a stick and held it over the flames. He could scarcely wait for it to warm up, so tantalizing was the aroma of the meat. But he forced himself to wait, knowing it was unwise to eat raw meat.

Filip's spirits rose appreciably. It no longer mattered that he was a fugitive. It no longer mattered that he was uncertain of his whereabouts. He was warm now. He turned the meat over with loving care, reveling in the sight of the juices running out of it. At last, Filip decided his feast was ready. He withdrew the skewer from the flames.

Out of the darkness behind him, something small and ice cold was pressed into the nape of his neck.

"Keep your hands high." The voice was quite close to Filip's ear. Reacting automatically, Filip dropped the meat into the fire and watched it char. Foolishly, all he could think of was, "I must not break down."

Very slowly, he raised his hands. His eyes stayed rooted to the spot where the flames consumed his dinner. Rapidly and expertly, the man behind Filip located the revolver, and transferred it from Filip's waist to his own pocket. Then he stepped back.

"Turn around. Very slowly." It was a flat, even voice. Filip obeyed carefully. After having looked so long into the bright fire, his eyes could make out only a dim shape in the darkness. But there was no mistaking the Luger aimed at Filip's midsection.

As his eyes grew accustomed to the darkness, the outline of his captor became clearer in the flickering firelight. He wore the uniform of the Red Army, surmounted by captain's bars. The captain was a tall, lean man with a long, craggy but attractive face. He had white, even teeth, and he was smiling.

"You are the man who helped Peter Slezak, aren't you?" The question was asked politely, in a conversational tone.

Filip studied the captain before answering. He had been caught. Cleanly. He had been tricked by a fire that had been laid for him alone. He was sure of it. His bodily weakness had betrayed him into following a plume of smoke in the sky, in the hope of finding warmth, food, shelter. Instead, he was facing death at the hands of an agent of the enemy. Clearly, he was up against an exceedingly clever man, a man clever enough to reduce Filip Polhora to the status of a moth beating its wings to death against the fire it instinctively seeks.

Yet there was something that did not quite add up. The captain was alone. Filip sensed this, though he could not be certain. It seemed inconceivable that the Red Army would send a single man into the mountains to hunt him down. The captain's bars plainly said that he was in charge of the manhunt for Filip, and it logically followed that he would have a patrol with him. Still, he confronted Filip alone, and with a smile on his face.

He might fire that pistol if I am not careful, Filip thought.

Answering the captain's smile with one of his own, Filip took a chance. "Where are the others?" he asked.

It had been a shot in the dark, but it had a telling effect. The captain held his smile, but his eyes told Filip plainly that his enemy was indeed alone. The others were not near. That reduced the odds considerably.

"May I sit down?" Filip asked politely.

"Of course. Your name?"

"Pavel Harustiak," Filip said unhesitatingly. It was a name he had never used before, but it sprang to his lips naturally. "And you are Captain. . . ?"

"Captain Urban. How do you do?" He nodded pleasantly, but did not offer to shake hands. He moved closer to the fire and sat facing Filip. He handled the Luger casually, but without permitting the barrel to deviate from its target. "I'm sorry if I startled you, and made you drop your venison."

Filip shrugged. "I wasn't sure what kind of meat it was. I never did get to taste it."

Captain Urban rummaged in his field pack with his free hand, and pulled out a bigger joint than the one Filip had been cooking. He tossed it at Filip. "Here. Start cooking this one. There's more than enough for both of us." His smile could not have been friendlier.

As the meat sizzled over the fire, Filip decided to press his advantage. "I don't believe you answered my question, Captain. Where are the others? Certainly the Army isn't reduced to sending out one-man patrols."

Urban laughed. "We will meet the others tomorrow. The rendezvous is only half a day's march from here."

"And you intend to bring me with you?"

"Of course, Harustiak. You are a prisoner of the Red Army, wanted for sabotage. And I'm bringing you in. It's as simple as that."

The captain's self-confidence worried Filip. His self-confidence and the fact that Captain Urban had both Filip's weapon and his own. Still, Filip was getting a chance to eat, and the prospect of food and a night's rest before setting off for the rendezvous would give him an opportunity, if only a slight one, to compete with his enemy on more advantageous terms.

After they ate, Filip lay down on a blanket Urban provided from his field pack and covered himself with his coat. He closed his eyes, pretending to sleep, and hoping Urban would drop off before him. But the warmth of the fire and his tiredness overcame his resistance and sleep overtook him as the Red Army captain was still feeding logs into the fire.

Filip awoke, but made sure there was no change in the rhythm of his breathing before he opened his eyes. The darkness was slowly giving way to day. He could feel that the fire had long since died down to embers, and he heard nothing to tell him whether his captor was asleep or awake. Perhaps this was his chance.

Captain Urban was smiling at him from five feet away. The Luger was aimed at Filip's head. "Go back to sleep, Harustiak. You have another hour, at least, before dawn."

Filip stifled the impulse to say something, shrugged his shoulders once, and went back to sleep.

But sleep did not come easily. Never before had he felt so completely alone and powerless. Help from the Underground seemed out of the question here deep in the mountains. And Captain Urban disturbed Filip. He made no attempt to question Filip about the Underground, or his role in the sabotage at the Stalin Enterprises. He seemed content merely to have captured Filip. The implication was that Filip would be questioned later on at length. He tried not to think about that, resolving only that he would die before the Reds learned anything of value from his lips.

Eventually, the Underground would hear exactly how Filip had been put to death, and the news would reach the tiny village on the banks of the Morava. Leonora would hear of his death and be saddened. That hurt worst of all, for the first time in his life to have met a girl he could think of in terms of marriage, then never to see her again.

Suddenly Captain Urban was shaking him awake.

After a meager breakfast of canned Red Army rations, Urban and his prisoner started off at a brisk pace toward the east. As the morning wore on, Filip, half-numbed by the cold and knife-like wind, made a mental note of the fact they seemed to be climbing higher and higher into the mountains. But he had long since lost track of his whereabouts. It was of little value to know he was heading east when he could no longer be sure of where he had started from.

Much of the time Filip and his captor were above the timber line, and the force of the wind became almost unbearable. Snow had begun to fall again. Filip began to worry now not so much about the treatment at the hands of the Red Army, but whether he and Urban would reach the rendezvous point alive.

By now Filip's shoes had holes worn through the soles, and each step had to be made carefully. His overcoat did little to keep out the wind, and his hands felt withered and raw from the cold. Several times he lagged behind, and Urban had to prod him to keep going. Urban did not seem to notice the cold. Indeed, he appeared to thrive on it, which added to Filip's misery.

At length, as they topped the crest of a ridge, Filip felt he could go no further. He sank to the ground, not even caring that he fell into the snow. Let him kill me, ran through his mind, and get it over with.

Urban smiled. "I was just going to suggest we rest a while, Harustiak. You picked a good spot for it. There is less wind here."

Filip didn't trust himself to answer. He hugged his knees to his chin, in a futile effort to keep warm. As far as he could see, there was no hint of warmth, no hint of shelter, only the barren loneliness of the impersonal mountains.

If only I had the strength, I would kill Urban with my bare hands, Filip thought. But when he flexed his hands, they did not react properly. Filip studied the captain for a long time,

94

hating him more each moment for his calm and self-assuredness. The man has no right to be impervious to cold. He has no right to be so damned confident.

Filip prayed: "Please God, let me kill this man before I die."

Urban lit a cigarette, then offered one to Filip. "Smoke, Harustiak?"

Filip hated himself for accepting, but the thought of the warmth of the smoke in his lungs was irresistible. "Thank you," he said sullenly.

Urban had long since returned his Luger to its holster, confident that the watched prisoner no longer offered a serious problem in resistance. Casually, he told Filip they should reach the meeting place with his troops in another two hours.

"Two more hours of this?" The incredulity in Filip's voice was plain.

Urban laughed. "I thought you 'freedom fighters' were made of sterner stuff. If you're an example, I don't think we'll have too much trouble with Underground after all."

Filip bit his lip to keep from replying.

Urban arose, obviously refreshed by the brief rest, and motioned for Filip to do the same. "Come on, Harustiak, let's keep moving. You'll feel warmer walking. Good for the circulation, you know."

Wearily, Filip dragged himself upright and shook some of the snow off his clothes. Goaded by hatred, he started off down the slope toward the next ridge, followed by his enemy. It was a point of pride now to keep going, to match Urban step for step over the uneven terrain. The snow lay deep as they crossed a gully between two pinnacles of ice-encrusted rock, and Filip stumbled again and again.

There was no telling how deep the snow lay at this spot, Filip realized. As one foot sank in, he quickly stepped on the other while pulling the first out. It was as if he were walking through quicksand.

Then Filip noticed it. Ahead of him was a depression in the snow. It was no more than two feet wide, and only two or three inches below the surface of the surrounding snow, but it ran as far as he could see to either side. If only this was what he thought it was, Filip prayed.

He glanced back over his shoulder cautiously, to see if Urban had also noticed it, but the captain's eyes were fixed on the summit ahead. Filip slowed his pace until Urban was perhaps only a foot or two behind him. As Filip reached the depression, he lifted his right foot without breaking stride, then suddenly twisted to the side away from Urban and threw himself backward.

The depression was, as Filip had hoped, a crevasse in the field of snow. As he leaped back, he could see the fleeting look of incredulity on Urban's face as the latter tried to bring himself to a halt in the middle of a stride, fail, then disappear in the snow.

The whole thing had happened in less than a second. At one moment, Urban had been completely in command, bringing in a prisoner. At the next, Urban himself was a prisoner, helplessly trapped in a deep fissure filled with snow and ice.

Filip tested the snow he sprawled on with infinite care, then cautiously crept forward to the edge of the crevasse. Urban had managed to break his fall before he had dropped very far. He was wedged sideways into the narrow but seemingly bottomless pit, his head about three feet below the surface. His left arm was jammed fast against the ice wall, but the ubiquitous Luger was there in his right hand. By stretching his arm straight up, Urban was able to aim the gun at Filip's head as it peered over the side of the crevasse.

Filip looked deep into Urban's eyes. The cool, self-assured look had given way to fear, hatred, disbelief and hopelessness.

"You know what will happen if you shoot?"

Urban continued to stare.

"If you kill me, you will never get out, Urban. I am your only hope."

The trapped officer considered this. The Luger wavered.

"Your hand is shaking, Urban. Suppose you miss. Or even

if you hit me. The noise of the shot may cave in the walls and you will be buried alive. Even if you kill me, you will die, Captain Urban."

In a gesture of utter defeat, Urban lowered his right arm.

A wild sense of elation came over Filip. He could just get up and walk off now. No power on earth could keep him here. He could leave Urban in the crevasse, make his way to civilization, make contact with the Underground. Perhaps he could even reach Leonora.

Still, he realized as sanity returned, there were perils ahead. He was a hunted man who had no idea where he was. The remainder of Urban's patrol awaited him. He was unarmed. That was the answer. He must get the two guns from Urban.

Filip peered into the crevasse. "Do you want me to get you out, Captain Urban?"

A glimmer of hope crossed Urban's face. "Yes," he gasped, "please, yes."

"Give me the Luger first."

"Oh God," Urban pleaded, "Get me out of here!"

"Hand up the Luger, butt end first."

Filip realized there wasn't much time. Urban was beginning to crack. "Hand up the Luger."

Urban handed it up in desperate haste.

By reaching ever so carefully, and bracing himself with his other hand, Filip found he could grasp the pistol. He swiftly yanked it up out of the captain's hand and laid it on the snow beside him.

"Now, Captain Urban, I want my own revolver."

"Help me," Urban begged. "Help me, I can't hold on much longer."

The terror in Urban's eyes communicated itself to Filip. "Quickly then, my revolver."

Urban managed to slide his free hand into the pocket of his tunic and pull out the gun. He stretched it up toward Filip, grasping the barrel as a drowning man clutches at a straw.

97

Filip lowered his right hand, wrapped it around the revolver grip.

"Pull me up," Urban pleaded. "In the name of God, pull me up!"

Filip stared directly into his enemy's eyes. How thinly separated are life and death, Filip reflected. I can pull the trigger and Urban will die. I can pull him up and he will live.

With astonishing clarity, Filip analyzed his feelings. The helpless man below him was his natural enemy, a man who stood for tyranny, the police state, communism, everything Filip had learned to hate. Yet he was another human being, a man who ate and drank and slept and made love, a human being trapped by the implacable forces of nature, a man who had begged Filip, invoking the name of a God he had supposedly disavowed. He was worth killing and he was worth saving.

Filip tightened the grip on the revolver. Slowly, ever so slowly, he began pulling Urban upward.

For the rest of his life, Filip could never be sure if what happened next was an accident caused by fatigue or an act of will. His hand tightened on the revolver, the trigger squeezed. A bullet crashed through the short space between the hunter and his prey, and Urban's face shattered under the impact.

Urban's right hand unclasped itself from the barrel of the revolver and dropped slowly, almost gracefully to his side.

Filip looked at Urban's body twitch once, then go limp. He had the strange feeling that he had been standing apart from the two figures on the snow, watching the scene as a disinterested observer and not as a participant. Then he moved back from the crevasse and vomited.

The important thing now was to get as far away from this place as possible. Urban's patrol was sure to have heard the shot in the mountain stillness. Panic restoring his flagging energy, Filip fled the tiny snow field as fast as he could without any clear sense of direction. Stumbling through the snow, he instinctively sought trails leading downward, away from the furious winds of the mountain peaks.

For hours he trudged on automatically, no longer thinking of a destination. His body was numb beyond aching. I could lie down and die but I won't, he told himself over and over.

By nightfall, he was well below the timberline on the northern side of the Vah River and he sought refuge in a thick cluster of trees. Huddled beside the bole of a great tree, Filip lay down at the command of his bone-weary body, and waited for sleep to overtake him, still clutching his guns. I won't die, he told himself, I won't die, I won't die. The wind, softer here below the peaks, soughed through the treetops above him, repeating the refrain—you won't die, you won't die—until he heard no more.

Book II THE CHURCH OF SILENCE

Wherever the Communists gain control, they seek to destroy organized religion or bend it to their will. There is no God, no immortal soul in the Communist order of things, only materialism, only the here-and-now.

But the Communist suppression of religion is more than just a matter of philosophic belief. It is a practical necessity for Communist survival. So long as a man believes in a power greater than his own, so long as he believes in God, whether it is the God of the Christians and Jews or any other faith, his mind and soul has not succumbed to communism and he remains a potential enemy of the State.

The Slovaks are a deeply religious people; most of them are Roman Catholics. They were the first among the Slavs to embrace Christianity. In the year 863, Saints Cyril and Methodius, "the Apostles of the Slavs" as they later came to be called, came to Slovakia from Byzantium to bring the new faith. They translated the Bible into the Old Slavonic tongue and from Slovakia, the Word was spread to the other Slavic peoples.

The parish church was an important part of the life of Slovakia when the Communists came to power. For many villagers, its music was their opera; the drama of the Mass the only theater they would know; the beauty of the church and its holy art their major opportunity for artistic appreciation. The square in front of the church on Sunday was their forum, where they would meet and discuss the news of the day, politics, sports, recipes and gossip. The church was their fashion show, where the embroidered costumes of men and women displayed the skill of the women whose fingers made them. It was the center of their lives, and to be denied the church was almost to be denied life itself.

To the Communists, therefore, subjugation of the Church in Slovakia seemed to offer an excellent chance of winning over the minds and souls of the Slovaks. The Red rulers succeeded in taking over control of all open and organized religion. But they did not reckon with the depth of the Slovaks' faith, nor with their determination somehow to keep the spark of that faith alive through the Church of Silence. . . .

5. Bread and Wine

THE CAVE had a sand floor, paved with slabs of rock. A long straight tunnel branching off the main path of the cave formed a natural nave. The rock walls rose along the side like the vaulted arch of a church. Along the walls, set in niches cut out of the sides, were heavy candles. At the far end of the nave was a rough-hewn table, covered by a white cloth and flanked by a pair of white candles.

The figure that rose from the altar was a giant—big and rugged. He genuflected to the tabernacle, asked Christ's forgiveness for the interrupted Mass and hurried to the prostrate form below the altar.

"Leave him with me," he told the two men who had carried the limp figure into the cave.

"As you wish, Father Vendel," one of the pair bowed.

Father Vendel pried the Luger and revolver from the unconscious man's hands, tucked them into the belt beneath his cassock, then hoisted the man easily over his right shoulder and carried him out of the makeshift church.

Following a labyrinthine path through the passages leading away from the natural nave, Father Vendel finally reached an enclosed chamber. The sparsely furnished room served as his living quarters. He put the body down gently onto his bed, turned up the kerosene heater and removed his cassock and surplice. Extracting a key from his pants pocket, he unlocked a steel cabinet standing against the stone wall of the cavern.

Methodically, he hung up his priestly vestments. Then, remembering the revolver and Luger, he pulled these out of his belt and put them on a shelf of the locker alongside a submachine gun, four rifles, six hand grenades and four other guns. He locked the steel cabinet and dropped the key back in his pocket.

Finally, he turned his attention to the prone figure on his bed. Father Vendel searched the man's clothes in a thorough and practiced manner. He examined the man's pockets, the lining of his coat, the cuffs of his trousers.

Failing to find anything menacing, the priest set about making the man comfortable. He removed the wet torn clothing and piled blankets over him. He forced a few swallows of brandy down the man's throat, examined him for fever, counted his pulse and listened to his respiration. He gently massaged his patient's hands and feet and ears, then applied a warmed cloth to the frost-bitten parts.

Lacking medicine, Father Vendel decided the wisest course was to let him sleep. He settled into a straight chair, picked up a small black book and began reading his daily office. From time to time he looked at the sleeping figure. The suffering etched on the face of the man on his bed brought a sympathetic smile to Father Vendel. He remembered when he, too, had looked so desperate, so forlorn, suffering from shock and torture.

All morning, Father Vendel busied himself with his household chores, tidying the church, the "parish house," and the other rooms of the cave, stopping once for a meager meal of bread and cheese. Occasionally he dropped in to see the sleeping man, but there was no change in his condition.

The quiet of the afternoon was interrupted only by a new storm outside the cave. Harsh winds and snow battered the High Tatras. Branches of trees, already bent with snow and ice, swung loosely back and forth under the impact of the winds. Father Vendel stood near the mouth of the cave looking at the swirling whiteness, then went back inside to complete his breviary.

A strange foreboding came over him as he was murmuring

his prayers. He put on his warmest coat, donned a fur cap and walked out into the snow. There, far in the distance, he thought he saw movement. The glare of sun reflected on the snow made vision difficult, but it seemed to Father Vendel that a column of men was moving in his direction. He stared steadily at the slowly enlarging blur, searching for a clue that would tell him if the advancing mass was friend or foe. From time to time, the dark blot on the snow would stop, then move again. The guerillas weren't expected until Christmas, three weeks off, he ruminated. But was it likely that the Communists would send patrols out in weather such as this?

The cleric watched warily as the column came closer, moving over the tricky terrain with sure familiarity. In front, Father Vendel could now make out the broad outlines of the leader who was supporting—could it really be?—what looked like a woman. Hope surged back to Father Vendel, for a party with a woman in its midst could hardly be a Communist patrol.

As the intruders came nearer, the priest saw they were wearing no uniforms. Across the chest of the heavy-set leader, Father Vendel saw a familiar bandolier. On the leader's face a drooping mustache could be made out. The priest ran down the slope to meet his visitors.

"Jan Labuda, Jan Labuda," he shouted as he ran. "Labuda, Labuda," came the echoes from the valley. The guerilla leader tore himself loose from the column, and rushed to embrace Father Vendel wordlessly. He pulled back sharply, gestured with his carbine to the group behind and said quietly, "Father, we bring a dead man with us. It is Martin Hatala. Anicka is heartbroken. Do what you can."

Father Vendel, observing the great emotion in Labuda's face, braced himself for the encounter with the rest of the guerilla band. He knew what the loss would mean to the guerillas, for Hatala was destined to succeed Labuda. But the pain would be even greater for Labuda, for it was only a few months before that Father Vendel had married Labuda's daughter Anicka to Hatala in the very same cave that stood behind him.

Slowly uncovering the face of Martin Hatala, Father Vendel spoke: "Friends, I see that a bloody death snatched a valiant man from among his brave companions. In mourning him and praying for his eternal rest, we must devoutly thank our Saviour that Martin Hatala has died in battle, in freedom, and is to rest here in the earth around us that we still consider free. Yes, we still have the grace of a death of our own choosing. And therefore to see aright the grace in which God lets us live, we must think again and again of the thousands from whom such grace was withdrawn, of those thousands who have died in the worst bondage, who lie unburied or in mass graves, or whom the enemies of freedom simply cremated.

"Martin Hatala will be buried in consecrated ground, in dignity and with the blessing of the Church. So let us then, in this hour in which we mourn our brother in Christ, Martin Hatala, remember what real misfortune is and that it is located not here where we stand but down the mountains in the territory of the slave."

The guerillas groaned assent, and carried Hatala's body into the church and laid it down near the altar. Father Vendel shook his head sadly when he saw that Hatala was still dressed in clothes of combat and not in a fresh suit as is usually worn on the last trip beyond. There was only the washing of his face as comfort to the dead. Then came the tying of Hatala's feet for the Judgment Day. A crucifix and two candles were placed near the head of the body and the guerillas, despite their exhaustion, took turns watching over Hatala at the altar.

Labuda felt the gentle touch of the priest's fingers on his shoulder, asking him to follow. They walked through dimly lit passages until they came to an empty chamber and sat down. "How did it happen?" Father Vendel asked.

"Martin was killed two days ago in the skirmish near Podolinec," Labuda began. "It was madness to attack that concentration camp. I was against it." But with adolescent zeal, Hatala had joined the crowd of several hundred peasants who wanted to liberate the monks and priests from throughout Slovakia who had been detained in Podolinec. The guards in the observation towers were equipped with automatic machine guns, and mowed down the onrushing peasants, armed only with scythes and forks. The field around the camp was soon littered with bodies, among them Hatala, whose machine gun was nestled in the crook of his arm.

"As I looked through my binoculars from a distance," Labuda went on, "it seemed that nothing could be done to rescue Martin. A sortie was out of the question. It would have cost too many lives and even then would have done no good. The only thing I could do was wait till the bloodshed was all over, then send two of my men to search for Hatala in the hope that he was only wounded. But that was a vain hope. In the evening when Dubny and Lisska found him, Martin was dead."

"Jan," the huge priest muttered, "I can only pray that this impulsive attempt to save the prisoners in the camp will have no unfortunate consequences for them."

Labuda, his eyes red and his hands pounding aimlessly on the rocky wall, cried, "What right did Hatala have to join the unarmed peasants? What right did he have to risk his own life under such circumstances? Tell me, Father, what right did he have?"

The priest shook his head. He put his arm around Labuda and said, "He was an idealistic youth, a hotheaded one. He was always boiling to fight for his beliefs, but he had not yet learned to temper his thirst for battle with wisdom. Someday he would have learned that under you, Jan, if he had lived."

Labuda sat with his head in his hands, sobbing soundlessly. Seeking to end Labuda's suffering, Father Vendel asked, "When shall we bury him?"

The guerilla leader quieted down. He was dealing again with facts and decisions. "I will have my men make a coffin tomorrow morning. The burial should take place about four in the afternoon."

"There is one problem, Jan," the priest said. "I did not expect you and your men to come for some time. I will need more wafers and sacrificial wine for the funeral Mass tomorrow. I know your men must be exhausted after their long journey, but I think you will have to send someone to the village below to get some wine and enough wafers for all your men to receive the Communion."

Labuda quickly agreed. "We left Podolinec so fast that we did not have a chance to round up food for our band. I don't suppose you will have enough for them to last till Christmas."

Father Vendel shook his head. "Perhaps three or four days' supply, no more. And that would be stretching things."

"The Reds will be extra vigilant after the attack at Podolinec," Labuda said, "so it may be too risky to hunt for animals. The shots would only attract them. We might as well try to get food in the village tonight. Perhaps we can recruit some from the farmers."

"I think you will find the farmers eager to help," the priest said. "They are near revolt themselves." The Reds had forced the farmers to give up their land, he told Labuda, so it could be turned into a collective farm. The peasants were called into the local school and held there without food until they were near physical exhaustion. They had no choice except to sign away their ancestral farms.

"In that case," Labuda commented, "the temperature of the water is most favorable for our fish. Maybe we can even convince the Communists at the storehouse to share their bounty with us," he added, smiling thinly.

The sleeping figure in Father Vendel's room opened his eyes. He lay there quietly for awhile, accustoming himself to the dim light. The sound of approaching footsteps roused him to his feet, but he was struck by dizziness and dropped back to a sitting position on the bed. He reached for his Luger and revolver, but they were not there. Only then he remembered vaguely being dragged into a cave.

Two men walked into the room. One of them broke into a

broad grin as he saw the sitting figure. "Filip Polhora," Labuda exclaimed as he embraced the young courier. "I haven't seen you in years. What on earth are you doing here?"

"I have just escaped from the clutches of a devil named Urban, whom I have sent to hell."

Father Vendel's initial look of surprise turned to pleasure. Though he had never seen Filip before, he knew the name and had heard of his exploits as a courier for the Underground. "I did not think you were a Communist agent," he said, "but I had no idea the prince of couriers was my guest. I am honored to have you here."

Filip recounted to Labuda and the priest his flight after the sabotage of the Stalin Enterprises. "But what brings you here, Jan?" he asked.

"Martin Hatala is dead, Filip. He is lying now before the altar." Labuda pointed toward the altar room. "Go there, Filip, and comfort Anicka."

Altar? An altar in a cave? Filip was puzzled at first, then remembered a hazy vision of a priest rising from an altar. It seemed like a dream.

He rose from the bed, stood swaying for a few seconds before the wave of lightheadedness passed. Each step he took was painful, for blisters had begun to form on his frostbitten feet. He winced once, then hid his distress as he left the room with Father Vendel and Labuda.

The body of Hatala, lying in state before the altar, was never left alone. Though his death had been violent, Hatala's face still had the smile of delight he always wore in time of trial. He seemed at perfect peace with himself.

Kneeling over Hatala was Anicka. From her folded dress, Filip saw her take out a tiny glass phial, sealed with a drop of wax. Months before, Martin Hatala had brought back from one of the guerilla expeditions a bottle of expensive perfume. In the tiny pellet of glass Anicka kept her precious treasure. She stood up now and crushed the thin glass ball over Hatala's cold forehead. A heady scent of perfume rose and remained hovering in front of the crucifix.

"It might have been me lying there if Urban had been successful," ran through Filip's mind as he made the sign of the cross.

Anicka looked at Filip wordlessly as he put his arm around her, her eyes perplexed, like an animal mortally wounded in its own lair. Labuda motioned to Filip to take her away. She went, swaying a little, supported by Filip. Not till the two were far from the altar enclosure and Anicka's own room in sight did Filip speak. "Anicka, my friend, do not think that he has left us forever. Think that he has only gone ahead of us and that he is waiting for us to join him. That is our fate in the way of life we have chosen."

The stocky girl did not answer. She stopped at the entrance to her room, and spread her arms to bar the way to Filip. "Thank you, Filip, thank you," she said and ran quickly into her cave.

Father Vendel was leaning over a heavy wooden table in his room, writing by candlelight in apparent haste when Filip returned. The priest stood up. "It is time for you to sit down and eat. You must be starved."

Without waiting for a reply, the priest set bread and smoked bacon in front of Filip. He put a kettle of water on top of the kerosene heater to make fresh tea for both of them. Only when Filip was half finished with his bread and cold bacon did he speak. "When did Labuda and his men arrive?"

Father Vendel rose to pour the tea before he answered. It was the first hot nourishment Filip had tasted in forty-eight hours and the steam that curled up from the cup brought a feeling of content to his weary body. The priest stood staring off in space, holding the tea in both hands, as he told Filip of the events leading to the guerilla's arrival in the cave.

He put the cup down on the table. "Before I forget," he said as he went to the steel cabinet in the room, "here is your Luger and some of your other belongings."

Filip took his possessions and remarked, as he was putting the guns back into his belt, "I must confess I am surprised to see a priest living in the caves, and with a church set up to boot."

"Did you know, Filip, that I too was a courier for awhile?"

Filip shook his head. He had never known of any priests among his cohorts.

"Perhaps not a courier in your sense of the word," Father Vendel said as he noticed Filip's perplexity. "I did not work for anyone in the Underground. I was a courier for the bishops, carrying messages between them before their arrest. At that time I still believed it would be possible for the Church and communism to live together. I believed in some kind of a compromise."

"What changed your mind about the possibility of a compromise?"

"The Communists' idea of a compromise was no compromise at all," Father Vendel replied. "In Eastern Slovakia, as you know, as in the Ukraine, the Russians simply outlawed the Greek Catholic Church. They sent many of the clergy to Siberia and tried to absorb the rest into the Russian Orthodox Church. They made no bones about it. But in Western Slovakia they were much more insidious. They did not try to abolish the Church. They tried to take over control for themselves, staying within the letter of canon law, but perverting it."

The Soviets were not out to ban religious worship as such. They sought to force priests to cooperate with the Red regime, to tell their parishioners to work hard for their Communist leaders. A few priests embraced communism quickly, Father Vendel noted with regret. Many who disagreed were imprisoned and tortured until they relented, and if they still refused to cooperate with the Communists, were killed or denied the right to wear the priestly garb. They were sent to work in factories or on farms. Many churches were shut down, since

111

few new priests were being trained. The Soviets were banking on the gradual withering away of the Church.

Even the bishops were subjected to Communist pressure and torture until they agreed to toe the line. They were told the priests in their dioceses would be maltreated or killed unless the bishops followed the orders of the Communists. Those who would still not bow were thrown into jail on trumped-up charges of treason or espionage. When a bishop could no longer serve, it was up to the canons of the diocese to elect a vicar of the chapter, a kind of a temporary bishop to administer the diocese until the Pope could nominate a new bishop.

But the Pope cannot nominate a new bishop unless the existing one has died or resigned from his post. The fact that a bishop is in prison did not change the requirement. And even if a bishop had sent his resignation from a prison cell, the Pope could not have accepted it, for it would obviously have been dictated under extreme duress. And even if, legally, the Pope could have named a new bishop, he would refuse because to do so would have been interpreted as a tacit admission that the Communist charges against a particular bishop were well-founded.

So the Communists would advance their own candidate for temporary administration of a diocese, a priest who had embraced communism or would willingly cooperate with the Reds. If the canons of the chapter chose someone else, their choice would be quickly imprisoned. Eventually, the canons had to accede to the Communists' choice.

Once the leadership of the Church in Slovakia had been captured, many priests gave up the fight. If a bishop whom a parish priest had followed all his life was cooperating with the Soviets, even under pressure, how was the priest himself to know what was wrong and what was right? Even the titular vicars imposed by the Communists were followed by many of their priests, who were used to Church discipline. Confused, lost, cut off from any true inspiration, many priests yielded to the Reds.

"At first," Father Vendel related, "I too cooperated. I could not condemn my fellow priests, because I felt that a good shepherd does not run away from his flock. I cannot accuse them even now, for it is not my right to judge. The people want Communion, they want a priest to listen to their confessions. And if the priest refuses to cooperate with the Communists, his flock would soon be without someone to minister to its spiritual needs. Even the Holy Father suffered Communist regimes as long as they permitted the Church to perform a minimum of its functions. His hope has been that the Word of God can be brought to the greatest number and, so far as possible, to spare the faithful from the fullest impact of persecution and martyrdom. Only those who willingly embrace communism are excommunicated."

It was during the spring of 1951, Father Vendel told Filip, that he finally realized that compromise under pressure is no compromise at all.

"I was dressed as a workman, carrying secret papers for delivery to another city. As I reached the town of Borsky Svaty Mikulas, I saw a group of men fighting a detachment of police who had come to arrest the local priest. Since I had the secret documents with me, I could not risk my own arrest and I hid in the house of a friend near the church."

From the window, Father Vendel saw the people drive off the first small group of police with stones and clubs. But he knew what would follow. The people were still milling excitedly about the square when reinforcements came from nearby Bratislava, a strong detachment of Workers' Militia and Security Police.

The villagers surrounded the church. Many of them were women fighting only with their bare hands. One of the women, Hedviga Rozborova, mother of five, led a charge against the police. "Mothers, do not let them take our pastor," she shouted. "Fight! Fight!"

In the cave Father Vendel took another sip of tea. "The women fought like furies, tearing and scratching with their fingernails at the hands, the faces and the eyes of the police. But you know that bare hands cannot hold out long against guns. The police fired several volleys into the crowd, and I saw men and women and even children—for there were children in the crowd—fall to the ground. Many were wounded and killed that day.

"Hedviga Rozborova was struck by a rifle butt and carried off to prison in Bratislava, where she was beaten and tortured. Four months later she died in the jail, pleading for one last look at her children. That, of course, was denied to her. She was sent home in a sealed coffin under the eyes of the Communist police, so that her family and neighbors would not see her mangled body. She died without the sacraments and without a priest to assist at the burial."

"What happened to the pastor?" Filip asked.

"Naturally, he was carried away the day of the fight. It was then I realized that we cannot compromise with evil. One can surrender to it, or one can fight it. For me it was better to accept the fight."

The mission Father Vendel was engaged in when he passed through Borsky Svaty Mikulas offered him the opportunity to strike back at the Communists. The documents he carried to various priests included copies of a letter that had been drawn up years before by the bishops of Slovakia for just such an emergency as the Church then faced.

As long ago as 1944, when the Communist Armies were storming the Carpathians, the bishops had recognized the fact that the Church might in time be captured by the Reds. And so in anticipation of that black future, they prepared a secret document called "Pastorization in Difficult Times." Later, after the coup d'etat of 1948, new directives came from Rome.

The time might come, the letter said, when the public or official spiritual administration of Slovakia might fall into the control of the Communists. When that happened, a secret spiritual administration would be formed. A Secret Church or, as it came to be called, the Church of Silence.

Priests recruited into the Secret Church would have to disappear from public life. They would live as workers or farmers and change their names for safety's sake. They would minister to their flock in secrecy, in homes, in the woods, in the mountains, wherever they could without drawing the attention of the Communists. At least one secret bishop would have to be named, for a true Church cannot function without a bishop, and preferably three secret bishops should be selected if the Church is to be perpetuated, for three bishops are necessary to consecrate a new bishop once his appointment is approved by the Pope.

The papers outlining the structure of the Secret Church were brought to many priests by Father Vendel that summer. Once he had reported back to his bishop, he went underground. While many priests of the Secret Church melted into their parishes and assumed other identities, Father Vendel set up his secret church in the caves and attached himself to marauding guerilla units. He lived with the guerillas, led them in worship, performed weddings, baptisms—and burials. More than once he had given a dying guerilla the last sacraments.

When the guerillas seized a town temporarily, he was there to perform the offices of the Church for the townspeople. For the citizens of a town whose church had been shut down, Father Vendel's infrequent visits were greeted with jubilation. Even in the towns where the churches were still open, many of the people refused to attend, out of fear the confessions and other rites performed by a priest who collaborated with the Communists were not valid in the eyes of the Church. For these skeptics, Father Vendel's appearances, too, were eagerly awaited.

The teacup had long grown cold when Father Vendel finished his story. Filip looked at the priest in silence, twice starting to speak, but each time halting himself in obvious reluctance. The cleric lifted Filip's hand and touched it to his powerful chest in encouragement. "You still have another question, Filip?"

"Yes, Father. I know it is presumptuous of me. But since you were active at the very birth of the Secret Church, I cannot help but wonder if you yourself are a secret bishop."

Father Vendel laughed heartily. "So that's what was troubling you. No, Filip, I am not. I am what you might call a field general, executing the orders of my secret bishops, just as Jan Labuda, for example, leads his guerillas under the orders of the Underground general staff.

"But I will tell you this. Although I am not a bishop, I have many of the powers of a bishop in the Secret Church. For that matter, each and every priest of the Church of Silence—there are only a hundred or so of us—has the same powers. The Secret Church operates under such difficult conditions that we have been given special powers, we call them 'faculties,' that normally belong to bishops. If you were not confirmed, Filip, I could confirm you. If you want to marry and you need a dispensation from canon law, I can grant it."

Filip listened in fascination. He had been aware, of course, of the persecution of the Church. But he had not heard before of the Secret Church. Father Vendel rose to light a new candle from the flickering flames of the one that was now dying out, and Filip jumped up, too. "Father, I did not realize how much of your time I had taken up. Excuse me, please."

Father Vendel smiled. "It is good to have someone to talk to from the outside world after all these weeks." But he made no effort to stop Filip as the latter walked gingerly out of the room.

While Father Vendel was telling Filip of the Secret Church, three well-armed guerillas were descending the slopes of the mountain toward the village in the valley below. A dry southern wind had begun to blow so fiercely that branches of trees and pine needles were torn loose, and dodging the projectiles slowed the trio down.

Jan Baar, a big black-haired brute of a man, led the way. He strode with a barely perceptible limp, the result of a bullet that had entered his hip during a guerilla raid and was never removed. The limp did not slow him down, however, and the other two, Kazimir Hlavina and Stefan Dubny, were panting as they kept up with him.

As they came closer to the valley, the trees thickened into a deep forest that separated the arable land of the village from the mountains. Reaching the outskirts of the village, they heard faintly in the distance the clock on the tower of the church pealing nine times.

Here the three men separated. From now on each was on his own.

Jan Baar's assignment was to enter the church and obtain the wafers and sacrificial wine. He had been told the priest was a "patriot," the Communists' term for a cleric who collaborated with the Reds, and thus could not be trusted. That meant Jan would have to steal the wafers and wine.

From behind the barns he headed toward the dark shape of the church tower. The big clock announced each quarter of an hour and the sound served as a guide to Jan in the darkness. Soon he came to the old church structure. He looked both ways, then slipped around to the back where the sacristy was located. From his pocket Jan took a skeleton key, and tried it on the heavy door of the sacristy. If Father Vendel was right, the keyhole of the old door would be so worn, so smoothed out that it would offer no resistance.

The key squeaked in the hole, but it turned easily. Gently as he could, he pushed the door open. It creaked continuously as it turned inward on the centuries-old iron hinges. Jan stopped to listen for signs that he had been noticed. When he was sure he had not, he hurried into the vestry, leaving the door open to avoid the noise that shutting it would entail.

Holding a small lantern, Jan started to search for the objects Father Vendel wanted. He opened one drawer after another of the huge carved cabinet that hid the church's accumulated treasures. "Such a beautiful white alb and stole," he mused. He fingered the richly embroidered maniples and chasubles.

117

Christmas is coming, Jan thought. He debated with himself for only a few seconds before rolling the alb carefully with the stole and stuffing them into his knapsack. "Merciful God, take this not for thievery, since it is done for your glorification," he said quickly, then turned toward the upper part of the cabinet.

He made the sign of the cross as he opened the wooden doors, for what he saw then was shining at him like the sun itself. In front of him were three golden chalices and a great monstrance, shaped like a sunburst, that was studded with many-colored gems.

There, alongside the sparkling monstrance, were hundreds of small white wafers, waiting to be taken. His hands trembled slightly as he reached in and took the thin round sheets of unleavened flour by the handful, placing them with care in the knapsack.

Elsewhere in the sacristy Jan found four bottles of wine. The wine might break if I just dumped the bottles together, he reflected. Perhaps I had better take the chasuble too. He took the sleeveless mantle from its drawer and wrapped it around the wine bottles so that each bottle was separated from the other by several layers of the garment.

This should last a month, he judged, as he lifted the knapsack and moved toward the open door and slipped out into the darkness.

He heard the barking of dogs. A Red patrol was in the streets. Was it coming his way? Next to the church Jan saw a house. It could be the home of the pastor or perhaps of the sacristan, he reasoned.

If the priest was a collaborator, he might betray Jan to the Communists. It might be safer then to try to reach the mountains. The sacristan might be a collaborator, too, but that did not necessarily follow.

The baying of the dogs seemed only blocks away now. That decided it for Jan. He slipped into the courtyard of the house, flinging the knapsack over his back. There was light inside, he noticed, as he turned the knob. The door was unlocked.

"Anybody home?"

He saw the old woman first, standing over the stove. Then he caught sight of the old man, rising from his chair to greet the intruder. At least the house belonged to the sacristan, not the priest, Jan noted with relief.

"Are you the sacristan?" he asked.

"I am. What do you want?"

"I only wanted to ask whether it might be possible for me to speak with your priest at this late hour," Jan lied piously.

Uncertainty clouded the old man's dull face as he tried to grasp the situation. He took the pipe out of his mouth and looked Jan over. His wife came to his side and pointed to three white wafers that had fallen out of the knapsack to the earthen floor next to Jan. "Don't you see," she whispered, "that he is in trouble."

The aged sacristan had barely opened his mouth to speak when four loud shots broke the evening stillness of the village.

Before a word could be said, a heavy-set woman ran into the house. She took one look at Jan and gasped. "Orendas, there is a raid on the main street at the food store." It was plain from the way she stared at Jan that she thought he was involved.

"How do you know?" the old man snapped in disbelief.

"I was visiting my aunt and I saw the police chasing two men towards the barns."

The sacristan turned toward Jan. "That's too bad, my son. We will have to hide you. Otherwise you will never see our priest. Go and hide yourself in the old German bunker by the fence there," he said, pointing toward the window at the side of his house. "It's a good hiding place."

As an afterthought, he added, "If they ever find you, please don't tell them I helped you.'

Jan ran out the door and leaped into the deep pit, pulling the heavy wooden lid shut on top of him. He took a few deep breaths to regain his wind, then lay quietly. He had been through similar situations many times before.

Straining his ears, he could hear footsteps in the courtyard. Then came the peremptory knocking on the door.

"Where did you hide them?" came a gruff voice an instant after the door was opened.

Jan marveled at the old man's daring. "How smart you must be," he heard the sacristan say, "to know that we have hidden someone before you even enter our house. Why don't you search it?" Jan could swear he heard the old man spitting on the floor.

In less than a minute, the police were out of the house. "I see there is a bunker in your yard. That's where you have hidden them, eh, old man?"

No response. This was the end, Jan thought. Three rifle butts were now pounding against the wooden lid of the pit. An iron bar was forced through the hole the rifles had made. "Die heroically in the eyes of your God," a phrase that Father Vendel spoke before each guerilla raid, ran through Jan's mind as he put his hand on the grenade tucked in his belt. He paused, determined to wait for the best time to explode it so he could take as many Communists as possible to death with him.

The lid was lifted. "Come out, both of you," rang through the air.

"I am alone," he said, his voice shaking as if from fear.

As he was lifted out by rough hands, he saw there were five Red troopers, all carrying rifles. One of the police held two panting dogs on a leash. Two of the others leaped into the bunker, poking around with their rifles.

"No one else here," one of the police in the pit reported.

The leader of the patrol turned to Jan. "Hand over your arms."

"Yes, sir," Jan said meekly. It did not seem possible that such a small, timorous voice could come from the lips of so virile-looking a man. He handed over his revolver. Behind the police he saw the sacristan huddled with his wife. The daring had drained out of the old man. In his face Jan saw fear. Fear mixed with contempt for Jan for giving up so easily.

Jan's eyes darted back to the three troopers guarding him. He saw his chance, a slim one, but the only opportunity he would likely have before the two other policemen climbed out of the bunker. His feigned cowardice, his nervous celerity in handing over his revolver had put his captors off guard. They still held their rifles ready for action, but they dropped the barrels down, away from Jan, so they were pointed to the earth.

All this Jan saw in an instant. In one motion, he pulled the grenade from his belt, which had been covered by his jacket, pulled the pin, twisted himself as he fell face forward to the ground and tossed the grenade over his shoulder toward the Red police.

The blast killed all three officers above ground instantly. The two climbing out of the pit were thrown back into the bunker by the force of the explosion, shocked and cowering, but uninjured. Jan himself lost consciousness but only for a few seconds.

He got up quickly, picked up his knapsack and ran toward the barns. Looking back he saw the old sacristan and his wife waving to him, apparently unharmed. The two surviving policemen poked their heads carefully above the top of the bunker, then clambered out. Slowed down by the heavy bundle, Jan ran as fast as he could across the fields toward the woods at the base of the mountains. Rifle shots whizzed past him.

Jan broke into a zigzag running pattern, to throw his assailants' shooting off, clenching his teeth as he sped in anticipation of a bullet in his back. He could make better time, he thought, if he dropped the knapsack. But he could not bring himself to abandon his booty after he had come so far.

Suddenly, Jan's agony came to an end. From behind he could now hear other shots, revolver shots, mixed with the rifle fire. Then wild shouting and laughter. He turned around. There running toward him with broad grins were Hlavina and

Dubny, lugging bundles of their own. Behind them he could see the supine figures of his two pursuers.

"We heard an explosion coming from the church," Dubny explained, "and we figured you were in trouble."

Jan opened his mouth to thank them but Hlavina interrupted. "Come, come, no time for idle chatter. Let's get on our way before more of them come after us."

Filip awoke early the next morning, eager to breathe some fresh air after his unbroken confinement in the cave. He walked through the twisting passages, the pain in his feet considerably diminished, until he came to the entrance. Though it was cold in his lungs, the air was dry and invigorating after the constant dampness of the underground cavern.

The snow had stopped and the mountains were absolutely calm. To his right, a group of guerillas were already at work felling trees, sawing lumber and hammering it into a simple coffin for Hatala. Far down the slope Filip saw a group of indistinguishable figures scurrying about. The occasional clanging of metal told him they were preparing a grave for the slain guerilla.

Filip started down the mountain to join the diggers. But the upper crust of the snow was icy and he had not taken more than a dozen steps when he slipped and fell tumbling to the ground. He got up clumsily but promptly fell down again, this time rolling over and over down the slope.

From below he could hear roars of laughter as he tumbled downward. The mocking guffaws angered him into clutching frantically at the unyielding ice with his hands to brake his slide, but the attempt was unsuccessful and the picture of ineffectual frustration he presented sent the men below into even louder bursts of laughter.

Filip's slide ended with a jolt when his hurtling body came to a narrow leveling of the slope halfway down to the diggers. He sat up, gasping for breath. Anger flooded over him as he looked down at the guerillas, four in number, whose merriment was still evident. He started to raise his fist to accentuate the epithet that came to his lips, but he caught himself short.

His wrath subsided as quickly as it began. He was aware of the tension, alternating with boredom, that was the lot of the guerillas, who lived in danger and isolation. And sorrow, too, when one of their number was killed, as Hatala had been. The realization came to Filip as he gazed at the four grave-diggers that laughter did not come often to them in the mountains, that laughter, even at his expense, brightened the drabness of their lives. "Let them laugh," he thought.

But Filip was not completely without a sense of pride, or a streak of playfulness. He lifted himself up gingerly and started up again to join the diggers. Stepping awkwardly, he slipped again, rolled down the slope and finally came to a halt flat on his back, his feet sticking up in the air without any visible means of support.

The four guerillas dropped their spades instantly and scampered up the hill toward Filip. "How the hell could Filip have fallen down in that position?" said Stefan Dubny. He and Jozef Lisska each grabbed one of Filip's protruding feet and pushed it down to the ground. At that moment, Filip leaped up and hurled himself with all his might against Dubny and Lisska, forcing them down into the snow under the impact.

"You asked for it," he yelled jubilantly, picking up handfuls of snow and throwing them at the other two. All five were soon hurling snowballs at each other with reckless abandon, running down the hill toward the gully where Hatala's grave was being dug.

When they reached the spot, surrounded by snow-covered, red-berried shrubs and clumps of lonely trees, the merriment halted abruptly. The open grave quickly sobered the frolicking crew. It was gouged out of the snow and earth, four feet deep into the ground. No cross was planted near the head of the hole to bear the name of the body that would lie underneath. Only a large flat stone lay near the pit, ready to be placed over the thin crust of earth that would cover Martin Hatala.

Filip watched as the guerillas put the finishing touches on the grave. The five men marched slowly up the hill to the cave, each somber and silent, deep in his own thoughts.

The funeral Mass for Martin Hatala was almost over now. Filip sat there puzzled, for the chalice used by Father Vendel had remained uncovered during the entire ceremony. Usually, he knew, a veil covers the chalice completely during the preparatory and concluding portions of the Mass, and yet there was no veil to be seen at all.

Nudging Jozef Lisska, who was sitting next to him, Filip whispered his question. "You haven't seen anything," Lisska replied. "The priests in the Secret Church have the power to make many changes in the Mass because of the difficult conditions under which they worship. We don't have a veil, so we don't use one. At least we have a real chalice. If we're at services in the field, the priest may use only a regular drinking glass."

Filip's attention was drawn back to Father Vendel. The priest stood rigidly upright at the altar, garbed in his black cassock covered by the new chasuble with its richly embroidered cross on the back.

"Requiescat in pace," the priest's melodious voice echoed through the uneven vaults of the cave.

"Amen," responded the crowd crouching around the bier of Martin Hatala in front of the altar.

Labuda was the first to rise. He lifted up his grieving daughter and began the procession around the altar. Moving slowly, they stopped on the left side of the altar where on a small plate a number of coins had been piled. Labuda took two coins, placing one into the unsteady hand of Anicka. Her eyes were closed tight as if by shutting them she could will away the scene before her.

She opened her eyes now as she proceeded around the primitive altar to give her offering to Father Vendel for her husband's soul. The offering would ensure the safe journey of Martin's soul, she thought, when it reaches Purgatory and must make atonement for its earthly sins before achieving eternal life. Her pace quickened as she approached Father Vendel, who waited with a cross in his hand. She dropped her coin in an empty plate near the priest and kissed the crucifix he held. As she turned away, the men behind her could see that the look of grief that had seemed to be permanently etched on her features had now given way to calm resignation.

Labuda dropped his obol in the plate and kissed the cross, and the rest of the men did the same, as Father Vendel stood in the flickering candlelight and blessed the hero's corpse over and over.

Then the last earthly journey of Martin Hatala began.

As the youngest male, Filip led the procession out of the cave, bearing the cross. Behind him were the four coffin-bearers, the same group that had dug Hatala's grave. On each side of the bier Vincent Halmo and Gabriel Dobias, two of the oldest guerillas, carried a torch so that Hatala would not be received in his permanent abode unlit and unhonored. Behind the bier came Jan Kratky, bent double under the load of the wooden box that contained the consecrated earth.

Only then came Father Vendel intoning "Dreaded day, that day of ire, when the world shall melt in fire." Jan Labuda and Anicka, sobbing freely for the first time in days, followed with the rest of the mourners, murmuring their prayers for the dead.

Out of the cave the funeral train came, marching slowly over the crisp snow on a circuitous path that descended gradually enough to the gravesite for the mourners to manage without losing their footing. All that could be heard as they neared the gully was the crunching of the snow beneath their feet.

At one end of the grave Father Vendel stood in silent thought, while Filip, holding the cross, faced him at the other side. Anicka, composed once more, knelt beside the bier as it stood next to the grave. She placed her cheek on top of the coffin and ran her hand fondly along the bier from end to end, as the priest prayed.

"Oh, God," he concluded, "Whose property is ever to have mercy and to spare, we humbly supplicate Thee for the soul of Thy servant Martin Hatala which Thou hast this day called out of this world, that Thou deliver it not to the hands of the enemy nor forget it forever, but command it to be received by the holy angels and taken to Paradise, its home. . . ."

Father Vendel opened the wooden box that Kratky had borne and strewed the holy soil into the open grave. Anicka, Labuda and the others did the same. Then the coffin was lowered into the grave and covered with dirt. On top the large flat rock was placed so that only those present would ever know that here was the last resting place of Martin Hatala.

6. The Agony of Father Michael

LEONORA DANKOVA waited in vain for Filip to return from his assignment in Vienna. She had prepared dozens of *kolacky* for him, small white pastries stuffed with plum jam. The harvest had been good that year and the big copper kettle in the cottage at Levary was crammed with ripe plums to be turned into marmalade. The house had been tidied up in readiness for Filip.

But the flooding of the Morava changed the return route Filip had planned. Leonora waited long into the night, expecting the secret knock on the door that never came. She slept poorly and when she woke she busied herself around the house to keep her mind occupied.

After breakfast, her father announced, "Did you know there was some shooting upstream during the night? I understand a courier was shot in Holic and another one as he crossed the river. They haven't identified the bodies."

Leonora stifled a sob. "The lives that have been swallowed by that river!" she exclaimed. "No wonder they call it the 'cemetery of couriers.'" She vowed to keep her concern over Filip to herself, for her father had enough anxieties of his own as an Underground contact near the Iron Curtain.

But Karol Danko knew exactly what went through Leonora's head. A few days later, when the last apples from the orchard were carefully laid aside for the winter on the wooden boards in the cellar, he asked her, "How would you like to go to Bratislava and bring Aunt Kristina a basket of apples? Perhaps you can visit with her awhile and see some of the sights in the city."

Leonora quickly agreed and packed her suitcase. "She will forget him there," Karol thought when she left. He tamped the tobacco into his pipe and started to smoke contentedly.

Kristina Adamova was a widow in her sixties and a bad sleeper. She would get up at five in the morning, pace her apartment, then leave at six for the early Mass at a convent church several blocks away. There, after the service, she would gossip with her friends. Now she would wake Leonora up and take her along.

Leonora had her own reasons for going. After the Mass one morning, instead of joining Kristina and her cronies for gossip, she went back inside the church, saying she wanted to pray some more. Actually, she had recognized the Father Provincial of the ancient Catholic order that morning and wanted his advice and guidance. Leonora had known the Father Provincial as a child when he passed through Levary frequently to preach in the village church. So struck by the piety and simplicity of his words had she been then that she thought for a long time about taking orders as a nun. But her mother died and as the only child, she did not want to leave her father alone in his bereavement.

"Leonora, where have you been the whole summer? You look well. How is your father?" the priest asked. Now the head of his order in Slovakia, he was a tall spare man in his early forties who looked younger than his age. His face was pale but a broad smile crossed it as he stood up in his bare feet to greet Leonora. Thick auburn hair surrounded his skull-cap and his beard was short and neatly trimmed.

"Father Provincial, I am visiting my Aunt Kristina, but I am in trouble and I would like to know if you can spare a few moments for me," Leonora implored.

"So, as young as you are, a bird that can hardly fly, how can you be in trouble?" he said, half in jest. The priest motioned her to sit down. To Leonora's surprise, he walked to the door of the monastery parlor to make sure it was shut before he sat down and asked what was on her mind.

He sat in a red armchair, leaning his head on his delicate hands as he listened to Leonora tell of her meeting with Filip, and of how she had fallen in love with him so quickly.

"What is wrong with falling in love, Leonora? It is God's gift."

"There's nothing wrong with it, since ours is an honorable love," she said with feeling. "But I fear for his life. Perhaps you know of him, Father, his name is Filip Polhora and he works for the Resistance as a courier."

The priest gave a nod of assent. "So it is Filip Polhora, is it? I know him, Leonora. Do not fear for his life. But do not tell anyone about him. God's plans are inscrutable and you must trust Him. He will take care of you and Filip and He will bring you together according to His will, not according to our desires."

Leonora's eyes filled with tears of joy.

"How is your father?" the priest asked as he stood up from his chair.

"We have finished in the fields and in the orchard and he is well. Next Sunday he will be at the pilgrimage in Marianka. I know he is looking forward to seeing you there, Very Reverend Father. My aunt is taking me there, too." Leonora rose and picked up her red leather bag.

"Then I shall see all of you in Marianka next Sunday," the priest said in parting.

The outward cheerfulness of Father Provincial Michael Bobula, however, was only a mask. His mind was a sea of worry that haunted him day and night. Throughout Slovakia, the Communist regime was closing down the monasteries and convents of many orders and deporting or imprisoning the monks and nuns. His own order was one of the few to escape thus far, though the time would come when it, too, would fall beneath the Red boot. But if he were to speak out in condemnation of the Communists, the liquidation of his order would come more quickly.

Some time before, the Communists had already vilified the order by sending a spy posing as an honest man who wished to become a priest. He talked well and humbly, this man named Szecs, and he was admitted to the study of theology in the congregation of the order. But while he wore the priestly garb, he studied Father Michael's moves, the bishops he talked to, the trips he took to Prague to see the papal nuncio, and reported all to the secret police.

Spying, however, was not the most important part of Szecs' services to the Reds. The chief weapon they planned to use against Father Michael and his order was ridicule, to undermine him with the people. When the Communists thought the time was ripe, Szecs threw off his robes, left the congregation and wrote articles in the Communist press in which he tried to make Father Michael's simplicity appear as stupidity, his loyalty to his faith as blind ignorance and treason to the State.

After that Father Michael acted more cautiously for a time. He avoided visits to bishops and others high in the Church. He destroyed some papers which, innocent in themselves, might have had their meaning twisted if they had fallen into Communist hands. But caution before the Communists did not come naturally to Father Michael and he was sick at heart.

"So many have died, so many martyrs were made and I am ashamed that I have not been one of them," he mused as he prepared for the pilgrimage to Marianka, where he was to deliver the sermon.

Sunday came and Father Michael was still undecided. What shall I tell the people? Will it be wise now that churches and monasteries are being closed to speak strongly against the enemy? Would it not be better to try to calm the excited faithful, rather than say something that might inflame them?

Such were the questions that ran through Father Michael's mind as he walked in the garden of the church in Marianka. The fresh clean air blew cool from the mountains down upon the sanctuary to the Virgin that had become a rallying point for thousands from miles around.

He went back into his cell, knelt with his head in his hands and prayed for guidance and courage. When he got up from the prie-dieu, he could see the crowd through the window pouring into the church.

The ringing of bells told him his time was at hand. He adjusted his cassock of plain white wool and walked down the stairs into the sanctuary. The candles were already lighted when he reached the church and the organ was playing the Veni Sanctus Spiritus.

Kneeling before the altar, Father Michael could feel the eyes of the people on him, watching his every movement with burning intensity. With calm, deliberate movements, he arose and walked erect to the pulpit. As he grasped the cross, the words of St. Matthew came to mind: "For he that will save his life, shall lose it; and he that shall lose his life for my sake, shall find it. For what doth it profit a man, if he gain the whole world and suffer the loss of his own soul? Or what exchange shall a man give for his soul?"

His voice was quiet and low at first and the worshipers leaned forward in their seats, straining to catch the words. The silence in the huge nave of the church was absolute. In less than a minute, the burden of his sermon had become clear. The pilgrims turned to look at each other's grim faces as he unleashed his most severe attack against the Communists. The words flowed from his mouth like a stream, slowly at first but gathering momentum as his voice grew louder. He felt that God was with him, that he was igniting a flame of faith that would burn throughout the lives of those who listened. And then it was over.

When the last hallelujah had been sung, the people rushed toward him to touch him or kiss his hands and he knew the sermon had been his "entry into Jerusalem." Now, he was sure, he faced arrest, for it was the custom of the Communists to have their spies planted in each assembly of the faithful.

Leonora came to him, her eyes aglow, as he stood under the portals of the church. He told her, "You must pray now, not only for Filip, but for me. Above all, be strong under all circumstances and never lose your faith."

"Father, why don't you leave the country now, before they get to you," Karol Danko pleaded. "I can help you get away."

But Father Michael would not listen. "I am married to my own order even unto the cross" was his only comment.

He returned to his monastery in Bratislava that day, but soon set out to visit all the parishes in the country that were under his jurisdiction to warn them of the dangers to come. While at the monastery at Trenčin, in the Vah valley, news reached him that a priest of his own order had been arrested in Michalovce, at the eastern tip of Slovakia, for having refused absolution to a Communist. Fear and tension mounted. Priests everywhere were being arrested and those who were still free slept with a tiny bundle of personal belongings near at hand, for the police, when they came, allowed their prisoners no time to gather anything before they were dragged away. Like Judas, the police came in the night, when there was less chance of precipitating a riot.

Leonora came again to see Father Michael when he returned from his abbreviated tour. She was in tears, certain she would never see him again, when he told her: "You must be brave, for the time approaches when you will be called on for even greater services for your country and your faith. The day will come, Leonora, when it will seem that all is dark and lost. But that is when your courage must reach its height."

Neither knew how soon those words would prove true.

To a last plea to flee the country, he replied: "I cannot desert my brothers in their need. Many follow Jesus in the breaking of the bread, but few to the drinking of the chalice of His

132

Passion. Many admire His miracles, but few accept the ignominy of His Cross."

At midnight one night in October, the police swarmed into his monastery. Fearlessly, Father Michael placed himself in front of his monastical community, barring the way to the intruders and cried: "By what warrant do you invade this monastery?"

The leader of the police pointed to his armed men and spat out insolently, "There is my warrant."

The priests were taken away, each with his small bundle, but Father Michael and the rector of the monastery were held there until five in the morning. Then they too were hauled off, forced into a car that took them south to the grey edifice of the old Franciscan convent in Bac.

There Father Michael saw priests from every part of Slovakia, and new prisoners were arriving every day. He was herded into a room so crowded with priestly captives that there was no place to sit down, and as he looked over the bedraggled captives he repeated the words of the ancient song of Good Friday, "Oh, my people, am I your enemy?"

At the convent church in Bratislava that morning, Leonora and her Aunt Kristina found the main gate closed and sealed. Two guards were standing in front and one of them, barring the way with his rifle, warned, "There will be no Mass here today or ever again."

"What a fresh young man you are," the sharp-tongued widow shot back, turned abruptly around as the guard's face flushed and pulled Leonora away.

So began the agony of Father Michael. He was kept in the monastery at Bac for three weeks. At first he was left alone in his cell. He stretched his tired body on one of the two iron cots in the tiny dark room and rested awhile. But not knowing how long they would leave him alone, he soon rose to recite the daily office. Fortunately, he had managed to hide his breviary and psalterium from the police.

133

Next came the Holy Mass. He stood in a corner of the cell without moving and recited and analysed each prayer. Then he shut his eyes and saw the faces of his friends and workers for the Church and together they approached Christ in spirit and sang Glory to Him.

The sound of the key turning in the door interrupted Father Michael. A cellmate was brought in. His name was Julius Botek, an engineer with a wife and three children. His unshaven face was an intelligent one, furrowed with suffering and worry that made him look more than fifty years old, though he was only in his early forties. In his dreams, which Father Michael could recall years later, Botek would call to his wife and children and play games with them in his sleep.

From morning till evening they would take Botek from the cell for his interrogation. Not once did they question Father Michael.

One day while Botek was away the priest noticed for the first time that there were faint etchings on the back of the cell door. Right in the middle was an apostolic cross over three hills with the words nearby: "For God, Life; for Nation, Freedom." Underneath was scratched, "God will not forsake" and the name of the writer, a priest Father Michael had known long. All over the door were other names, other dates, other words. One could see the door had been painted several times to try to obliterate the scratchings, but the nails of prisoners are long and untiring.

Reading the words on the door was Father Michael's afternoon recreation. He thought it remarkable that all the writings were directed towards God. To think that there was no trace of hatred. Could it be, he wondered, that the Communists were arresting only devout Christians, whose suffering had purified them?

A week later Botek returned to the cell early one afternoon, much before his usual time. He sat down on one of the boards that served as chairs and wept. Raising his head, he told Father Michael in a voice that broke often, "I think they will give me

134

peace. They finished the interrogation and I have signed the record book. Soon they will transfer me to the regional court jail for trial. Father, perhaps they will release you, for they have not called you for questioning at all. If you are let go, please go to my wife and children. Tell them that their father is no criminal. Tell them that even if I confess at the trial, tell them not to believe it. I have not committed any crimes for which they should sentence me."

When he quieted down, Botek told Father Michael his story. He had been the head of a state factory. The raw materials it used never came in the necessary quantities and production in the plant went down. Warning came from above that the plant's quota must be fulfilled or else. His deputy, a capable man, was arrested and in his place was put a callow youth, lacking the proper training, but so impertinent and filled with self-esteem that Botek was sure he was a spy. Two months later, Julius Botek was arrested and charged with embezzlement of the plant's funds and sabotage in the service of "Western imperialists."

How they got Botek to confess Father Michael did not ask, nor did Botek tell. There were no marks of physical suffering on the parts of his body that the priest could see.

But the Communists were not so gentle with his next cellmate, Laco Fintora, the owner of a small wine-processing plant.

Each day Fintora was beaten, kicked and slapped whenever he denied charges of activities against the State. At night he would sit near Father Michael, his face trembling, and repeat over and over, "They want me to confess to things I never did, not even in my wildest dreams, and they torture me and torture me."

Still they left Father Michael alone. He became convinced this seeming indifference to him was part of the Communists' plan. They wanted to fill him with doubt, to show how they treated others so he would be instilled with fear and anxiety

135

over what they might do to him. That way, they would be able to break his will to resist more easily, or so they thought.

It took them only a week to shatter Laco's resistance, too.

At that time, the Communists had passed a law nationalizing every private business in which fifty or more workers were employed. Laco's plant employed fewer men. "Today, they did not torture me," Laco told Father Michael. "They said that if I voluntarily agree to the nationalization of my plant, they will close their eyes to my anti-state activities. I promised."

This was exactly what the Communists had been after all along, but Laco was too numbed by the torture to realize it. And so he was released, after signing away his livelihood, with a cracked rib, an ear drum that was torn and the fingers of his left hand crushed.

"At least my life was saved," were his parting words to Father Michael.

For the first time since the beginning of his imprisonment the priest was left without a cellmate. On the second day of his solitude, he was reading from the breviary when a guard, an unusually sadistic one named Palo Mlkvy, came into the cell and said, "You can go to church with me if you like."

Father Michael's heart leaped for joy. It was as if the Holy Spirit Himself had heard his prayer. Perhaps he would even be allowed to celebrate a Mass. Joyfully, he followed the guard.

No words were exchanged between the two as they walked. As they came nearer the church, the priest caught sight of the bent, weak figure of the saintly Greek Catholic Bishop of Prešov, Pavel Gojdic. He looked at Father Michael mutely, for he was too feeble even to talk.

"So you lead me here to show me that bishops are tortured too," Father Michael said to himself. It was obviously another step to break his will.

When they reached the church, however, the priest was still in a hopeful frame of mind for he felt that any degradation he received was worth a Mass. It was then that Palo Mlkvy

136

turned around to him sharply and flung his arms out to bar his way. With great howls of sadistic laughter, he brought his face inches away from Father Michael's and said:

"Did you take me for a fool?"

Father Michael looked at him without saying a word or betraying an emotion, for he knew the guard wanted him to show anger or frustration. When Mlkvy saw that the priest did not react the way he expected, Mlkvy pounded on Father Michael's chest with his hamlike hands. "Say something, say something, don't just stand there like a calf!"

But the priest said not a word.

He was led back to his room, happy to be alone again, and resumed his prayers. As he prayed he stood before the one small window in the cell. The sun was up, bright and beautiful. He watched with fascination as the leaves fell from the trees. It was autumn and Father Michael had always felt that autumn was his season. He could not take his eyes off the leaves as they spiraled downward in the oblique sunlight and he thought, "They die and fall, but new ones will grow again." It was another manifestation of the eternal life he had always preached.

Into his line of sight came a group of monks, tilling the garden near a small cluster of birches. There were no guards around the monks. There seemed to be little need of guards, for the whole area was fenced. But to the priest's surprise five of the monks suddenly ran toward the birches, quickly took off their heavy cassocks and started climbing the fence. One of the five, a rather fat man, lagged behind, but finally even he reached the fence, where the tallest of the fleeing monks, gesturing wildly and acting hastily, boosted the others up the fence. Was he strong enough to lift the fat monk? Father Michael wondered. The whole thing went rather smoothly and soon all five were on the other side of the fence, fleeing toward the Danube.

"Here is your breakfast, friend of the people," a voice snarled from behind the priest.

In his absorption with the escape, he had not heard the guard entering. Trying to hide his excitement so as not to arouse the guard's suspicions, Father Michael calmly took the piece of bread and rusty cup of black coffee that was the standard breakfast for the prisoners at Bac.

For six days he was left alone, wondering what tortures they were preparing. But they laid not a hand on him. During the second night, while he was asleep, the guard opened the cell door and flashed a light in his face, awakening him. "I just wanted to know if you were asleep," he said and left.

This was repeated on three consecutive nights. Then, on the sixth night, they came for him. "Take your bundle and follow us," commanded a new shrill voice. Father Michael drowsily donned his cassock, took his little pile of personal belongings and was led through the long vaulted corridors into a waiting car. Three Security Police, heavily armed, escorted him without any ceremony or pretension of politeness to the courtyard.

Was this deportation? Was he going to the Soviet Union? These questions ran through the priest's mind as a heavy black bag was put over his head. It was a warm autumn night and he was soon perspiring heavily. Father Michael thought he would suffocate in the bag and he could not help but envy the simple monks who had escaped the convent a few days earlier. Had he not been the head of a religious order, he, too, might have been asked to scrub floors or work in the gardens and perhaps he might have escaped with them. But for him there was no choice and he felt a pang of guilt that he had even had a thought disloyal to his order.

"Drink willingly the chalice of the sweet Lord, if you wish to be His friend and partake with Him," John's words sounded in his mind. "Drink willingly" he repeated to himself again and again.

After three hours of fear, the car stopped and the guards got out. Two men took Father Michael by the hands, two others pushed him out of the car from behind and he was led, still blinded by the bag, up some stairs and into a room. The

138

bag was finally removed from his head and he was ordered to take his clothes off.

They examined each piece of clothing minutely, apparently hunting for secret papers. When they were through, they gave the priest back only a shirt, a pair of pants and a towel—nothing else. His psalterium, his breviary and rosary were gone.

Only a priest or the most devout can know the sense of loss, the sense of spiritual nakedness Father Michael felt when he was left without the physical tokens of his faith.

"Follow!" one of his captors ordered. The priest followed through long halls into the open air and then into a five-story building, a structure surmounted by a cupola, and surrounded by balconies. He recognized the building immediately as an old Hapsburg fortress, used in the defense against the Turks, that had been converted into a prison by the Communists. Father Michael was in Leopoldov.

The guard opened a heavy iron door and pushed him into a small room, lighted only through a tiny, grilled window and furnished with an iron cot, one blanket and a pail. Father Michael was left alone for two hours until another guard came, ordered him to stand at attention and said imperiously:

"These are the rules. When you hear the bell at 5 A.M., you will get up, wash, and sweep the room, you will straighten out your mattress. You cannot sit or lie on the bed during the day!"

And so, seventeen hours a day, the beleaguered priest paced the floors of the cell, barefooted, day after day, until he thought he had reached the limit of his resistance. At times he would collapse on the cold, damp floor. "Get up, you parasite!" the raw voice of the guard would shout as he looked through a tiny hole in the door. If Father Michael was too exhausted, too sick to get up, the guard would come in and shout oaths and kick him over and over with his heavy boots until the priest summoned up enough strength to rise.

Once a day an inspector would come into the cell to see if it was clean. The cleric had to stand at attention facing the wall during these visits and if the inspector was not satisfied—

and it seemed that he could never be satisfied—there was a fresh torrent of abuse and blows.

The only other interruption in the drab routine of the day was the meals. At six-thirty in the morning there was a dark tasteless liquid called coffee, and a few pieces of bread that were to last Father Michael for the day. At noon, a thin watery soup, a little piece of lard, beans or dried peas and potatoes, if he was lucky. At five, dinner came—more of the liquid called coffee, bread if he had saved any from breakfast and, at rare intervals, a potato. At ten, a bell rang and the Father Provincial was allowed to go to bed.

But sleep was almost impossible. Other prisoners were moaning and sobbing, some out of fear and loneliness, some as the result of torture and bodily injury they had suffered during the day. And the guards would shout and laugh, roar over a game of cards, play harmonicas and sing, or curse and deride the prisoners.

Father Michael never actually saw anyone except the guards and the inspector. He was being broken, mentally and physically, in preparation for what was to come, the brain-washing, the scouring away of everything the mind believes, and its replacement with Communist ideas.

Denied his psalterium, prayer book or rosary, the priest would meditate on the Stations of the Cross. Recreating in his mind Christ's suffering as He bore the cross to Calvary and was laid in the sepulchre, Father Michael would try to feel Christ's agony as if it were his own and to realize anew what He endured to redeem man. But even that consolation grew more difficult to attain. The guards interrupted so often that meditation became meaningless. It seemed as though they were following a calculated course to prevent any real concentration. It was uncanny the way the guards broke into the priest's thoughts at almost exactly the moment when he was about to physically relive, through his concentration, the suffering of Jesus.

When meditation seemed useless, Father Michael prayed the

rosary on his fingers, saying the Hail Marys to himself, so the guard would not know what he was doing. Every prayer he knew, long and short, he would repeat to exercise his determination to withstand the Communists' pressure.

The mind, he knew, is the most delicate of all instruments. It is so finely adjusted, so susceptible to the impact of outside influences, that if he did not make a greater effort of will his own mind might prove a malleable tool in the hands of his enemy. Repeating the prayers to himself was his strongest weapon. It would keep his senses sharp and preserve his mental balance and peace of mind.

"From now on, I must control every day my ability to state my own thoughts," Father Michael swore as he started his rosary.

The solitude itself was torture. The priest had no knowledge of the fate of his brothers in the order, of his friends, or his country. Am I truly alone in a world of triumphant communism? he wondered.

After a month, stronger measures were taken. A bright light was affixed in his room that was left burning all night. He slept fitfully when he slept at all. But the periods of somnolent tossing and turning were no rest at all. His mind was as tired when he awoke as when he went to sleep.

Then came the first full-scale investigation. A guard woke him from an unsettled sleep and took him into a small room where there were two men in civilian dress.

"Please sit down, Michael," said the man sitting behind the desk in a gentle voice.

"A cigarette?" offered the other standing nearby.

The first man said, "Now, Michael,"—he never used the priest's title—"Now, Michael, we do not want to see you hurt. Just tell us about your life and the things you have done against the State."

Father Michael smiled back and said in a quiet voice that he had never done anything against the State, that he worked only for the people's spiritual good.

"But we have a file against you," the second man interrupted. His voice was the epitome of reasonableness. Then he added, with sudden harshness, "If you don't speak voluntarily and confess, you will suffer and die for your crimes."

"But I have done nothing, absolutely nothing. I am innocent of any crime. I was a friend of the poor, if that is a crime."

"All right," the man behind the desk said soothingly, "if you don't want to talk, we will send you back to your cell and speak to you again in a week or two."

And so in ten days they questioned Father Michael again, and again he gave the same answers with the same result. He was sent back to his cell in which the light never went off. There was no unusual physical torture, only the kicks he received when he could stand on his feet no longer and slumped to the floor. Why were they not more cruel, he wondered, when he had seen how they had beaten his former cellmates in Bac. He could only surmise that in his case they wanted a voluntary confession and that they feared if he were tortured into a quick confession that he might just as quickly recant.

But even without extensive torture, Father Michael's physical condition was deteriorating. He was sick and feverish much of the time. There were days when he could not keep down even the scanty food they served. His only strength and consolation was at night when, lying on the cot, he could think, without interruption, of his Redeemer.

"How long, how long, O my God, will this last?" the priest prayed. At times it almost seemed that he could hear His voice telling him, "Your time of labor and tribulation will not last long. Wait, wait only a little while."

It was already the end of autumn and winter's cold had penetrated the prison. Just as other sick and weary prisoners had been shown to Father Michael when he was first captured, now he, too, was shown to other new ones to throw fear into them. But for several weeks he faced no further interrogation and he regained a greater portion of peace of mind. He won-

142

dered about Leonora and Filip Polhora, not knowing that even then Leonora had been searching for him in vain.

In the midst of such thoughts one day, the priest heard heavy boots approaching his cell. A guard opened the door and commanded, "Take your soap and towel and follow me."

Where do I go now? Father Michael thought. I have already seen two high priests of communism, perhaps now I shall see Pontius Pilate.

Again his face was covered with a black hood. As the guards pushed him to the car, he could feel the snow falling and hear chains placed on the tires. They traveled day and night, stopping only to eat or buy gasoline. When mealtime came, Father Michael's hood was lifted only as high as the bridge of his nose and the guards fed him. He could not see the countryside they passed through. Perhaps I am already in Poland or the Soviet Union, he thought, for despite the black bag he could feel the sun on his face the next morning, which meant they were heading east.

Finally, the car arrived at its destination. It was a modern jail with central heating, clean toilets and big windows. Even the guards seemed more polite. But Father Michael was soon to learn that they were more dangerous. Whether or not he had been taken out of Slovakia, he was certainly hundreds of miles away from his native Bratislava, across the length of Slovakia, and near the Soviet Union, if not in it. He could not help but feel cut adrift and moving toward disaster, and he sought refuge in further meditation and prayer.

Father Michael's cell was lighted day and night by strong reflectors outside the door that burned far brighter than the bulb in the room at Leopoldov. The food was bad and insufficient and his thoughts grew more confused each day. All his grown life he used to pray "to be crucified with Him," but he had never truly suffered more than the "crown of thorns." Now he almost looked forward to the torture he expected at the hands of the Communists, for he thought it might be the road towards fulfillment of his wish to relive Christ's suffering.

Yet, deep down, Father Michael was also afraid of what his enemies had in store for him.

Through the large window he could see mountain peaks on the far horizon, but they gave him no clue as to where he was. Nobody told him, nor was there anyone but the uncommunicative guards for him to ask. By now four months had gone by since his arrest. The trees, he saw from his window, were bare and a feeling of utter loneliness took hold of him.

For days this sense of alienation from the world fought within Father Michael with the feeling of joy that his suffering, his effort to follow and imitate Jesus, would purify his soul. No one disturbed him and he was able to fill the days with meditation. To the guards he acted with almost servile obedience so that they would never have occasion to use God's name in vain.

One day, a guard came into the priest's cell and asked him in a polite manner if he would like to have some cigarettes. The offer seemed perfectly in keeping with the not unfriendly atmosphere of the prison. Father Michael said he would and from then on he was given two cigarettes a day. He began to hunger for tobacco, to look forward eagerly to the moment when the guard would bring in the cigarettes, and he enjoyed smoking them to the fullest—even though their taste seemed a little strange.

Soon the black, watery coffee was replaced with another kind of coffee that had the same strange taste as the cigarettes. Father Michael did not then think of drugs. But he wanted those cigarettes, that coffee, more than he could remember wanting any creature comforts before.

Then one wintry evening, when the tenth hour had sounded and it was time to go to sleep, the priest found himself more drowsy than usual. He attributed this to the lack of sleep the previous nights and to the slow pace of his life in the cell. But as he lay there a memory flickered. There was a young boy from the remote village of Oscadnica who had "visions" in 1947 and predicted the fall of communism. This was most uncomfortable for the Communists, for many Slovaks believe in miracles, so they decided to make an end to his visions. He was taken to a clinic in Bratislava, injected with scopolamine and that was that. No more visions, no more dire predictions of harm to the Communists.

But I did not get any injections, Father Michael thought as he fell asleep, convincing himself that he had not been drugged as yet.

The sleep was fitful and he dreamed he was falling into an abyss that had no bottom. When he awoke in the morning, he felt stiff and and his muscles ached. He was lying on the hard cot, uncovered, for in his drowsiness the night before he had failed to pull up the prison blanket. For a moment the priest felt panic. He shook his head to get rid of that ugly dream. When he sat up he felt utterly dejected.

Father Michael got to his feet and, though weak and exhausted, managed to put the cot in order and wash his face. The shock of the cold water revived him somewhat.

But it seemed hard to praise God that morning. His Name did not raise the joy in Father Michael's heart that it usually did. He tried to contemplate one of the mysteries of the faith, but he could not meditate clearly. Instead he repeated the prayers he knew by heart, mechanically and without real feeling.

When the guard came in and brought coffee and a cigarette, he reached for them greedily.

"Michael, your cot is not quite in order," the guard said.

"Michael," he repeated in a louder voice, "I said that your bed is not tidy."

"I am sorry, I did not hear," Father Michael replied, for indeed his reactions seemed slower and he had trouble fathoming what the guard meant.

"Holy Mary, Mother of God, pray for us sinners," was constantly on his lips. He could not concentrate, could not meditate. All he was able to do on the following days was to pray spiritlessly the links that make the chain of a Rosary. Slowly and gradually, physically and mentally, he was breaking down. His mind seemed uncertain; his voice was faint; and his lips seemed to grow small as his mouth grew dry. His sight became dim and weak.

The day came when he could not even repeat the Rosary. That day, the only prayer that he could say was: "My God! My God! Why hast thou forsaken me?"

That was all Father Michael could think of. He was alone, abandoned by his friends and his Lord. Where was God that he had let me sink into this desert of body and soul? he asked himself. His head was turning in a thousand directions. He could feel no link with God.

The next day, at nine in the morning, two guards came into the cell and took him into a large room. The first thing he saw when he entered the office was two large screens, which he was sure must conceal some instruments of torture. Three hard-faced men sat at a long table in front of the screens, a pistol lying in front of each. The guards who had escorted him left the room, locking the door behind them, and Father Michael stood alone in front of the desk.

Though the situation was designed to frighten him, the three investigators did not act harshly. Instead, they spoke normally as if it were a routine matter.

"Where were you born, Michael?" asked the man in the middle. He had a smooth face and small, sharp eyes.

Hesitatingly, the priest answered "Prievidza." To the next question, he told them his parents had been farmers and when the investigator to the left asked where he had been educated, he said, "Innsbruck and Rome."

"But you forgot that you also studied in Paris," the sly-looking one in the center interrupted. "Don't conceal anything. Remember we have the file on you."

Indeed, Father Michael had difficulty in remembering and when he spoke his voice was weak. He managed to answer other questions about his family, even though he could not remember all his relatives and had to be reminded of their names.

When the questioning was finished, the priest was led back to the cell. They gave him the inevitable cigarette and coffee and though he thought that perhaps he should refuse, he was unable to, for he craved them. His will was no longer his own.

The next day the routine was the same except that this time they asked Father Michael to tell everything that he had done against the State.

"I warn you, Michael," the investigator on the right said, his voice harsher than the day before, "we have the documents to prove that you conspired against the State."

"If you confess," the man in the middle said more kindly, "your punishment will be greatly reduced, because the People's Democratic regime is merciful and good."

"But gentlemen," Father Michael protested faintly, his eyes on the middle investigator for he seemed the most reasonable, "I never conspired against the State, nor against the welfare of the people."

At that point, the cleric was sure they would open the screen behind the desk and take out some instrument of torture. But they did not. Instead he was told, "Think it over, Michael, and tomorrow we will see you again."

Father Michael knew they could not possibly have any incriminating evidence against him. But he was more tired and weak that second day and he longed to get back to the cell. The subsequent coffee and cigarette put him at ease, though the nausea and dizziness he felt afterwards was greater than ever.

On the third day of questioning, the charges became more specific. Accusation after accusation was hurled at the priest before he could answer the previous one.

"You and your order have been trained to spy against the State."

"You are the leader in Slovakia of a conspiracy that originates in the Vatican."

147

"Your conspiracy is organized by the Pope himself."

"The general of your order even came from Rome to see you in Bratislava, can you deny that?"

From one to the other, Father Michael looked, until they were silent, waiting for him to speak. "Gentlemen, gentlemen, I am only a simple priest. It is true that I have seen the Holy Father in Rome, and it is true that I have seen the general of my order both in Rome and Bratislava. But what I discussed with them involved only religious matters, I assure you, gentlemen."

Still the charges came thick and fast.

"But did you not plot with the papal nuncio and with the bishops of Slovakia to issue instructions that created the Secret Church? Can you deny that? Here is a photograph of you entering the papal nunciature in Prague."

Toying with the pistol in front of him, the chief investigator said, "It was you who went to the bishop here in Prešov to tell him the clouds were getting darker over the Greek Catholics."

"And it was you," he added, now pointing the pistol casually at the priest, "who went to the convent in Michalovce, after we abolished the Greek Catholic Church, and received the monks into the Roman Catholic Church so they would escape absorption into the Russian Orthodox Church. Is that not so?" He pounded the pistol butt on the desk.

Oh, how cunning the Communists were, Father Michael thought. Each of the charges had a grain of truth in it, but the truth was twisted. What he had done to save the Church and serve the people was twisted into a crime against the people.

Utterly tired and unable to think clearly, the priest could nevertheless still discern the truth from falsehood and he did not surrender. Not as yet.

The days merged into each other and time ceased to have any meaning. Relentlessly, they pounded into his head the charge that he was a spy, determined to make him believe it, then confess it. Throughout all the hearings his questioners remained fresh and full of energy. They had food and refreshments in the next room, while Father Michael was forced to stand on his feet all day long. They saw how tired and confused he was, and they intensified their attack, asking the same questions over and over.

In the twilight between sleep and wakefulness, his imagination played tricks on him. He saw himself in a vast hole below the ground which he recognized as a great empty cistern. To his terror, his father and mother were descending a narrow ladder through a hole in the domelike roof. Down, down they climbed to reach him while the frail ladder swayed and bent. He could do nothing but watch with fright-filled eyes. But the nightmare ended just as they were about to reach the floor to save him.

One night Father Michael tried to count himself to sleep as he used to do when he was a little boy. Never as a child, he recalled with a sudden clear vision, did he ever pass twenty-one without falling asleep. His mother used to stand over him smiling as he tried to keep his eyes from closing. But now, twenty-one came and he was still awake. The cold wind broke in waves against the window of the cell.

He could not get his mother out of his disturbed mind. There she was, taking him to the field where Father was harvesting the wheat. Father was hungry and waiting for the food Mama was bringing him. He appeared from behind a tall heap of dry wheat, dressed in snow-white linen pants and a light white shirt. Mama beckoned to him. When he saw the small boy trotting behind her, Father opened his arms and lifted the boy effortlessly to his radiant face, then higher and higher above his head. Then he put the boy down, very gently, made the sign of the cross and began to eat.

Why did Father make the sign of the cross? Father Michael wondered that night in his cell.

Then came a day when he was left alone in the room, without questioning. He felt a stronger urge for food and he ate everything served that day, including coffee that tasted stronger

149

than usual. But by the end of the day, he vomited the food. He tried to pray, but as soon as he began, he stopped. It was not only that he was too weak in body. His mind rejected the prayers he had wanted to say. There seemed no reason for prayer. He tried to force himself, but could not say a single Hail Mary!

Father Michael's spirit had drained away. Where was my God? Why had he deserted me? "Perhaps, He doesn't even exist." As this blasphemy crossed his lips, his heart seemed to stand still. Never before had the priest felt such cold fear. He was indeed standing on the brink of an infinite void.

The interrogation was resumed the next day. Father Michael could hardly walk, so weak was he. Two guards had to push him. Now there were six men in the hearing room.

"Michael, kneel down," one of the newcomers ordered, a man with wavy blond hair dressed in an immaculate new uniform. The cleric knelt down. Then the two other new inquisitors, standing behind him, stamped down on his bare heels with their boots. They struck his back, his face, his stomach.

Only then did the interrogation begin.

"Confess that you are the leader of the Vatican's spy ring in Slovakia," said the one with the sleek blond hair.

"And tell us everything you did to help set up the Secret Church," the chief investigator snapped.

Father Michael's mind was a vacuum. Had he reached the limit of his will to resist? He was no longer sure of what was true and what was not. Into this vacuum, thoughts were sucked. Perhaps I really am a spy. No, I could not be. Yet so many of the actions my questioners accused me of participating in really did happen. Could I have been a spy? I am not sure. I am not sure.

But he kept silent. After three hours of shouting and kicking and table pounding, he was taken away. This time the priest was placed in a new cell, one without windows. It was pitch black. He was ordered to stand against the wall and not to move. How long he stood there he did not know, for he could no longer measure time.

Then Father Michael was back in the hearing room. Was it that same afternoon or the next day? He could not tell.

"Tell us, who are the administrators of the Secret Church?" The voice was calm.

"Who consecrated them?" The pitch had risen.

"Tell us, tell us," came a shriek.

Finally, Father Michael broke his silence. "If you know all this about the Secret Church, why do you ask me?"

The insolence was too much for them. Clubs and fists smashed into his face. He could feel the blood rushing down his face, the ghastly pain, then unconsciousness.

Father Michael woke up in the black cell. In the darkness he was overcome with despair. He was unable to utter a single word to his Creator. He was unable to say the Name of God. He was utterly alone, without hope, without faith, without love.

As he stood there, he could feel two persons fighting within him for control. One, the person he had been, was dying in the dreadful loneliness of the cell. There was no God, Father Michael now thought, so that part of him which used to believe and serve Him had to die.

But the other personality, the one slowly conditioned by the brainwashing technique the priest had undergone, was growing stronger. To the new personality, the lies of Father Michael's tormentors now appeared to be the truth, and all that the priest had thought and worked for during his life seemed false.

"I lost all memory of my previous life dedicated to God," Father Michael told friends many years later in recounting his experiences. "Since I was deprived of that memory, I appeared to myself as the poorest of the poor and the emptiest of the empty. I owned nothing but the rags that covered my nakedness, and I was a slave of my investigators to dispose of as they pleased.

"But the emptiness was nothing compared to the sense of betrayal of my faith and my refusal to suffer the martyrdom

151

to which so many valiant bishops, priests, nuns and laymen had submitted before me. For the first time in my life, in that dark room, I was confronted with a reality that did not allow evasion. As the other person that was born within me took control, I had made my decision not only to deny God, but even to sell Him. This was the most shameful decision of my life; and furthermore, I made it without any doubt or hesitation. At that moment I felt as if I had cleansed myself and was prepared to begin life anew. I was ready, no, eager to cooperate with my inquisitors."

The questioners took Father Michael back for another hearing after handing him a cup of coffee. Always the coffee. He was trembling from the effect of the drugs, from exhaustion, hunger, dizziness and pain. He was pale and emaciated, his eyes were bloodshot and his face was covered with cuts and bruises. The lights in the room were bright, so bright that his eyes hurt. All he wanted to do was say yes, yes to anything they asked.

What was Truth? Truth was what they wanted. Truth was what they said. They were the only reality in the world, their lies the only truth.

"You want to know, comrades, what is the truth?" Father Michael began in a shaky voice. They must have seen they had won.

"The truth is," he said, "the truth is everything you have said about me." And then, the hard floor came up fast to meet him.

Brandy was being poured into his throat when he came to. "Bring a chair for the prisoner," one of the interrogators said. It was the first time the priest had been allowed to sit at the hearings.

"Michael," the chief investigator said, "you will now give us your confession." His voice was fatherly. "You have admitted all the points in the accusation. It now remains for you to check the accuracy of the charges as you read your confession aloud." He pushed a pile of papers toward the priest.

"How can it . . . How can it . . ." Father Michael started to say, but his mouth was too parched to permit speech.

"Bring him some water," the presiding officer commanded.

When his thirst had been quenched, the Father Provincial tried again. "How can what I want to confess already be written up?"

"Now, now Michael," the chief interrogrator said gently, as if talking to a child, "Don't try to change what you have already generally confessed. Didn't you agree that you were the head of a conspiracy directed from the Vatican?"

"Yes."

"And doesn't your confession cover the fact that you opposed the People's Democracy and that you and the bishops set up a Secret Church?"

"Yes." Father Michael was intent on confessing.

"Well, then, just go ahead and read your confession and let us have it over with, so we can all go to sleep. It is quite late."

There was no point in refusing, so the priest started to read. It came slowly. He was not even sure of what he read, for his mind was clouded and his stomach pained him as never before. He was aware his words were being recorded on a machine, however. And he was aware that he confessed to being a spy and that the whole Church was filled with spies from top to bottom.

After four difficult hours, Father Michael was finished with the reading. Next he was asked to sign each page of each document. His fingers could barely hold the pen at first. He wrote slowly and uncertainly. Then with each succeeding page, he felt a little victory at being able to write his name. He signed more quickly, with a growing feeling akin to exaltation. The vast loneliness, the black despair of spirit when he was alone was disappearing. To his enslaved, captive mind, truth seemed to live again in these lines. The void left by the God he had lost was filled by these men, his tormentors. They were God, and life and hope!

They led Father Michael back to the cell, and he collapsed

on the bed. He could not eat, nor could he sleep. Day and night merged into continual nightmare. He just lay there, staring at the grey ceiling. This time, when the guards came into the room, they did not order him to stand or tidy up the cell. They left him alone.

But the Communists were not finished. On the fourth day after Father Michael's confession, they pushed a man into his cell. The priest had to force himself to look at the stranger who had no face, only a bleeding mass of flesh. His body was a mass of burns and bruises. It was hours before he could speak, and the wonder was that he was still alive.

At first he was terrified of Father Michael. But after he realized that the priest was a prisoner, too, he began to speak slowly. He told Father Michael how he had been tortured, how his body and the soles of his feet had been burned, his head beaten with clubs, his fingernails torn out.

Later they took him from the priest's cell. He was their warning to Father Michael. A graphic illustration of what he could expect if he recanted his confession, if he refused to follow them in every way.

They kept the cleric isolated for seven more days. His coffee and food were still drugged, but the dosage was gradually lessened. At the end of the week Father Michael was called again for a hearing. The investigators were kind and gentle. They were eating ham, bread, butter and beer and they gave some to him.

The chief of the interrogators praised his confession, then stared directly at him and said, "The fine will be heavy."

He gave Father Michael time to ponder what he had said before adding, "But you know, Michael, there is a way to avoid the punishment." A pause to let that sink in. "Perhaps we can have the trial dropped—if you will do some services for us. You will find that the People's Democracy can be grateful. The People's regime seeks only the people's good, and you will be serving the people."

The words sounded like honey, but the priest said nothing.

When they saw his hesitation, the chief went to the filing cabinet in the room and took out a folder. From it, he removed a document and showed it to Father Michael.

"Is that your signature?" the chief asked.

"Yes, it is," the priest answered.

"Read this document."

It was an agreement to spy on his fellow priests.

"You see," the chief said, "you have already given your word. And you will do it."

"Yes," Father Michael said, resignedly. "I will carry out what I promised." There was no other choice, his captive mind agreed. He had given his word.

After days of rest and undrugged food, after the dizziness and dryness of mouth had begun to diminish, Father Michael was taken to Podolinec in the High Tatras, where the Communists had turned an old Redemptorist monastery into a labor camp for priests and monks from all over Slovakia. Not only had he lost his faith in God and surrendered his soul to the Communists, but he also had agreed to betray his fellow priests.

7. Resurrection

WHEN Father Michael was taken from Bratislava, Leonora Dankova returned to her home in Levary. The loss of both Filip and Father Michael was difficult for her to bear. Unable to unravel the whereabouts of Filip, she tried to trace the Father Provincial's travels. Rumors reached her that he was in Pezinok, north of Bratislava. But when she went there, the reports proved false. Then she heard he had been moved to Bac. But when she arrived at that town, he had already been taken away. Long months passed without a word of his fate.

Then early in April, her father was called to a secret meeting with the leaders of the Underground in Bratislava. When he returned, he brought with him Jozef Maryan.

"We have found Father Michael," Karol Danko said.

"Where is he, when can I see him?" Leonora asked impulsively.

Danko was silent. Maryan, normally an intense man not given to the social niceties, spoke in a sympathetic voice. "He was drugged by the Communists, Leonora. He has confessed to crimes he never committed."

"How do you know?" she inquired, uncomprehending.

Her father replied, "That's why we had the meeting with General Duplin in Bratislava. All the bits and pieces of news from the grapevine were pieced together."

"But where is he now?"

"In Podolinec, in a concentration camp." Karel Danko replied.

Leonora sat down, still numb. "So, then he is still not free."

"No, Leonora," Maryan interjected. "And that is the reason I came here to see you." His manner was businesslike again, his dark eyes peering intently into Leonora's as if to emphasize the importance of his words.

"We need a woman to help free him. You know him and he knows and trusts you. We want you to visit him in Podolinec. He is in terrible shape, physically and mentally, and I am not at all sure he will recognize you or listen to you even if he does remember you. But it is our only chance."

Leonora protested her inexperience. But Maryan brushed the objections aside. "Everything will be worked out for you to the smallest detail. You won't have to explain any of the details of the rescue to Father Michael, since you may be watched when you see him. You'll only have to bring him a food parcel that will contain instructions for him."

Leonora looked at her father for guidance. He was noncommittal.

"Remember, Leonora," Maryan went on, "that this is a mission of the utmost importance. A live and free Father Provincial can reveal to us and to the whole world the whole technique of brainwashing. If we can free him, we plan to bring him to the Vatican, to the Holy Father himself, to tell of the Communists' methods."

"Then I will do it," Leonora said resolutely.

Her father smiled, though his eyes were not free of concern. "Now, Leonora, you must start packing, for there is not much time."

That afternoon and the next day as she made ready to depart, Leonora experienced a resurgence of joy. Filip was still missing and Father Michael was a captive, but she no longer had to sit in her house and languish. Now there was a great to-do of packing clothes and food and stuffing trunks and boxes.

Hovering around her, Karol Danko flashed anger and shouted a great deal, unlike his usual self. "Don't take that . . . you need this," he ordered imperiously. He did not smile much any more, for his only child was about to embark on a dangerous mission. But while Karol frowned and sighed, Leonora felt like a bird on a bough ready to burst into song.

Maryan and her father sat at a table on which they had spread out maps, planning her trip and going over the details of the rescue plan. "Run along into the kitchen," her father shouted at her, interrupting her reverie. "Don't you smell the bread burning?"

Her father's roar and a sudden push in the back sent her flying. Before she left the room she saw her father stand and say to Maryan, "I have never laid a hand on her, but by God, this has to be perfect."

"Holy Mother, help!" Leonora cried as she pulled the door of the oven down, and quickly took the loaf of bread out. The bread was steaming and the kitchen filled with smoke. But she saw that the loaf was golden brown and not yet charred. She set it down to cool while she finished packing.

When the big trunk was full, her father lowered the top lid and sat on it while the locks were forced shut. The bread, now cool, was wrapped carefully in a hand-stitched white cloth and laid gingerly in a box full of smoked bacon and sausages and cookies and other food. The box with the bread, she was told, must be carried by her at all times for it would play a vital role in Father Michael's escape.

Leonora hurried into her own room, tidied herself, combed her long golden hair, put on the lambskin shoes she used to wear to church on Sundays and went back to her father. He buried his face in her neck, wetting it with his tears. She stopped smiling now, lifted her father's head and kissed him on the forehead.

"Papa, you just stay here and be ready for my return, for I know that everything will go smoothly," she said and kissed his hand.

With Maryan, she went in a shabby taxi to the local depot at Levary. "We should be in Bratislava in two hours," the Underground leader said, "then you take the express up to

Poprad. There is a very good connection in Bratislava, and you should be in Podolinec by tomorrow morning.

"But let's not forget this. Here is your Party emblem." Maryan pinned it to her coat. "I expect you to behave accordingly," he said, "for the devil never sleeps." She smiled back in understanding.

Once she boarded the night express at Bratislava, Maryan left her. Now Leonora was on her own. She curled up in a crowded compartment, the small box of food between her body and the window. Avidly, she pretended to read the Communist daily, ignoring her fellow passengers. Two of the travelers seemed bent on passing the trip in telling jokes against the regime, but Leonora could not be sure of them so she pretended not to hear what they said. They could very well be *agents provocateurs,* she mused, peering more intently at the newspaper on her lap.

The first stop was Trnava, known as the Slovak Rome because of its innumerable churches, convents and seminaries. As the express pulled out and headed north, she caught a glimpse of the two huge towers of the ancient cathedral. They seemed to be saying "goodbye and good luck" to her as she entered territory she had never visited before. The towers, which had withstood the Turkish and Napoleonic wars, stood in silence now, their bells stilled by the Communists.

Her thoughts were interrupted by the loud talking of the men next to her. One, a burly fellow with bushy chestnut hair, said to his companion, "You want to hear the latest, Jan?"

"What is it?"

"Just listen and I will tell you," the first man said, obviously trying to interest other passengers. Leonora looked away. Instead, she took from her foodbox a roll of wool and began to work on a scarf she wanted ready when she met Filip again.

"The local commissar at Urmin was making an inspection tour of the farmers' cooperative when he heard a conversation between two rabbits:

" 'When did we have it better, when did we have it better?'

the older rabbit asked, as both chewed on the sugar beets left unharvested by the farmers on the fields that were covered with snow.

" 'What do you mean?' asked the younger rabbit.

" 'Have you forgotten the difficult times we had under the capitalist system, when the farmers gathered everything from their fields before the winter came, so that we were starved to death?' the older rabbit explained, and went on:

" 'And what do you see now? Under the People's Democratic system, we find enough abandoned on the same fields to last from one harvest to the next.'

" 'We never had it so good, we never had it so good,' the young rabbit agreed enthusiastically."

The narrator burst into laughter and so did his companion. Others in the car grinned. The two men looked at Leonora to read her reaction, but she would not be provoked. Instead, turning towards them with her Party emblem clearly displayed, she shook her head in apparent irritation. Surprised at her own glibness and daring, she scolded the two for being spoiled brats, not appreciating what the Party did for the poor farmers in pulling together their uneconomic farms into larger ones and providing them with tractors and other mechanical devices for the achievement of greater productivity. So convincing was Leonora, that at the next stop, Leopoldov, the two jokesters left in a hurry.

"Act normally," Leonora remembered her father's telling her. So she opened the foodbox and took out some pastries. The train rattled away from Leopoldov, following the picturesque Vah valley, and by midnight it was nearing the northernmost regions of Slovakia. The lights went out in the compartment and she clung more tenaciously to the foodbox. She feigned sleep, as she leaned over the box.

When the night express came closer to the massive High Tatras it slowed down considerably as it began its steep climb. At Štrba it went downwards again, and as Leonora came nearer to her destination she became more excited. "Act normally," sounded in her ears when the train finally stopped at Poprad.

There were few people on the platform in the chill of the early morning. She dragged the trunk herself into the station restaurant and sat down casually, as she had been told to do, at the small table in the corner facing the entrance. She ordered coffee and started to sip it when a balding man, also wearing the Party emblem, came into the restaurant and headed straight toward her. He was tall and athletic in build, despite his age, and a pipe was clenched between his teeth as he rubbed his hands to warm them.

"Could you tell me, perhaps, what time the next express leaves for Žilina?" he said to Leonora.

"It leaves at three minutes past seven," she said confidently but in a half-whisper.

At that, the man stopped rubbing his hands and exclaimed loudly, "Welcome to Poprad, my dear niece, and excuse the delay. We still have snow around here."

Leonora gently touched the forehead of the unknown man as if he were in fact her uncle and asked, "How is Aunt Veronika?"

"She is not as well as she could be, but perhaps your visit will make her feel better," Leonora's new "uncle" said with a chuckle. He took her big trunk, while she carried the box with the precious loaf of bread. A cold wind struck her face as they stepped out of the station and the fog hid the High Tatras from sight as they stepped into a waiting car. The old auto's tires still had chains on, for the road to Podolinec was a tortuous climb and covered with snow. They traveled from Poprad toward the Polish border, and soon reached Kežmarok. There the fog began to lift and the morning was suddenly radiant. They came to Spišská Bela, where the loudspeakers were issuing orders telling the farmers where to go to work, and the woodcutters where to go to fell trees. Despite her long journey, Leonora showed no sign of fatigue, so taken was she by the alpine beauty of the area.

"There behind those two towers," her "Uncle" Pavel said

when they arrived in Podolinec, pointing at the vast compound of buildings that stood behind the church of the former Redemptorist convent, "is Father Michael."

As the car passed by the convent, Leonora noticed guards all around but no other people. The auto headed toward the Lesny Zavod, which administered the lumber business in Podolinec where Leonora's new uncle was an accountant. Near the office was a neat-looking house and Leonora and her uncle went inside.

"Aunt" Veronika was a chubby, pleasant woman in her forties. She had been expecting her "niece" and a breakfast of potato pancakes and tasty country sausage was quickly placed on the table, with plenty of milk and coffee. As an important official of the state lumber enterprise Pavel lived well, while the farmers nearby barely scraped along.

When she finished eating, Leonora asked, "How can we get a pass to see Father Michael?"

"Leave it to Pavel," Veronika said. "He has his man at the SNB headquarters and he will talk with him about getting you the pass."

"I would like to bring Father Michael some food as soon as possible," Leonora insisted. She made no mention of just what her mission entailed.

"First, I think you are ready for a good sleep," Pavel said. "Let me tackle the pass while you rest." He left the house for work. At the end of the day, he went to the SNB office to see his friend, Sergeant Surovy.

"Why does your niece want to see the prisoner?" the Sergeant asked.

"I told you before that the prisoner knew her and her whole family and while she is here she wants to see him and deliver some food that my wife will prepare for him," Pavel said.

"We are allowed to issue such passes only in quite urgent cases, such as illness, and only in very rare instances at that, Pavel. After what happened when the farmers attacked the camp last winter, who can be sure that the priests didn't have a hand in it? Maybe they provoked the raid through the people who visited them. If I issue a pass to your niece, you must value it as a great exception to our rules." The sergeant stopped pacing the room and looked expectantly into Pavel's eyes.

"Rest assured, Sergeant, that I know how to appreciate this favor," Pavel answered, and pressed into the sergeant's hands an envelope stuffed with money.

Leonora set out for the convent the next day, accompanied by Aunt Veronika. Though it was spring by the calendar, the mountains were still covered with a fine sheet of snow, and the two women walked on snowshoes. Leonora carried her package in yellow wrapping paper. As they approached the convent, Leonora could see machine guns protruding from the narrow openings at the top of the towers guarding the compound.

When they came to the entrance, Veronika said she would wait outside. Leonora headed toward the guards who held their guns in hand as if expecting an attack momentarily. She stopped and, holding her package tightly with one hand, pulled out the pass from her pocket with the other.

"Pass inside," one of the guards said, "and present it to the bureau."

Her heart beat faster, for now she was inside the Communist-patrolled compound. At the end of the yard she came to a small building and showed her pass to another guard. He looked at it, ushered her into a waiting room and without a word gave her a form to fill out.

When she had written her false name and birthplace, lied that she was a Party member, and said whom she wanted to see and why, the guard took the paper and motioned her to a long bench while he went to an office next door. Within a few minutes, he was back.

"Unwrap the package," he ordered.

"Act normally," she said to herself as panic took hold. She took the paper off the package with shaking hands, then took a deep breath and willed her hands steady. She smiled at the guard. "Here is some tasty bacon, some good domestic sausages and of course a loaf of bread to go with it." She smacked her lips in relish.

The guard held each piece in his hands, turned them over, then set each down on the table. From a drawer he pulled out a long, sharp breadknife, and held the loaf steady with his left hand while he prepared to cut.

Leonora held her breath in terror as the guard sliced the bread in half. His knife went clean through without interference. Leonora relaxed, only to feel a cold chill come over her as the guard proceeded to slice each half in two. But his knife touched nothing but bread.

She smiled weakly as he turned to her and said, "You may go to the parlour next door and wait."

Leonora wrapped the bread in its white cloth again, then covered all the food with the yellow paper and went into the parlour. A large crucifix hung from the wall. The room was unheated and as she waited her breath came from her mouth and nose in a light mist.

Fearful, yet determined to show a calm exterior, she recalled the last words of Father Michael in Bratislava, "You must be brave, for the time approaches when you will be called on for even greater services for your country and your faith. The day will come when it will seem that all is dark and lost, but that is when your courage must reach its height."

After he was brought to Podolinec, Father Michael was allowed to rest for a week before assuming his duties as pastor of the community of more than a thousand clerics. As he lay on his bed, thinking of his promise to report on the thoughts and words of his fellow priests, a vague sense of guilt came over him. He could think of no reason why he should feel guilty, for after all he had promised to spy and it was for the good of the State.

Though he did not realize it at the time, the twinge of conscience he could not explain was the first indication that the

Communists had not captured his soul as completely as they had thought.

Sleep came easier and the nightmares were fewer. One morning he even awoke from a dream with a smile on his face. It was the first time he had smiled in months. He had dreamed of the time as a boy when he wore the first complete set of new clothes in his life—long pants, jacket and laced shoes. He was walking with his mother down the clean streets of the city on the way to school. It was a brand new school where, his mother told him, he would meet many nice children from the best families. He would be well looked after by kind sisters wearing large starched white hats like umbrellas and he would sit in whitewashed classrooms and if he learned well he might some day be a teacher or a doctor or a priest. For a brief spell that morning when he awoke from his dream, Father Michael felt a sense of security and peace he had lacked for months.

Toward the end of the first week in Podolinec, Father Michael was looking out the window of his cell, gazing at the snow-covered mountains, when hundreds of small birds appeared, circled over the courtyard, and set down on the gutters of the buildings in the compound. They were the first living creatures other than the guards and investigators he had seen for months.

"God, how beautiful!"

The words came from his lips automatically. He spoke them without a true sense of God. Nevertheless, he had spoken the name of God. His spiritual awakening had begun.

His old memories had not been entirely erased. His mind was still captive, but a spark remained. It was only the faint suggestion of light, glimmering just over the border of consciousness. He could not see it clearly as yet, and he could not grasp its meaning. But he was aware of that spark and his mind reached out for it, like a man trying to remember a haunting thought that always eludes him.

The words and rituals of his religion came back to him gradually. After learning to say God's name again, he recalled a few simple prayers. Then, a whole Rosary with its Hail Marys. Then all the other prayers and rites he had ever said or performed. All returned to his memory in just the reverse order they had left it while he was being brainwashed.

He remembered the words without feeling them. They did not rouse him emotionally, did not make him know God as he once did. His recitations were mechanical.

The Communists were still certain of Father Michael's loyalty. They let him conduct the Mass for the imprisoned priests, so that he might appear as one in whom they could confide. He was allowed to move freely about the convent.

At first, the ritual of the Mass had little meaning for Father Michael. Steadily, however, as he repeated each day the ancient words of the liturgy, he began to remember their true meaning. That light at the edge of his mind grew stronger. He had not yet recaptured his faith, nor was he even aware of such a goal. Rather, he was beset by doubt. He knew there was something wrong, something missing from his life that he wanted desperately to recapture. The knowledge of righteousness was struggling, feebly at first, against the evil that had been planted in his mind by the Communists. His mind was never at rest; the persistent spark of his old life never ceased its struggle for recognition.

He avoided his fellow priests except for the daily Masses, for he wanted to be in complete control of himself. He spent most of his time in his own cell. There he tried to remember the essence, the emotional content of all the prayers he could recite by heart. He gave himself to meditations and he read the theological books that he found in the old convent's library.

What is God? Which are His laws? How do they govern all things and how do they bring about balance and harmony? The questions he had asked and answered as a young man training for the priesthood he now asked again.

166

One day he read the Scriptures and his attention was drawn to this passage: "You must put on the new man, and be changed into another man."

What other man could I be? he reflected. At that moment, he heard a knock at his door. He opened it and saw two of the investigators at this new prison.

"Father," one said, "we have come for the report on the other priests."

"I told you that I must first recover my health," the priest said, "and then I shall give you my report."

"We will give you another week," the interrogator said. "We will expect it on your Holy Saturday. Please have it ready, Father." The words were polite but the tone carried a direct if unvoiced threat.

The strange twilight that had hovered over Father Michael off and on during the weeks after his drugging was discontinued came to haunt his slumber again that night. Strange noises echoed and re-echoed in his ears. He arose in the middle of the night to get a glass of cold water to quench a sudden thirst. If only he did not have to go through with the report, he thought, his recovery would go much quicker and his life in Podolinec, though restricted, might even be bearable.

The next morning was Saturday of Passion Week. As Father Michael celebrated the Mass for the imprisoned priests, he was struck by the liturgical text prescribed to begin the introduction to the services. For the second successive day, the Introitus began with the words:

"Have mercy on me, O Lord, for I am afflicted:
Deliver me out of the hands of my enemies,
And from them that persecute me:
Let me not be confounded."

The words seemed to apply especially to him. "If only I would be spared the writing of the report, O Lord," he prayed to himself and offered the Mass to that aim, that he would not be a traitor to his fellow worshipers.

A feeling of near-elation suffused him when the Mass was over. Certainly, a sense of God was growing in him again. Though he still had trouble recognizing former friends in the camp until they patiently explained who they were, Father Michael was sure the lapses of memory were only temporary and that in time he would regain complete control of himself.

But the dizziness and physical weakness had not disappeared completely. Once that morning he even had to interrupt the Mass to compose himself, and at all times the candles had to be kept close to the missal so he could read the text. His hands trembled as he read and he was so fatigued after the Mass that he returned to his room to remain in quiet meditation for the rest of the day.

But Father Michael's thoughts were interrupted that afternoon when a guard came to tell him a young lady he had long known was waiting downstairs to see him.

After ten minutes of waiting, Leonora saw the door at the end of the parlour open and a guard usher in an emaciated man. "This is your visitor," the guard said, "and you have ten minutes in all." He slammed the door and left the two alone.

The girl and Father Michael looked at each other without recognition. His skin was almost yellow and his eyes were dull. His auburn hair had receded considerably in the six months since Leonora had seen him and streaks of grey ran through it.

"Who are you, my child?" Father Michael asked in a low voice, nervously entwining the fingers of his hands that rested on his chest.

"Very Reverend Father Provincial, I am Leonora Dankova. Don't you know me?" She bent to kiss the hand he automatically offered her.

"My child, you must tell me more about yourself, for I have been sick a long time."

Tears filled Leonora's eyes. "Very Reverend Father, don't you remember Leonora, who knew you as a child in Levary, who came to you in Bratislava to seek consolation and ask your prayers for Filip Polhora? Don't you remember?"

His faced was turned away from her and he stared off into space. "Leonora, Filip, Leonora, Filip," he mumbled repeatedly, as Leonora crouched at his feet. Then a smile lit up his face.

"Of course, my child, I remember. Forgive me." He cupped his hand under her chin and lifted her to her feet.

"Very Reverend Father, we don't have much time. Listen to me carefully. I have brought you some food. But this is not the real purpose of my visit. I have come to help rescue you from your imprisonment. Take the loaf of bread that is in this package and when you are alone—be sure you are alone—break each portion until you find what is hidden inside. It tells the whole plan of escape."

Father Michael smiled. "My child, you cannot rescue me. Nor can anyone else. Only our Father who is above can rescue me."

"Yes, yes, Father," she corrected herself. "This can only be done if it is our Lord's will. But the Holy Father in Rome is waiting to see you," she added on impulse, twisting the truth just a bit.

She picked up the package and put it in Father Michael's hands to be sure he would not forget it. Then she waited until he rose and left the room first. He turned at the door and said, "Bless you, Leonora, and continue to pray that I may be strong."

Back in his cell, Father Michael realized he had been deeply touched by the unexpected visit. The remembrance of the love of Filip and Leonora helped remove the dam that was blocking his memory.

But escape? The thought had never entered his mind before and now the prospect bewildered him. It appealed to him enormously, yet he felt fairly secure and comfortable at Podolinec. What could he expect outside? He recalled the suffering and torture he had undergone and recoiled at the idea that he might be laying himself open to such treatment again if he escaped and was caught anew. But he was discovering God once more, and as he progressed along this path, he became increasingly uncomfortable in his role as a servant of the Communists.

And if he escaped, his mind leaped joyously at the prospect, he might avoid the need to turn in his report on his fellow priests.

Father Michael did not open the precious loaf of bread right away. He wanted to be sure he would not be disturbed, so he waited until after supper when no one ever came to visit him. Taking the four pieces of bread from the cloth covering, he broke each apart. In the third he tried, an end piece, he found two small folded sheets of paper and a key. He put the bread down and inspected the papers. One was a map with spots pinpointed on it. The other contained directions. The whole thing was rather simple, even to Father Michael's troubled mind, and he put both papers and key into his pocket and ate a piece of the bread with satisfaction.

Sleep was sweet that night. He saw his mother again in his dreams. She was visiting him at Innsbruck just before his ordination for the priesthood. He saw her coming with all sorts of pastries, with ham and sausages, for the ordination was his wedding and his mother wanted to celebrate the great event of his life in style. She brought wine, too, and they had a nice dinner, he, his mother and fellow priests. Mother was happy and smiled constantly. And then the following day, she received the Communion from the hands of her own son in the great dome of Innsbruck.

He woke from his dream thirsty, as always. He drank a glass of water and stuck his hand into the pocket to make sure the papers and key were still there; then he returned to bed happily. But his mind was so filled with anticipation, he could not fall asleep. The moon that appeared after the cold wind from Poland dispelled the clouds illuminated his room. Only toward morning did he finally doze off.

The night before Leonora came to Podolinec, a group of men were standing outside a cave in the High Tatra Mountains not far from that city. The air was sharp and clear as the full moon climbed the sky, the blanket of snow glowed silvery in the light.

"Nothing is more radiant than the April moon over the Tatras," Imrich Lisska said in a voice that brooked no disagreement. Each of the guerillas stood quietly, looking skyward thoughtfully and longing for his sweetheart or wife.

"Lent will soon be over," Jan Baar sighed, "and we can eat and love again."

An air of melancholy seeped through the band. "Why don't we go inside," Kazimir Hlavina said, breaking the stillness. "I can't provide you with women, but I can play my harmonica and Lisska maybe will part with some of his Slivovitz."

The men grinned agreement and, following Lisska, went to a section of the cave where their noise would not disturb Father Vendel, Labuda or his daughter.

Hlavina's harmonica brought a mixture of joy and nostalgia to the guerillas as they sat round the fire taking turns sipping the plum brandy. His fingers moved skillfully as he played their favorite love songs, songs that filled their homesick hearts with cravings and longings and reminded them of past conquests.

"No, no, Brother Halmo," Lisska broke the spell with an angry shout. "Not so much. You're due for sentry duty. You'll fall asleep on the job with all that liquor in you."

Vincent Halmo, one of the younger guerillas, finished with a deep gulp, smiled sheepishly and ran out with rifle in hand.

"Let's play twenty-one," Jan Baar said.

"What do we play for?" asked Tomas Kratky.

"He who scores the most points shall have the honor of

accompanying and courting the first female we encounter?"
Hlavina proposed.

"Agreed," the guerillas said and Baar began shuffling and
dealing the oily, dirty cards that would have long ago been
discarded if they were not the only pack in the cave.

The game had not gone fifteen minutes when Halmo came
running back into the cave. "Lisska, Lisska," he shouted,
"there is a man coming up the south slope heading our way."

Lisska rose to his feet quickly. "Don't lose control of yourself, young Halmo, when you see just one mouse. Two or three
men can handle the situation."

Lisska, Halmo and Jan Baar hurried out the entrance and
looked down below them but could see nothing. "He must be
behind the curve that obstructs our vision," Halmo said uncertainly. It was his first assignment with the guerilla band and
he was eager to make good.

"Jan, you go around the two rocks on the south," Lisska
ordered. "I will wait this side of the cave, should he come from
this direction, and you, Halmo, wait at your regular post."

Jan Baar ran for his skis and quickly descended the slope
toward the two large boulders that pointed heavenward on
either side of a path leading toward the cave. Anyone familiar
with the mountain would have to go past the rocks, Jan knew.

He took his skis off, put them down at the base of one of
the rocks and climbed to the top of the boulder. From the
height of almost nine feet he could see a lonely figure trudging
slowly toward him, sometimes walking, sometimes sitting as
if to regain his strength. The figure seemed to be walking quite
openly, making no attempt to hide his movements, and he kept
his hands in plain sight.

When he reached the rocks, he sat down again. As he wiped
his face with the sleeves of his coat, his foot slipped on the
thin sheet of ice that coated the path and he fell down. He
tried to get up instantly so as not to succumb to his own
fatigue. It was at that instant, when the newcomer was off his
guard, that Baar leaped down from his perch on the rock and

172

fell on the figure. The intruder was no match for the husky guerilla and was subdued after a short scuffle.

Only when his prisoner sat up and looked him right in the face did Baar realize whom he had captured. "Filip Polhora! What are you doing here again?"

Filip wiped the snow off his face with a good-natured grin, picked up his cap and gave his knapsack to Baar to carry without a word.

"We fought like Jacob and the angel," Filip finally said.

"Yes, but the question is, who was Jacob and who was the angel," Baar snapped back with a laugh.

The pair got up from the snow and started upwards toward the cave. Baar noticed Filip walking in his shoes and asked, "Where are your snowshoes? Don't tell me you came all the way in those things."

"Only since Ruzbachy. Someone recognized me there and I had to leave in a hurry without all my equipment."

"You must be starving," Baar said. "Let's see if we can find something for you to eat."

"And to drink, too, judging by your breath," Filip said.

When they neared the cave, Baar whistled a short, staccato sound that announced the arrival of a friend and soon Lisska and others surrounded them.

"I must see Jan Labuda immediately," Filip said.

"Is it so important that it can't wait till morning?" Lisska asked.

"My orders are to see Labuda upon arrival," Filip repeated.

"All right, all right." Lisska's pride was hurt by the challenge to his authority. "I'll get Labuda. You men take care of our guest."

Filip had warmed his stomach with a long drink from the bottle of Slivovitz when Labuda came into the room, grumbling and rubbing his eyes. When he saw Filip, his face lit up and he hugged the courier in his powerful arms. Filip's presence could only mean action for his guerilla band and Labuda was anxious to put his men to the test again, for they had done

173

little since Lent began and might be growing stale. They were thinking too much, Labuda thought, and too much time for thinking was not good for guerillas. It made them careless and hard to rouse to fever pitch when it did not actually goad them into reckless actions just for the sake of action.

"Welcome, Filip, what brings you here? An assignment, I trust."

"I have a very important message from General Duplin," the courier said and handed over two sheets of paper torn from the lining of his jacket.

"Filip, my eyes are not as good as they used to be and this candlelight isn't any too strong," Labuda said as he held the papers to the flame to verify the signature of General Duplin, one of the leaders of the Underground. "Read it to me."

The message Filip read told of the drugging of Father Michael and his confession to the Communists, leading to his imprisonment at Podolinec. Filip paused long enough to let Labuda curse the Communists' cruelty, then continued with the Underground's orders to Labuda: Rescue Father Michael at any price. The rescue plans were spelled out and a map was enclosed to show where the Father Provincial was located and where he would leave the convent, if all went well.

During the next week, the guerilla camp hummed with activity as preparations were made for the rescue. Labuda put his men through rigorous physical exercises to harden their limbs and build up their wind. Daily skiing, in groups of only two or three to avoid suspicious eyes overhead, was part of the regimen. And then Holy Saturday dawned, the day of the rescue.

Father Vendel was one of the first to arise. He performed his priestly duties and walked out of the cave. Near the entrance Filip and Jan Baar were already preparing a small fire from some old dry splinters, a fire known as the "Burning of Judas." For the guerillas, the Burning of Judas held special significance, for Judas to them represented the eternal traitor, and traitors were part and parcel of their life in Slovakia.

In a few minutes the guerilla band assembled for the dawn

rite. Hlavina carried the cross. Labuda followed the priest, a rosary in his hands. Lisska followed with Anicka, and then the rest of the company. When Father Vendel stopped at the fire, Filip held up in his hands a piece of flint and a steel pipe to show that, according to custom, matches had not been used to start the fire.

The crowd was hushed as the priest blessed the fire and lit his three-stemmed candle in the flames. As he rose the faces of his followers were creased with smiles and he led them back into the cave, to the church inside, intoning the traditional Lumen Christi three times in succession, each time in a higher tone until the worshipers reached the altar.

The Light of Christ dawn ritual, symbolizing the end of darkness in all-embracing light and the end of death through the triumph of the Resurrection, was followed by the blessing of water, the reading of prophesies, litanies to all saints and finally the Mass. And then it was time to prepare for action.

Labuda motioned to Father Vendel to step forward. The huge priest, his cassock clinging to his body, raised his hands in blessing:

"Men of the Underground," he began, "You are leaving soon on a mission that is important in the eyes of God and man. Up till now you fought, as guerillas, against the enslavement of men's bodies. Now you are not only guerillas, but a Legion of the Spirit, for you are going to liberate from slavery a man's mind and soul. Go, therefore, and resurrect a man whom our enemies have turned into a walking dead one. Godspeed to all of you."

Because of their roles in the rescue, Filip, Jan Baar, Tomas Sobol and Kazimir Hlavina were the first to leave. They put on their skis, looked down a long clear slope into the valley and were off. Here and there the party stopped and Filip would look through his field glasses to see if the enemy were ahead before the group moved on again. The early spring sun was growing hotter and the men removed their caps. There was little talk among them all the way to the outskirts of Podolinec.

Podolinec had long been under a spell of solemnity, for the procession of the Expectation of the Resurrection was to take place at six in the evening before Easter Sunday. Once the procession was over, Lent would end and the people rejoice. Those who had gone without meat for forty days would fill their stomachs and those who had been courting would marry.

Even the thousand prisoners in Podolinec could sense the joyous expectations. The Communist guards themselves bowed to the significance of the hour. They did not force the captive priests and monks that day to take part in the "re-education" courses that were designed to change the prisoners from recalcitrants into "patriotic" priests. Instead, the captives were allowed to spend the day cleaning their cells, mending their cassocks, sweeping the church or just standing idle in expectation of the great procession. Whatever their publicly avowed beliefs, many of the guards, too, quietly joined the crowd of prisoners to be a part of the worshipers, even if they would not march in the procession.

Father Michael, by Communist order, was to lead the procession as the highest in rank among the prisoners. The priests and monks were to assemble in the church and wait for him to come from the convent, at precisely 6 P.M. Holding the monstrance in his hands, Father Michael was to lead the celebrants around the church from the chapel to the main altar, where he would announce that Christ had risen. That same day, after the procession, Father Michael was to turn over the report he had promised to the Communists.

Those were the Communists' plans for Father Michael. But not the Underground's.

His nerves on edge in anticipation of the escape, the Father Provincial could hardly sit still. He ran back and forth between his cell and the church, first looking over the Underground's instructions, then making sure the flowers were properly placed on the main altar. Back and forth he went, afraid that if he remained in one place too long his anxiety would alert the Communists and the rescue effort would be thwarted.

At one point, Father Michael almost decided not to go through with the escape. A thousand of his brothers were waiting expectantly for him in the church, dressed in the finest vestments they could find, the candles were lit, and the high altar radiant with light. How could he disappoint them? Yet to stay and turn in his report to the Communists, he realized, would be an even viler betrayal.

At twenty minutes to six, before schedule, he entered the church, clean shaven and hair trimmed in the manner of a celebrant. He bowed deeply before the sepulchre of his Lord, then turned and walked out of the church again without a word.

To a puzzled guard in the sacristy, he said, "I forgot something in my cell. I will be back quickly." He broke into a run as if to show the guard he knew he must be back by six.

Once back in the room, he threw off his cassock, put on a tie, jacket, coat and hat. Then, instead of descending to the church, he took one last look at the map he had been given by Leonora, thrust it into his pocket and went down into the cellar of the convent building. The guards who were usually on duty were watching the services in the church.

The cellar led under the courtyard to the church where the priests were waiting and Father Michael felt his way across the dark underground room. When he reached the farthest wall, he lit his first match. There, as had been described in the instructions, was a loose panel of wood. He gripped it with one hand, dropped the match, and then tore it loose easily. Lighting another match, he found a wooden door. The master key he had been given fitted the rusty lock and turned it so easily that he was sure he could have unlocked the door with a hooked wire or other makeshift key.

Ahead of him was a long hallway stretching as far as he could see by the light of a match. The air was cold and clammy. The tunnel, Father Michael was later to learn, had been built centuries before, when the church itself went up. It was designed to let the inhabitants escape when the enemy besieged the compound. Many times the tunnel was used during the wars that beset Slovakia over her long history. And now the secret passage was saving still another endangered life.

Father Michael closed the door behind him, made the sign of the cross as he whispered *"Procedamus in pace"*—Let us proceed in peace—and then, using one match after another, made his way to the other end of the tunnel.

A door at the other end yielded to the key, too, though with considerably more difficulty. Beads of heavy perspiration were streaming down his face, cool as the passage was, as he pushed the door ajar. The door opened barely enough for him to squeeze his body through before he was prevented from moving any further by evergreen bushes. The shrubs were obviously planted to hide the door from outside view.

Near the bushes stood a slender young girl dressed in fur coat, ski pants and a multicolored kerchief on her head. Noticing the movement of the evergreens, she fastened her eyes there until she saw the face of Father Michael peer around a break in the row of bushes. She shook her head violently, hoping he would understand he was to move back out of sight, for there were SNB troopers nearby at that moment. He ducked back quickly behind the shrubs.

Leonora Dankova walked toward the pair of SNB gendarmes and smiled broadly.

"Good evening," one of the policemen greeted her.

"Good evening," she replied.

"Didn't your boy friend keep his date?" the other trooper asked.

"Oh, my Mike is always late," she said grinning. "That's his custom, but he will be here any minute." She tried to keep her voice natural.

"If he does not come soon, we may take you to the dance this evening ourselves," the first gendarme suggested.

"Happy Easter to you," Leonora replied, and added, "If he does not show up, I will remember that I owe each of you a dance."

The two SNB men continued on their rounds, watching

Leonora move away in the opposite direction until they turned a corner and were out of sight. When she was sure the police would not double back, Leonora quickly turned around and retraced her steps until she was near the bushes again where Father Michael emerged.

She waved her hand and the priest came out. Quickly straightening his tie and uncrumpling his hat, Leonora embraced him and then put her arm around his waist. He reciprocated. She led him slowly, stopping here and there to embrace, as if they were two lovers without a care in the world.

One guard in the observation tower even waved towards the couple in friendly fashion when he saw them walking on a lonely road, their arms intertwined. Though Leonora and Father Michael could not see his face clearly, he winked knowingly.

As they walked on, they met the two SNB troopers Leonora had encountered earlier. The police looked closely at the man who now walked hand in hand with her, not because they suspected anything, but because they were curious as to what sort of man had attracted such a lovely young girl. The dusk made it difficult for them to make out his features clearly, but they agreed afterwards they had never seen the lucky lover before.

Her heart sinking with fear, Leonora smiled and waved at the SNB men. Fighting the panic that was growing within her, she forced herself to walk slowly into the woods that surrounded the convent. The plan called for her to cut through the forest with Father Michael, but the priest was already near exhaustion, physically and emotionally. His long imprisonment had sapped his strength and his feet could not manage climbing the rough ground. Leonora led him back to the forest path. It would be more dangerous, but the ascent was less steep and the ground easier on the feet.

And then, before they had taken a dozen steps, two new SNB men dropped down from a pine tree onto the road just ahead of them.

In that instant, Leonora thought all was lost.

"Leonora," one of the SNB men cried, racing towards her. In the creeping darkness of evening she could only see a blur approaching, but the voice told her plainly the man dressed in the uniform of the Security Police was Filip Polhora.

They were in each other's arms for only a second. This was neither the time nor place for them to express the sentiments, the relief that enveloped them.

"Forgive me, Father Michael," Filip said, "for not greeting you first, but . . ." His voice trailed off.

The priest smiled benignly. "I know very well, Filip, what love is, for the first attribute of God is love and that is what I have lived for."

The conversation ended abruptly when footsteps were heard down the road, from the direction Leonora and Father Michael had come. Filip and Jan Baar pulled out their guns in readiness, then put them back when they saw two more SNB men— Tomas Sobol and Kazimir Hlavina.

"Now Father, there is no time to lose," Filip said. His voice was crisp. "By now they will be missing you. Sit here please," he ordered as he and Baar joined hands to form a seat to carry the priest deeper into the forest. A mile further on they came to the end of the woods. Ahead of them was a long bare snow-covered stretch sloping gently upwards.

The sight of the clearing struck home to Father Michael how far they had come from the convent at Podolinec. Till then he was so wrapped up in carrying out the plans of his escape, that he did not fully realize he was once again a free man. Now the fact impressed itself on his agitated mind, and he broke into uncontrollable weeping.

Filip and Leonora quickly embraced him and wiping his face she whispered words of comfort. But he could not stop his sobbing until almost ten minutes had passed. When he was quiet again and had regained his composure, Filip told him:

"Now Father, we have six pairs of skis here, one for each of

180

us. But I don't think you are in any condition to stand on them. We will have to carry you about three kilometers to the forester's house, where our comrades wait for us. Three kilometers will take approximately an hour in this rough terrain, but then we will have a warm, comfortable place to rest awhile."

"Do whatever you think is necessary," Father Michael said.

Traversing the open space on a bright moonlit night, however, was not so simple. By now Communist patrols would be searching out in all directions from the convent for Father Michael. Even a small crowd of six would stand out against the white snow. From his knapsack, Jan Baar took six white sheets. Each of the members of the party donned one, tearing out eyeholes with his fingers, and what had been six dark blotches now formed a white on white pattern against the snow that could only be distinguished from close quarters.

The sheets did the trick and an hour later, at eight-thirty in the evening, the six reached the forester's house. The forester was an avowed Communist, but Labuda had chosen his home for the rendezvous because the well-built wooden structure was the only suitable place between Podolinec and the guerillas' cave in the High Tatras for a rendezvous and for Father Michael to rest in.

The cottage was not without danger, for the patrolling guards and security officers who kept the area under surveillance would often stop there for a cup of tea or just to warm their cold hands on the fireplace. When Labuda arrived, the forester, his wife and grown daughter were at home, eating their dinner of Easter bread, called *paska,* cold ham cuts with horseradish and homemade pastries. The lonely house at the outskirts of a pine wood was completely surrounded by Labuda's men before the guerilla leader kicked the door open and plunged in, followed by Lisska and Hlavina.

Up jumped the forester, leaping for the telephone that connected him directly with Podolinec. But he was not quick enough, for Labuda with one strong pull of his huge hand tore the wires out of the wall, and the hut stood more isolated than ever.

The display of strength and the sight of the two other armed guerillas shook the forester into quiet submission. Even more frightening was the polite, almost apologetic way Labuda spoke to the cowering family. He excused himself for interrupting the traditional Easter dinner but, he said, he must occupy the house and the area around it for just a few hours. To make things absolutely secure for everyone concerned, he asked the forester and his family to spend the few hours in their own bedrooms, where Labuda assured them they would go unmolested. Just to make sure the captive family gave them no trouble, they wouldn't mind being bound and gagged and placed down on the beds, would they?

Soon after the guerillas had made themselves at home, Filip arrived with Father Michael and the rest in tow. The priest, uttering not a word, as if to speak would shatter the dream of freedom he was having, was seated in a comfortable chair near the fire. There was food and wine in abundance as befitted the house of a Communist. But the guerillas did not eat right away. They looked with concern upon the silent priest, who breathed heavily and with obvious emotion as he looked into the flames. When the fire had brought a glow to the pale, emaciated face, Father Michael broke his silence.

"My friends, all of you here, for the rest of my life I shall not forget to pray to God for what you have done for me this day, for you have helped a dead man come to life again."

He stopped talking. The guerillas waited for him to continue. But those were all the words he could get out of his mouth without breaking down again. Father Michael stood up and moved with outstretched hands to Jan Labuda, who at that instant was wiping the tears from his own eyes. When he realized the sick and feeble priest was coming to him, Labuda jumped up and met him halfway to spare Father Michael even that effort. He grabbed the priest's hand warmly.

"We, too, thank God, Very Reverend Father," the bearded

guerilla chieftain said, "that He showed great things to us this day, for He has chosen a frail woman to be His instrument in leading you out of an impregnable fortress, and not the might of weapons." Filip pressed Leonora's hand tightly at his side as Labuda spoke the words of praise.

"Now, Father, you must be very hungry," Filip said as he rose. "There is ham, there is *paska* . . . and excellent pastries," Leonora continued. She prepared a plate for the priest and soon all the guerillas were stuffing themselves. They were talking and eating at the same time, happily reliving the rescue of Father Michael, when all of a sudden, the door opened.

Two SNB men hurtled in. The guerillas reached for their guns but stopped themselves quickly. The green-uniformed police were blindfolded and their hands were tied behind their backs. They had been shoved through the door by four guerillas, who had been on guard near the house.

"What do we do with them?" one of the captors asked gruffly.

"Just tie their legs and put them in the next room," Labuda said. "Today there will be no killing and no shooting. Not even Communists. This is a solemn day for us all, and we must behave as Christians." All throughout that eventful day, Labuda reminded his followers, they had heeded his warning not to fire a shot or spill a drop of blood.

A stretcher was quickly constructed with sheets torn from the beds in the forester's house for Father Michael to rest on. He was carried by a pair of guerillas who were changed frequently as the party ascended the slope.

Filip and Leonora walked hand in hand, telling of what had happened to each other in the months they had been apart. Interspersed throughout their excited conversation were frequent periods of silence, during which they looked at each other and smiled and walked along content.

Father Vendel greeted them at the cave, long after midnight, his face wreathed in a smile of relief. "Thank God, you are all

183

safe. I was getting strange ideas that something went wrong. It's three o'clock in the morning already."

Then he noticed the emaciated face, wet and half frozen, a face he had never seen before but whose deeply etched lines told a story of suffering and sorrow. He walked soundlessly to the Father Provincial, his huge, vigorous body towering over the thin figure who was trying to sit up. The guerillas grew silent as the two priests met.

"Welcome to my church," Father Vendel said.

"Thank you," said Father Michael.

They shook hands and looked at each other without a sound. Their silence conveyed as much emotion as a torrent of passionate words.

Father Michael was taken to Father Vendel's room and before many minutes had passed, all the denizens of the mountain cave except the lookouts were fast asleep.

It was noon before life was stirring again. Spring was in the air, a month late by the calendar, and the ice and snow were melting. Under a radiant blue sky, the mountains glittered brightly as the wet snow reflected the warm sun.

Father Michael sat on the edge of his bed, still unable to comprehend fully his happiness. Only yesterday he had been a prisoner, and now he was a free man. Only a week ago he had introduced two consecutive Masses with a prayer for delivery from the hands of his enemies. Only a few days before, he had been tormented by the thought he must betray his fellow priests. And now he would soon celebrate the Mass of Resurrection in freedom.

By one o'clock, everything had been prepared for Father Michael. The heavy wooden table that served as an altar was placed at the entrance to the cave, instead of its usual place deep inside the cave, for the Father Provincial wanted this Mass to be held under the glorious dome of the sky. An Easter service in the sunlight seemed to him more appropriate for this day in which all darkness was dispelled.

He came out of the cave, dressed in the beautiful long white alb that Jan Baar had given Father Vendel months before, followed by Baar, who was joyously shaking a little bell to summon the faithful to witness Father Michael. But his urgent pealing was superfluous, for the whole community had long since assembled for this Mass. Still the little bell of Baar's tolled on and on over the heads of the congregation to announce to the mountains and to the world that this was the hour of triumph for Christendom.

Standing erect now before the altar, Father Michael closed his eyes and felt the intense fervor of the group penetrate his own frame. His heart began to pound and he was filled with an indescribable sense of the holiness of the hour as he began:

"I arose, and I still am with Thee, alleluja:
Lord, Thou has proved me and known me:
Thou has known my sitting down, and my rising up."
And he intoned in a trembling but solemn voice:
"Gloria in excelsis Deo."

From rite to rite and prayer to prayer he went, his spirit soaring as if carried on pillows of clouds that made its movement soft and elegant. Soon he grew into one with his sacrifice on the makeshift wooden altar, and as the Mass neared its end it seemed to him the shortest one he had ever conducted. His eyes never left the cross that stood before him and even as he turned around to face the congregation the cross was fixed sharply in his mind's eye.

His eyelids closed gently and in his fevered imagination he saw himself nailed to the cross.

The sun's steady heat was proving too much for the worn but exhilarated priest and underneath his vestments his body was covered with perspiration. Sweat oozed into his eyes as he opened them and his vision was blurred. There, off in the distance, he saw his Communist tormentors again, coming towards him armed and laughing. "We will get you," he heard them say.

Then the bells pealed again, the small bells of Jan Baar, and

Father Michael recovered his senses. "The Mass is over," flashed through his mind when he heard the bells, "and the men are waiting for the benediction."

He wiped the sweat from his eyes, and the phantoms that had terrified him in the distance now turned to be nothing more than the twin rocks that guarded the path to the cave, the voices nothing more than the wind gently rustling the pine trees.

But the brief shock left him suddenly exhausted and a wave of nausea passed over him. The six long months he had spent as a prisoner of the Communists had taken their toll and it would be many months before he could ever regain his former vitality. Now, summoning up the last reserve of energy, he shook off the feeling of faintness and turned to the people around the altar, who had fallen to their knees.

Cutting a cross in the air, he intoned, "I bless you in the name of the Father, and of the Son and of the Holy Spirit. Amen."

"Lord Jesus has risen from the dead," the men sang as they rose to their feet. And as their voices filled the air, Father Michael's eyes were drawn heavenward.

The lingering shadows seemed to fall away from his mind, and the light that had been growing stronger in his consciousness came flooding through him, illuminating all the dark corners of his mind.

The vision came to him sudden and clear. His imprisonment had been his own crucifixion. His denial of God's existence, his confession and promise to betray his fellow priests were the signs of his spiritual death.

And now, in the celebration of Jesus' rising from the dead, his own spirit was resurrected. He saw God clearly at last, and his soul reached out to Him and called:

"My God! My God!"

Weeping with joy, Father Michael was led back to the cave.

8. Brief Interlude

"HAVEN'T you had enough already?" boomed the voice of Jan Labuda as he slammed his spoon down on the back of Filip Polhora's outstretched hand.

Filip drew the hand back fast from the wooden plate still half full of meat in the middle of the table. He turned angrily to Labuda, expletives forming on his lips, when he saw the hulking guerilla leader grinning playfully.

"That wasn't for me," Filip explained with a straight face. "I was getting a piece for Leonora. Don't you see that her arms are shorter than any of ours?"

Labuda roared with laughter. He had been drinking wine steadily all during the Easter Sunday dinner and his mood was jovial. It was contagious, too, and all the guerillas and even the two priests ate with gusto and light heart.

All, that is, except Leonora and Anicka who sat next to each other talking seriously. The slender light-haired stranger to guerilla ways was fast becoming an admirer of plump dark-haired Anicka, as the latter told matter-of-factly of her experiences with her father's band. Leonora was eager to learn about the way Anicka lived, in case she herself would ever work by Filip's side.

"Do you go with them even if there will be shooting, and do you use weapons yourself?" she asked wide-eyed.

"No, I do not use weapons. My father would never permit me, even if I wanted to. But I do go with them when they fight."

"What do you do then?"

"Oh, I usually carry the supply of cartridges on my back. Or

I might have some bags on my shoulder full of dynamite or whatever else is necessary for blowing up track or a supply depot." Anicka's voice was quite natural.

"Isn't that dangerous?"

Anicka shrugged. "Not really. You get used to it. When I hear the shooting begin, I throw myself onto the ground and hug the ammunition and explosives beneath me.

"Sometimes I shout at my father or at my husband, when he was alive, 'Are you still there?' not daring to look up myself." There was no tremor in her voice any more as she spoke of her slain husband.

"And when everything is over, you get up." Leonora said with a smile.

"Or they get me up," Anicka laughed.

She speared a piece of marinated deer and put it on Leonora's plate. "Take another piece, for you will be hungry again before you reach your aunt's house in Podolinec. It's a long way."

When dinner was over, Leonora took off her bracelet and placed it on Anicka's wrist, insisting over the latter's protests that she take it. "When all this warfare is over," she said, "you must come visit me in Levary."

"My father says that the Communist system is about to crumble. But he's been saying that for years already. I don't know when this kind of life will ever be over," Anicka finished with a sigh.

With the end of the feast, the time had come for Leonora to return to Podolinec where she would take the train home to Levary. The farewell was a painful one, for in the short space of a day she had tasted the freedom and camaraderie of the guerillas that had been lacking in her own tense but monotonous life in the Iron Curtain buffer zone. But there was the satisfaction of what she had done for the Underground and the Church of Silence. And best of all, though she would soon be parted from Filip again, he would at least accompany her, alone, as far as Podolinec.

Filip dried the tears from her face after she said goodbye to Father Michael. The two young lovers put on their skis and skimmed down the slope, past the twin rocks. As soon as they were out of sight, Filip put on a burst of speed to pull ahead of Leonora, then turned sharply so she would collide with him. They tumbled over and over in the wet snow, laughing and clutching at each other. Filip helped her to her feet and embraced her. The laughter stopped suddenly as their lips met hungrily.

Holding her close, Filip said, "Nora, Podolinec is not so far and the weather is perfect for travel. How would it be if we could go dancing somewhere? What do you say?"

Her eyes glistened. "Yes, but where?"

"Well, Ruzbachy would be closest to Aunt Veronika, but I don't think it would be too safe, there." He did not explain why, nor did Leonora ask.

"Matliare is the closest place to here with a good orchestra, but we would have quite a distance to go yet to Podolinec."

"I don't care, as long as you are with me. Besides, I can sleep in the train back home from Podolinec."

"All right then, we go down to Matliare."

They dashed down to the resort, one of the finest in Northern Slovakia. Filip held himself in check at first, but he soon saw restraint was unnecessary, for Leonora was an excellent skier, too. Though she had been raised in the Morava Valley, she had often gone skiing with friends in the Little Carpathian Mountains or the White Carpathians that bounded the fertile lands along the Morava. She kept up well with Filip and soon their cheeks were glowing in the bright dry air of the awakening spring.

He shouted alongside her to stop. "Who can see you and not love you, Nora?" He came to her with outstretched arms, but as he reached out, she took off and left him clutching air.

"Nora, Nora, stop, don't you hear me!" he cried as she laughed. Filip grinned sheepishly and started after her. But not until she reached a small brook did he catch up to her. She had taken off her skis and was preparing to wade through the icy waters, so recently melted, when he put his arms around her from behind, squeezed her against his chest, then turned her around gently and kissed her.

Evening had just fallen when they reached Matliare. In the large dining hall of the resort hotel, a crowd had already gathered. Most of the guests were holiday visitors from Prague and Bratislava, high government officials who could afford the steep price of the luxuries in this exclusive place. Filip knew what sort of clientele the hotel drew, but he reckoned the danger of being recognized would be much smaller than in a less ostentatious place where he might meet fellow workers or people of his own age who knew him. And he still had plenty of money left.

He felt a twinge of guilt in spending funds that had been contributed to the Underground by Americans and other sympathetic Westerners as well as by wealthy Slovaks who supported the Communists outwardly but whose hearts lay with the Resistance. But his conscience did not bother the fun-loving courier for long. He convinced himself he had a gay time coming after many months of hard service.

Before entering the lobby of the hotel, Filip and Leonora shook off the snow that sparkled in their hair and covered their clothes and dried their faces. Leonora combed her hair hurriedly and put on new lipstick.

In the lobby they heard the strains of a sentimental love ballad and followed the sound, hand in hand, into the sumptuous dining room. They walked oblivious of the crowd around them. Once inside, however, Leonora was quick to notice that most of the ladies sat at their tables in dresses and gowns of the newest fashion. The men were impeccably dressed, too. But she felt more at ease when she noticed at least three other tourist couples who wore ski outfits as she and Filip did.

"Table for two, please," Filip said to the head waiter.

"You are not formally dressed," the waiter's lifted eyebrow punctuated the insolence of his tone.

"Would this do?" Filip pressed a banknote with a knowing grin into the waiter's outstretched hand.

The waiter found a table near the center of the dining room, just two rows away from the dancing platform, and winked back to Filip and Leonora at the entrance. He took a "reserved" sign from the table and motioned them to come. Filip took Leonora by the arm and made his way toward the waiter, whose hand was extended again.

Filip reached into his pocket and pulled out some more banknotes. Like most suitors he was anxious to impress the object of his affections as a man of the world. Moreover, he realized the table was an excellent one and he did not want an unfriendly head waiter to repay stinginess by moving him somewhere else and drawing attention to him and Leonora.

"Can I get you something to drink?" the waiter asked ingratiatingly.

"Don't you have a wine list?" Filip asked.

"You know that paper must be used only for absolute necessities during our present five-year plan," the waiter said apologetically.

"Well, what do you have then?"

"You can have Tokay, Pezinok or Limbach wines. Or do you prefer some three-star cognac, like Hennessey or Napoleon?"

"Is there any champagne?"

"Yes, but it is very expensive."

"Who asked you about the expense? Just bring it," Filip ordered. The waiter bowed and left.

"I never have had champagne in my life," Leonora whispered in faint protest.

"Tonight is as good a time as any to initiate you," Filip said, reaching across the table to take her hand in his and caress it softly. Their eyes met and held each other. Filip's hands squeezed the small, thin ones they held until Leonora bit her lip in pain. Their bodies slowly leaned forward across the table toward each other, as if impelled by a power beyond them, and all the sounds in the room faded away, all except the wild gypsy music that intensified the sudden desire that came over Filip.

A small explosion brought Filip out of his rapture.

Neither he nor Leonora had been aware of the waiter as he returned with the champagne. But the popping of the cork from the bottle broke the spell and Filip jumped up, alert. He grinned shamefacedly when he realized what had caused the sharp report, sat down and watched the waiter pour the champagne into their glasses and set the cloth-covered bottle down in a silver dish.

Filip realized he had to watch his step. Casually his eyes swept over the dining room. A dark, stocky SNB trooper was sitting in uniform several tables away. The other place at the table was unset, so the green-clad officer must be alone, Filip thought. He must be on duty, otherwise how could a policeman afford to eat in such a luxurious hotel. Filip's eyes fixed on the SNB man's eyes a second too long, for the trooper turned and caught Filip's stare before he could turn his head elsewhere.

The SNB man seemed to be the only danger spot in the room. Everyone else there was drinking or professing love to their ladies or dancing a tango or waltz on the platform. The officer's back was at a right angle to Filip, the courier noticed, and the odds were that he didn't see Filip's nervous reaction to the popping of the champagne cork.

Relaxing again, Filip turned back to Leonora, who had been watching him with anxious eyes, and raised his long-stemmed goblet.

"To us, Nora."

"That we may have a long life," she added, lifting her glass, "and that we may live as the swallows on the beam, happily together."

They sipped the wine. Not until Filip saw the blush redden

192

on Leonora's face did it strike home that her toast had implied a proposal.

Filip put his glass down deliberately. "Darling, it is the man who is supposed to propose. I have been thinking of the right words to say ever since I saw you with Father Michael on the road away from the convent."

"I knew it was coming, Filip, I could feel it. And I can only say that nothing is dearer to my heart than to marry you, and make a home for you. But tell me, how shall we live? Will it be up in the mountains, or will it just be a secret marriage or will we leave this land of ours and go elsewhere?"

"Why all these serious questions all of a sudden, Nora? This is our night for fun."

Her eyes fell to the table. "I am willing to go to the mountains and live with the guerillas like Anicka Hatala, if that is what you want."

"But that is no life for you, Nora. Anicka is a big strong woman. She has been living in the mountains with her father ever since she was just a girl. Besides, I am a courier, and I don't stay in the same place more than a few days, so your living with the guerillas doesn't improve things at all."

"Then what will we do?"

"Enough of the questions. I will think of something. But you haven't given me your answer, yet. Just say yes or no."

"Of course it is yes," she said, her earnest mien giving way to a broad smile of happiness.

The words stuck in Filip's throat. He had been dreaming of this moment for months, and now that it had come he could think of nothing to say. He bent over her white hand, kissed it and pulled her up to dance.

The gypsy musicians were playing a slow tango. Filip held Leonora close in his arms, pressing her to his chest, his head leaning against hers. He whispered words of love again and again into her ear. Through their heavy sweaters he could feel the firm curves of her slender but well-formed body press against him in the sensuous curiosity of innocence. His own body answered back in longing.

"Only a few more assignments, my love, and I will leave with you for some place where we will have nothing more to fear," Filip murmured in her ear.

"Where?"

"To the West."

"But you must still ask my father, darling."

"I know, and I will try to get to Levary as soon as I can," he said softly.

They were still dancing on the platform after the gypsies had finished the song and left their places for a short break. Filip and Leonora laughed at each other, and Leonora said, "One is blind and deaf when in love."

At least she doesn't look so solemn any more, Filip thought.

"To you again, Leonora," he said, raising another glass of champagne before her glowing eyes. People were coming and going during the orchestra's respite, ladies were dabbing at their lipstick, the men were greeting friends at other tables asking if they had their wives or other women with them, elderly officials from the capital were discussing their business problems. Only the crystal chandelier, hanging from the high ceiling seemed to hold still.

The leader of the orchestra reentered the dining room, followed by four violinists. They made their way, twisting and turning around the tables, to where Filip and Leonora were sitting engaged in intense talk. Filip was gesturing to Leonora in explanation of something when the gypsies broke into a wild Hungarian czardas. It was meant for the loving couple, this music, and Filip reached into his pocket for a handful of banknotes.

It was at that moment, as he was handing over the tip, that Filip recognized the gypsy leader. He was the same gypsy musician Filip had often seen in the nightclubs of Bratislava way back when as a student he led a carefree existence befitting his social status.

"Play, Jancsi, play," Filip shouted excitedly as he grabbed Leonora's hand and pulled her to the dancing platform. The gypsies followed them, playing as they moved, and the two lovers danced to the music with wild abandon.

"*Milostpanko,* Filip Polhora!" Jancsi exclaimed. "That was great, that was simply great, like the old days!"

The SNB man leaped up from his table. He heard the name Polhora distinctly. Moving with a speed that belied his stocky, bull-like body, he rushed forward, upsetting a crystal bowl filled with water and the wine-filled glasses on the next table. The water and wine spilled over the dresses of the elderly ladies who had been gossiping at the table.

"What is this?" a portly man at the table exclaimed, rising to his feet. "Can't you even apologize?" he shouted to the back of the green uniform rushing past his table in disregard of what had happened.

"Show me your identification," the officer ordered Filip. Leonora's face showed panic for an instant but she managed composure before the SNB man had seen her.

Filip was indignant. "What kind of investigation is this? I am a tourist here and I have as much right to dance as anyone else. And you have no right to behave like a bull. Just look behind you and see what you did."

The trooper turned and noticed his clumsiness for the first time. His face whitened when he saw whose table he had upset. He turned back to Filip, trying to keep his brave imperious manner. But the sudden loss of color in his face had not been lost on Filip.

"I heard the name of Filip Polhora. I heard it distinctly when Jancsi spoke to you. You don't deny that, do you?"

"Why don't you ask Jancsi himself," Filip said, deeply offended by the insinuation. "He's the man to tell you if you've been hearing things or not. Go ahead, ask him."

The officer was perturbed. He did not know whether to ask Filip for his identification or go to the orchestra stand and speak to the gypsy. If the suspect, who certainly did act with an air of confident authority, really was an important official of the Party, the SNB man thought, he might very well resent an unjustified inquiry and perhaps block the promotion he coveted.

To be on the safe side, the officer decided to approach Jancsi.

"Gypsy," he said, regaining his arrogant manner, "who is that man with the young woman you played for just a few minutes ago?"

"Which man?" Jancsi asked innocently.

"That man, there," the SNB trooper spit out, turning around and pointing to Filip, who had gone back to his table with Leonora.

"He is a complete stranger to me. Please do not be angry with me, but I do not know him," the gypsy said, bowing deeply before the SNB man.

But the angry officer, whose self-esteem had already been damaged by his clumsiness, would not accept the defeat. He pressed further.

"Didn't you say Filip Polhora? I heard the name." The officer shook Jancsi in his powerful hands.

The gypsy laughed, or tried to as he rocked back and forth. "Oh, yes, yes, my lord. I said to that man that he dances like Filip Polhora. Polhora was a fellow student of that man. That's what I said, my lord. But that is not Filip Polhora."

At the table, Filip's hand rested on his pistol as he strained to hear the gypsy's words. He could not make them out but, judging by the scowl on the SNB officer's face, Jancsi had protected his identity. This supposition seemed to be confirmed when the Communist trooper returned to his own table and sat down glumly, looked at Filip and Leonora thoughtfully, as if debating whether to apologize to the courier, then poured the rest of his drink down his throat and left the room.

"The danger is over," Filip said, reaching for Leonora's hand. She returned his smile.

But the idyllic mood had been shattered. After five minutes, when the SNB trooper had not returned, Filip rose. "We might as well play it safe just in case, Nora. I think we had better leave and get you home. Our friend in green may have quit for the night, or he may be contacting his office for further orders."

Filip dropped some banknotes on the table, pulled back Leonora's chair and guided her at a pace neither fast nor slow out of the dining room. Outside the hotel they slipped into their skis and moved toward the woods, careful to avoid unseemly haste, but once they were out of sight of the resort Filip put on a burst of speed and motioned Leonora to follow suit.

The moon, which had been moving in and out of the mountain peaks, was in full view when Filip and Leonora reached the forest above Podolinec. Their hearts were beating furiously and their bodies covered with perspiration from the long hard trip. Under an old pine tree they stopped, and Filip held Leonora close to him to calm her.

"Why must we live like this, always on the run? Why, why, Filip?"

He did not answer at first, but hugged her more tightly, as she sobbed. When she had quieted down, he said:

"Because we didn't act when there was still time to keep the Communists from grabbing power. Because we were all concerned too much with our own personal problems and ambitions to know what was going on until it was too late.

"Only now are we building a dam that we should have built ten years ago to stem the tide. Sometimes I think it is impossible that we shall ever win out and drive the Communists away. But we should not regret what we are doing, Nora, for every day of our struggle keeps alive our determination to be free."

Leonora had never before heard Filip speak with such deep feeling about his work. She remembered, as she watched Filip look off into the distance behind them, that he had always described his exploits in a devil-may-care manner, emphasizing the humorous, the specific details, and not touching on the

197

deeper meaning of what he was doing. She now realized, as she must have known subconsciously all the time, that he could not give up his way of life so quickly and leave with her for the West.

But Leonora said nothing. Filip took off his fur-lined jacket, placed it at the foot of the huge tree and motioned for Leonora to lie down on it. He fell beside her.

Each was thinking of Filip's promise to flee Slovakia, knowing deep inside it could not be done so easily. But neither spoke of it, nor did they speak any more of the clandestine war against the Communists. Recognizing they might be spending their last moments together for many weeks or months, Filip and Leonora exchanged the endearments and promises of undying devotion that lovers have always spoken to one another, yet discovered their freshness anew in the blossoming of love.

And when their supply of words was exhausted, they lay quietly, gazing at the moon and stars, then turning to each other and pressing lips together, softly at first, but with increasing intensity. His hand slipped under her sweater and blouse and cupped her small firm breast, the longing for her growing within him again, seizing him, driving all else out of his mind.

He could feel her body stiffen as he fondled her. She relaxed as he stilled his hand, but she grew tense again when he moved it from one breast to the other. Her own hand fell on her sweater, covering his underneath. Through the garments she pried first one finger of his hand loose, then another, but made no effort to remove his hand or prevent his fingers from dropping back to their resting place.

His hand slid down her body, coming to rest as if midway in its journey over the soft downy skin below her navel. The tremor that ran through her body passed through his fingers. She covered his hand with both of hers. She had never known a man before, he had thought all along, but now her resistance, the resistance not of coyness but of innocence, removed any lingering doubt.

He lifted his hand, still clutched in hers, and dropped it to his own chest, sighing deeply. But she did not leave it there. After a moment, she gripped his hand gingerly and placed it, softly, on her breast. The meaning of her movement was unmistakable; she was beckoning him to take her.

He turned to her, but her face avoided his. She was a simple, devout girl, he knew, and he was certain that in her mind the first act of physical love should take place on the marriage bed; he was certain that what enjoyment she derived out of the act here in haste on the snow would be stained thereafter with feelings of guilt.

The knife edge of his desire was blunted by thought. He was deeply and suddenly touched by this young girl who, in the flush of her love and in the uncertainty of their future, had overcome her unwillingness, her fears, and offered him her body. To Filip, the urbane, sophisticated lover of other women, Leonora's ideals, her conventional morality, now unaccountably seemed the right way. Removing his hand from her body, Filip shook his head at her, smiling sadly, and lay back, looking skyward. The desire that had flooded him now gave way to a poignant melancholy in which he felt no need to take of her body but to give her of his courage to bear the months of separation.

Before he could speak, she leaned her body over his and kissed him. He felt a warm tear fall on his cheek and then she was rising. "Our love," she said, "is like a flower that is too beautiful to be picked. So we must hide it."

Filip was mute. In that lovely image, she had given voice to what both knew must come to pass.

"You must be on your way," Leonora said, "or else you will never get back to the cave." The calm matter-of-factness in her voice was an attempt to soften the blow of parting.

Filip replied in kind. "You had better turn your sweater inside out for safety's sake." Leonora quickly reversed the sweater from the red side to the black one.

"When will you be in Levary?" she asked.

"Perhaps in a few weeks, perhaps longer. I will be there again as soon as I can."

They gazed at each other briefly, then kissed and embraced, her head buried against his chest. Then she turned quickly, strapped on her skis, signaled one more goodbye and was off down the slope to Podolinec. Filip waved at her back till she was out of sight, then started the long climb back to Labuda's cave in the High Tatras.

9. The Odyssey of Father Michael

JAN BAAR dangled his feet over the edge of the cot, stretched his long arms over his head and yawned. He lay there, studying a cobweb around a beam above him, cursing the boredom. There was nothing for him to do in Michalovce, a town of ten thousand near the eastern tip of Slovakia, except wait for Father Michael to consent to leave the place and head for Rome as planned.

Baar lifted his large body off the cot, drew the curtains on the thick windows and looked at the sun, now almost directly overhead. Yawning and stretching once more, he took a cigarette out of the pants that were hanging on the chair near his bed and sent circles of smoke up toward the cobweb on the rafter. To relieve the ennui, he played a game with the cigarette smoke, blowing a small ring first, then trying to shape each successive ring so it was just a little bigger than the previous one.

He and Father Michael had been in Michalovce for three weeks now. Though he was alert to the peril, the danger of discovery by the Communists bothered Baar less than the unexpected prolongation of his assignment. He was restless and anxious to complete it. There was a demon within him that forced him to move. Enforced idleness weighed more heavily on him than direct physical danger.

He had been sent by Labuda to accompany Father Michael on his trip to Eastern Slovakia, then see to it that the Father Provincial reached Rome. The Underground leaders wanted the beleaguered priest to report firsthand to the Vatican on how the Communists had brainwashed priests and persecuted the Roman Catholic clergy, and how the Church of Silence was fighting back. Their plan was to send Father Michael directly to Rome from the guerilla camp in the High Tatras. But Father Vendel had suggested, and Father Michael eagerly agreed, that he first travel to Eastern Slovakia and minister to the Catholics there who had been deprived of their priests when the Russians outlawed the Greek Catholic Church and tried to absorb its followers into the Russian Orthodox Church. It had been a long time since a secret priest had visited Eastern Slovakia.

After two weeks of rest in the guerilla camp, during which time Father Michael had begun to fill out again and lose that pale, haunted look, the priest and Baar left for Michalovce. Using the town as a base, Father Michael traveled to farms and villages nearby to administer sacraments to people who could not come to Michalovce. Living first in one house, then another, he also held secret Masses and other rites for those who were able to reach the town.

The door to Baar's room opened a crack and an elderly lady peeped in cautiously to see if her guest was awake. But the door squeaked so noisily that Baar noticed her at once and invited her in.

"Good morning, Jan, or rather good afternoon," she said. Her smile revealed only one tooth in the round wrinkled face. "I am wondering if you want breakfast."

"Do you still have any of that sausage left, Auntie?"

"Yes, but I am keeping that for Father, you know that." With her fingers she combed back some grey hairs that pushed out from under her multicolored kerchief. "However, I will bring you the sausage and good strong coffee if you promise not to make Father leave us. It's been so long since we have had a priest."

"A good bargain," Baar said. "Bring it fast, Auntie." He began again the game with the smoke rings, feeling a twinge of conscience in deceiving his hostess, for he had no intention of delaying the priest's stay. On the contrary, he meant to prod Father Michael into leaving.

"Here is the breakfast, young man," the old lady said. "You must wash, too, because some visitors are coming this afternoon."

Reluctantly, Baar took off his pajamas, put on his pants, and washed himself from the waist up with cold water he had poured from an old jug into the porcelain bowl that sat on top of his dresser. Then he put on a shirt and ate his breakfast. He had just finished the last morsel of the savory spiced sausage when he heard a knocking at the window.

"That must be Father Michael," he said to himself.

But it was not the priest. There outside the window stood a limping hunchback. He was known as Dodo and he served as the go-between for Father Michael and those who sought his aid in and around Michalovce.

"Wait, Dodo, I will open the door," Baar shouted through the window.

From his guest room at the rear of the house he went to the other end of the one-story building. The dwelling stretched in a line like a railroad car, with the front room facing the muddy, ditch-lined street. In the center of the home was the kitchen, opening up on a yard that was part of the garden surrounding the entire house.

The distinguishing feature of the house, where "Auntie" Margita lived alone since her husband had been killed by the liberating armies of the Soviet Union, was a cellar that stretched under the length of the house. Its entrance was a wooden trapdoor on the floor of the kitchen, now covered by a rug Margita had woven herself.

Baar opened the bolt of the kitchen door and let Dodo in. The poor wretch of a man, holding an old oil-stained hat in his hands, barely came up to Baar's barrel chest. But his eyes were twinkling as he said:

"Zuza Balazova fell from a ladder and broke her ribs. She is dying and is in urgent need of confession, Communion and Extreme Unction."

"What else does she need, Dodo?" Baar could barely keep the irritation out of his voice. This business of going off to administer the sacraments in secret was sapping Father Michael's strength and delaying his recovery. Moreover, Baar could not see how it was doing anything to speed up the overthrow of the Communists.

Dodo had seen the strange expression on Baar's dark face. With his peasant shrewdness, he had an instinctive sense of not pushing things too far. "I just came to tell you what happened to Zuza Balazova. It's up to you to talk with Father," he said, scratching his filthy grey hair.

Baar realized as he spoke with Dodo that the peasants could sense his opposition, his hostility to a prolonged stay for Father Michael in Michalovce. The guerilla felt a pang of remorse for having offended these good people, who perhaps played no direct role in the clandestine war but who were nevertheless on his side.

He regretted his quick and gruff way of speaking to Dodo, who did run around the country, despite his disability, and produce a measure of happiness for people by bringing them together with a priest. After all, Baar thought, that too strengthened the spirit of resistance.

"Dodo," he said more amiably, "do you care for some coffee?"

"No, *Pan* Jan," the hunchback replied quickly, sensing the sudden change in Baar's attitude, "but do you still have any of that Slivovitz left?"

"Sure, Auntie keeps it for medicine. I think you deserve some."

As Dodo drank from the goblet, Baar said, "What else is new, Dodo?"

The cripple put down the drink, eager to gossip. "The Russian Orthodox bishop is now luring our youth to join his church. He even invited the son of Zuza Balazova to join him

204

on a trip to Prague. He is trying to induce the boy to give up his Greek Catholic faith.

"He even invites our boys to join his new seminary, for he needs new Orthodox priests for the parishes that became vacant when they arrested all the pastors who were faithful to Rome."

"Dodo, you are a good man. Wait here while I get something for you." Baar poured some more Slivovitz into the goblet, one of the few valuable possessions owned by Margita, and put the bottle back into a cabinet.

Baar returned with his ski jacket in his hands. "I know it is almost summer, Dodo, but perhaps you can use this when the weather gets cold again." He helped the old cripple into the handsome jacket he had brought with him from the mountains. Though it reached only to Baar's thighs, it fit Dodo like an overcoat.

The hunchback thanked Baar effusively, but even in the moment of Baar's compassion he did not forget why he had come here in the first place. "And what shall I tell Zuza Balazova, *Pan* Jan?"

"Tell her not to die until at least eight tonight. Father will visit her then." As an afterthought, Baar added, "But be sure her son is not present."

At that moment, Margita walked in with her shopping bag. "So we have a guest, eh? I see you had Slivovitz, Dodo," she said with a severe glance. But with Baar around, she scolded no further, for she wanted to keep her guest in a happy frame of mind. Dodo left to deliver Baar's reply to Zuza Balazova.

At about five in the afternoon, Father Michael returned from his tour of the town and surrounding countryside. His tall thin body fell heavily on a chair in the kitchen and he sighed deeply. He had been covering an area that once had been served by six priests and he was near exhaustion.

Baar was tempted to forget what he had to say. But he had promised. "Father, after the Mass this evening, you will have

205

to see Zuza Balazova. She fell and broke her ribs. Dodo was here."

"Then I must go, Jan. It is my duty." The priest placed his bag, which contained baptismal water and holy oils, on the table.

Hardly had the weariness begun to leave his body when there was again a knock at the door. Father Michael and Baar disappeared into the next room, while Margita asked, "Who is there?"

"It's me."

"Who is 'me'?"

"Barbora Janikova."

Only then did the old woman let the visitor in, a simple peasant woman with ruddy cheeks. The newcomer asked, "Where is Father?"

"Wait a minute, Barbora." Margita went into the adjoining room and reappeared with the priest.

"How are you, Barbora?" Father Michael asked, the ever-present heartiness he displayed to the natives still in his voice.

"I brought you these, Father," Barbora said modestly. She handed him a basket of eggs and a freshly killed chicken.

"You should not have done this, Barbora, for you have to fulfill your quota. You will get in trouble with the Communists." The reprimand was gentle.

"Look, Father, what they ask I will never be able to fulfill. And since I cannot meet the quota anyhow, we might as well enjoy what we have, for tomorrow the whole farm will be taken away from us. So please, just take what I bring you."

The priest thanked her warmly and gave the food to Margita to store. "You might as well wait now until the time of the Mass," he said to Barbora and went back to his room. Baar was waiting for him.

"What you do here for all these people is very touching, Father," the guerilla began, "but don't you see that your health is no better and you are no nearer to Rome. The time has come to leave for Bratislava. How much longer are you going to postpone our return? Last week you told me that we would go this Saturday. Yesterday you suddenly tell me that the old dean Timothy is too sick to do anything for his outlawed congregation and that you have to stay one more week. Now, Father, for your sake and mine, please tell me when we return."

"Why do we have to set a specific date?"

"Because I have to make certain preparations for the trip, such as having a car at our disposal."

"Well, since you are so insistent, let us therefore depart next Sunday. Is that suitable?"

"Nothing is better than a Sunday for dangerous travel. But we really must go."

It was agreed and Baar breathed easier.

That evening at six, the faithful came to Margita's house for worship. It was always in the evening that Father Michael met his congregation in the cellar of the house. One by one the people came so as not to arouse suspicion. Never did more than twenty attend one service, the people taking turns on different nights. After all the participants gathered in the cellar, Margita and Dodo would spread the handmade carpet on the trapdoor in the kitchen, and move the table over the rug. The old woman then would begin cooking supper as if nothing unusual were happening, while down below Father Michael would listen to confessions and then celebrate a secret Mass, using a plain glass to hold the wine in place of a chalice.

At about seven or seven-thirty, there would be a knock from down below and Dodo and Margita would remove the heavy table and carpet and the people would leave singly in the gathering dusk. By that time, supper would be ready and the priest and his companion would eat with Margita and the hunchback. After the meal, there were usually further rounds for Father Michael. This evening Dodo waited to take him to Zuza Balazova. Tomorrow there might be a marriage or secret confirmation.

Father Michael conducted the rites outside the town wherever he could—in a farmhouse, a barn, a cave, an open field. When there was no table to use as an altar, he would use a tree stump. And if there were no tree stump, he could—in an extreme case—lie down on the ground and use his breast as an altar.

The Sunday set for departure finally came and both Baar and Father Michael put on the green uniforms of the SNB they had hidden away for the occasion. Guns dangled from their black belts as they seated themselves in a small car, a Skoda, driven by a chauffeur also dressed in the garb of the State Security Police.

Father Michael and Baar both carried false papers. Since he was a wanted criminal, the priest wore a dark mustache to match his dyed black hair, and rimless glasses. The picture on his identification papers bore a remarkable resemblance to the disguised priest, mustache, spectacles and all.

Old Margita, Dodo and several of the neighbors came to see them off. Dodo wore his new coat for the occasion, even though the early June sun beat down fiercely. To his wellwishers, many of whom were crying, Father Michael said:

"Pray, good people and friends, pray, and above all keep your faith and stay strong, no matter what happens."

The car pulled away from the muddy ditch.

"Bring him back soon," Margita's shrill voice could be heard from a distance.

Baar closed his eyes and dozed off. He was vaguely conscious of movement and muted conversation around him but nothing penetrated his awareness. About half an hour after the car had left for Bratislava, he opened his eyes again. Instantly he sensed something was wrong.

"Where are we going?" he demanded of the driver. The chauffeur shrugged his shoulders in silence.

"This is not the way to Bratislava. The sun is behind us. We are heading east."

Again the innocent shrug from the driver.

Baar gave Father Michael a quizzical look. "Nothing is wrong, Jan," the priest said softly. "The driver is following my orders. It's just a little detour that we have to make to attend to some urgent business in Klenova."

Baar choked back angry words. Klenova was some forty miles to the northeast of Michalovce, at the very border of the Soviet Union. But he knew argument would be futile. He sat back, waiting for the priest to explain further.

"We are going to visit a man named Emil Kracun," Father Michael said. "He is acting as an elder to the little flock there which has remained true to the faith."

Kracun was a distant relative of Margita, and through the slow but sure communication system of the peasantry he had learned of Father Michael's presence in the region and had requested his services. The priest, who still harbored deep feelings of guilt for having confessed to the Communists and betrayed his God, even if only temporarily, was quick to acquiesce. It was only a few hours out of the way, he reasoned, and he could thereby bring great consolation to people who had gone for a long interval without a priest.

The travelers reached Emil Kracun's house, on the outskirts of Klenova, by evening. Klenova was a village of huts and brick and stone houses amid the forests that border on the Ukraine. The area abounded with oak and pine and the villagers worked mostly as lumberjacks or in the nationalized sawmill.

As soon as they were inside, the old farmer's wife busied herself in preparing supper for the travelers. Father Michael pointed out that he could not partake of any food because of the duties which he had come to perform that very night, but his companions would certainly not refuse the kindness.

In the meantime the farmer's two sons—lumberjacks at Stakcin Enterprises—and his daughter presented themselves. They greeted the priest with spontaneous warmth and no little curiosity at his disguise as an SNB man. But the sons didn't remain for long. Old Kracun dispatched them with precise instructions on whom to visit and inform of Father Michael's presence. The old man was exhilarated by the priest's presence and anxious, too, over the many things Father Michael had to do, all in one night.

While Baar and the driver began the first course of the meal, a simple bean soup, the priest was led by Kracun into the largest room of the house. There he took off his uniform and donned the white surplice and stole he had carried with him in a kit. The colors of the garments were not exactly those prescribed by the Church, nor did he have all the accessories called for in celebrating a Mass. But such requirements were waived in the Church of Silence.

While he was dressing, Kracun told him what had befallen the Greek Catholics of little Klenova. Four years before, their priest had been taken away and the villagers were forced to attend services in the church that were conducted by the state-imposed priest, a member of the Russian Orthodox church. This priest, immediately upon taking possession of the parish, denounced the Pope as an instrument of capitalist imperialism and consequently a sworn enemy of the working class. Next the priest tried to induce the congregation to give allegiance to the Russian Orthodoxy and recognize the Patriarch of Moscow as their spiritual leader in place of the Pope.

Some members of the congregation, to avoid conflict with the authorities, yielded and embraced the Orthodox faith right away. Others succumbed over a period of time when they saw that no Catholic priest was coming to lead them. But a minority, led by Kracun, refused to give in. Fearful that following a schismatic priest would deprive the sacraments of validity, they abstained from overt religious practices. They pretended publicly to be atheists, which pleased the State even more than turning to Russian Orthodoxy would have done, and thus carried off their defiance undisturbed.

Inwardly, of course, they were bent on remaining true to the faith of their ancestors. They congregated secretly in Kracun's house (his sons were prodigious workers for the

State and the Kracun family was looked upon favorably by the Communists) and conducted their services as best as they were able to remember them, without benefit of clergy. They baptized their infants with holy water until their supply had run out some months before. A long row of empty bottles in one corner of the spacious room testified to the shortage.

Father Michael finished donning his priestly vestments and began meditating on the terrible tragedy that these heroic people of Klenova had undergone, when the door was flung open without a knock. In came Kracun's son, Jan, bringing with him Ondrej and Maria Sotak and their little son Mikulas, who was less than a year old.

Maria, who had been carrying the baby, handed the bundle to her husband and bowed low, trying to kiss Father Michael's hands. But the priest withdrew his hands. He did not consider himself worthy of Maria's reverence, for these people in Klenova had kept their faith under trying conditions while he had betrayed it. With a contrite heart, he was desirous of serving them.

Sotak, a sawmill operator, explained why he had come. His marriage two years before had never been blessed by the Church, he muttered guiltily. The contract that made him and Maria man and wife had been executed by the local civil authorities and now that a priest had arrived he wanted to have their marriage blessed by the Church and their son's baptism solemnized by Father Michael.

The priest turned to Jan Kracun. "Will there be others with babies?"

The younger Kracun nodded assent.

"Then you had better bring as much clean fresh water as possible." Father Michael visualized a long night ahead of him and the sooner his work began the better.

The largest wooden table that could be found in the house was brought into the room and covered with the finest linen cloth the Kracuns owned. On the table the crucifix was placed and two candles were lit. Jan Baar pitched in, too, once he had finished his meal, for in Michalovce he had learned how to assist in the various chores that were necessary to conduct a proper service. Jan Kracun brought in a large basin filled to the brim with water, but that did not satisfy his father, who whispered something into his son's ear. Young Jan nodded, went out, and brought in several wooden buckets full of water.

"Why so much water?" Father Michael asked. "This is more than you will need for some time to come."

Emil Kracun looked apologetically at the priest. "Our brothers across the border in the Ukraine have been without a priest even longer than we. We will smuggle the holy water that we do not need to them."

Father Michael was speechless. The risks these people ran to preserve the faith!

Newcomers arrived steadily at Kracun's house in small groups. While preparing himself for the blessing of the holy water, he tried to estimate the work ahead of him—the confessions he would hear, the baptisms he would perform, the couples who would want their recent marriages blessed. And all the people present most certainly would want to partake of the Holy Communion.

His own longing for food and rest he brushed aside as insignificant in his admiration for the brave people who had assembled before him. The risks they were undertaking for their God, the security they could find in the greener pastures of Russian Orthodoxy and yet had rejected, the nearness of the Soviet borders—all these thoughts filled Father Michael anew with shame. Yet he could not help but feel an upsurge of energy for the drama that was to unfold that night.

Standing in front of the huge basin and wooden buckets of water, he began mumbling his prayers in Latin. The crowd watched intently as if its eyes were fingers with which it could touch him and discover that he was truly a priest of God. Though his back was turned to the assembly, Father Michael could feel their gaze and for an instant he imagined he was being watched by all the martyrs of the ages.

Dividing the water in the form of a cross, he invoked the Holy Spirit. Again he touched the water with his hand and repeated, "May this holy and innocent creature be free from every assault of the adversary and purged of every flaw of wickedness." And again he made the sign of the cross over each container of water, saying:

"Therefore I bless thee, O Creature of water, in the name of the living God, of the true God, of the Holy God, of the God who, in the beginning, by His Word divided Thee from the dry land; Whose Spirit was borne upon thee."

His voice rose as he finished so all present could hear that he was indeed blessing the water. Then he parted the water again with his hand and sprinkled drops to the north, south, east and west.

With silent reverence, composed of fright and joy, the crowd looked on, many members crossing themselves, until the last Amen came from the priest's lips. Then a stir ran through the congregation.

Five infants were brought forth for a solemn baptism. The ceremony, hurried along by Father Michael so that the young mothers could take their children home to put them to bed and return for confession, was a familiar one to most of the congregation. In only two ways did it differ from the countless baptisms they had seen when the Church flourished in Slovakia.

Instead of the traditional silver container to store the water that was poured over the heads of the baptismal candidates, Father Michael used a plain water glass. And in place of the white baptismal garment held close to the child as a sign of the new life of grace the infant had received, the priest simply placed a white handkerchief over the child's head.

When the baptized infants, bundled up in their blankets, left the house, silence descended once more. It was time for confession. One after another Father Michael heard as the night wore on. It was midnight when the last penitent's sins were absolved, but the end of the drama was not yet in sight. The time had come for a Mass.

At least once a year, each Catholic who has reached the age of reason must partake of the Eucharist in Holy Communion. It had been at least four years since the people of Klenova had been able to attend Mass and partake of the Eucharist, and the excitement in the room was almost palpable. This was a night they had long been waiting for, the holy night of an abandoned congregation when Christmas and Epiphany, Easter and Ascension and Pentecost would be celebrated for them all at the same time.

To their amazement, the Mass they participated in was like none they had ever seen before. It lasted little more than ten minutes, the shortest they had ever witnessed. It was bare of the splendour in which the ages had enveloped it.

Father Michael did not pray first at the foot of the hastily prepared altar as a priest usually did at the start of Mass. Nor was there any Introit, nor Kyrie Eleison, nor Gloria in Excelsis Deo, nor Collects, the short prayers petitioning for divine grace and blessing. Father Michael did not even read the Epistle. He skipped the Gospel and the long Nicene creed, the "Credo in unum Deum," embodying the fundamental beliefs of the Church.

Instead, standing at the wooden table, he plunged immediately into the Offertory of the host and the wine, the heart of the Mass.

Jan Baar had been standing at the foot of the altar, ready to serve as an altar boy, prepared with all the Latin answers to the prayers he had expected the priest to make at the start of the Mass. That was the way Father Michael had begun Mass in the cave in the High Tatras and in the cellars in Michalovce. Though he was not especially devout, Baar could not help but be moved by all the Masses he had witnessed and he had been rather proud of his effort, kept secret from the priest, to learn the proper responses to the opening prayers.

Thus it was incomprehensible and disappointing to Baar

214

when Father Michael excluded the preparatory prayers and portions of the Mass and began right away to knock at the gates of Heaven. To Baar's thinking, it was inexcusable that the celebrant did not start the Mass in the way the villagers were accustomed to hearing and were no doubt expecting it.

It was only after the night was over and they were on their way to Bratislava that Baar learned why Father Michael had acted as he did. The unusual Mass was another accommodation of the Church of Silence to the conditions under which Catholics practiced their faith behind the Iron Curtain. Priests of the Church of Silence had been specifically empowered to cut the Mass to its barest, unalterable essentials in time of extreme danger.

The hour was late, the congregation had already been assembled for a long time and there was still much to be done. Had the holy sacrifice been interrupted by Communist police, Father Michael would have had on his conscience the grave pain of an unfinished Mass, let alone the sacrilegious dishonoring of the sacrament by the enemy. By excluding all the preparatory portions of the service, he would be more certain of finishing the Anaphora of the Mass, when the bread and wine are changed into the Body and Blood of Christ, and of permitting himself and the faithful of the persecuted congregation to partake of the sacred meal as an ultimate symbol and effective means of preserving their unity with Christ and His Church.

Nor was the specific point at which the Mass was begun, Baar later found out, an arbitrary decision by Father Michael. The shortest Mass permissible, as practiced in the Church of Silence and as conducted that night, started exactly at the very moment at which, in the primitive Church of the first centuries after Christ, the catechumens, the new converts undergoing instruction in the Church, were excluded from the Mass and the oblation reserved to the faithful alone.

And so, making the sign of the cross and murmuring audibly the words, *"In Nomine Patris"* to signify that he and the worshipers present belonged to Christ, Father Michael kissed the altar and turned to the ardent believers. He saluted them with *"Dominus Vobiscum"*—the Lord be with you—and began the offering of the bread and wine to God.

With serene face and steady voice, the gaunt priest accomplished in a few minutes the first sanctification of the bread and wine, invoking the Holy Spirit to bless the gifts that would be transformed into the divine Victim, and asking the Holy Trinity to receive them to honor Christ, the blessed Mary, the apostles and saints and to save the present members of the Church on earth. Upon conclusion of the ancient formula, he then turned to the hushed worshipers and asked them, "Pray, brethren, that my sacrifice and yours may prove acceptable in the eyes of God, the Almighty Father."

With the rites of Offertory completed, the central act of the Mystery began: the age-old Anaphora or Canon, the central part of the sacrifice that traces back to early Christianity and which not even in the Church of Silence can be altered or abbreviated.

From the prayer of thanksgiving known as Preface, through the hymn of Sanctus, the service ran, bringing Father Michael and the awed worshipers to the very entrance of the Holy of Holies. First raising his hands, then bowing low and joining his hands on the altar, he kissed the wooden table, then prayed fervently to God to accept the sacrificial gifts for the Church, for its peace and unity, for the Pope and for the bishop and all the faithful, but particularly for His persecuted congregation of Klenova which had so faithfully clung to the faith.

The silence in the room was complete as Father Michael's prayers brought together the triumphant Church of all saints with the earthbound members of the Militant Church. And then the priest entered the Holy of Holies, praying to God that his offering of bread and wine might truly become the Body and Blood of Jesus Christ.

He took the host in his hands, raised his eyes heavenward,

made the sign of the cross over the bread, and then repeated the words of Christ at the Last Supper:

"For this is my body."

First bowing low, he then elevated the host above his head with trembling hands so the faithful behind him, now sobbing freely, could lift their eyes and see Christ present on the altar come to bring them His infinite love. This was their Christ, their Saviour for whom they had waited hopefully to see again for many years. Now He was among them, the divine Victim they were ready to receive in Communion.

As they stared transfixed, Father Michael lowered the host to the linen cloth that covered the altar and uncovered the glass that served as a chalice.

"For this is the chalice of My blood, of the new and everlasting testament, the mystery of faith, which for you and for many shall be shed unto the remission of sin." The priest repeated the words of Christ, and held the glass up for the congregation to see the chalice filled with Christ's blood.

To the simple folk of Klenova, the elevation of the bread and the wine was the Mass. Ordinarily, at that point of the service, the church bell would ring and if they happened to be far from church, either in the field or the forest, they would stop working and kneel reverently. But now they witnessed in person the Body and the Blood of Christ, and their joy was boundless, their excitement almost unbearable.

While Father Michael continued the Anaphora, the faithful behind him turned their minds to the Communion. So wrought up were they that they could not tell when the Anaphora ended and Communion began. Their starved souls craved the nourishment of Christ, for that alone, they knew, would give them strength enough to stand fast to their faith for the months or years they might again go without a priest to minister to their spiritual needs.

Soon they heard the familiar words of Pater Noster, and the Agnus Dei—"Lamb of God who takes away the sins of the world"—and the hour of Communion was at hand. The elder

Kracun first, and his family, shifted from one knee to the other, then stood up and approached the table that for them was the altar of God. Soon they were followed by the others in the room, all without exception, all mumbling the prayers before participating through the Eucharist, the consecrated host, in the life of their glorified Christ. The priest stood facing them with the Body of Christ in his hands, ready to place it into their mouths, and into their hearts to satisfy their spiritual hunger.

The Mass was soon over, yet the crowd stood in avid expectation of further spiritual consolation. Now the time had come to sanctify those marriages which had not yet been blessed by the Church. Maria and Ondrej Sotak were the first to come forward, but there were three more couples in similar circumstances. The marriages of each were solemnized and at last peace was restored to the congregation.

The faithful dispersed themselves, in twos and threes, each seeking their homes under cover of darkness. Weary but exhilarated, Father Michael looked forward to rest. But this was not yet to be.

Kracun still had another request. "You have performed everything for the living, Father. But what about the dead?"

"What do you mean? What can I do for those who are no longer among us?"

"You can still do something. At least you can bless their graves."

Father Michael could not keep the incredulity off his face. Dragging him out to the cemetery now, and exposing him and Kracun to unnecessary danger!

Kracun saw the look of disbelief and shook his head. With a twinkle in his eyes, he said, "Follow me, please, Father."

Lighting a candle, the old farmer led the priest to a dark room in the back of the house. The deceased faithful could not be stored there, Father Michael thought in bewilderment. And yet there in the room he saw a heap of earth.

"Do you have someone buried here, Kracun?" the priest asked wide-eyed.

"No, Father," came the answer gently.

"What then do you wish of me?"

"Just bless this earth for us, Father, so that our dead can each take a handful of sacred earth into his grave."

The priest nodded in mute wonder, then prayed over the heap of earth.

It was the final act of the drama that had begun hours earlier on a night Father Michael could never forget. The heap of blessed earth that he was to leave behind would be the last link of the Catholic outcasts of Klenova with the Church of Christ. Tears welled up in his eyes again as he thought of the depth of faith in these people who braved the hurricane of communism with simplicity and stubbornness. The hurricane blew, but the tree still stood, because it had a solid root.

Two days later Baar and Father Michael reached Vegelinova Street in Bratislava, where Leonora Dankova's Aunt Kristina lived. The trip across the length of Slovakia went without incident, and Kristina was expecting them. Until Baar could arrange to get the priest to Rome, the tiny, sharp-tongued widow would play host to the visitors as Margita had done in Michalovce. Her house would serve as a church and parish of the Church of Silence.

At night, after holding services in the cellar of Kristina's house, Father Michael would walk by his old monastery and church, dressed in the clothes of a laborer. Armed guards patrolled the structures, which had been taken over by the Communists as headquarters for the Security Police.

Baar, meanwhile, contacted Underground sources in Bratislava. A crossing into Austria over the Morava River was out of the question. The Communist patrols in the areas that offered the best jumping-off places had been strengthened recently and the mortality rate of couriers had taken a sudden jump. Moreover, Father Michael was still in no physical condition to make the crossing. He was to sit tight, Baar was told, until he would be approached.

The approach was made ten days after they arrived in Bratislava. At ten o'clock one evening there was a knock on the door of Kristina's house. The passwords the visitor gave indicated to Baar he had been sent by the Underground.

The contact was a sailor employed by the State-owned Danubian Navigation Company. That meant he was a Communist, since the authorities would never let someone whom they thought wasn't loyal to the State travel outside the country for fear he would defect. There was danger dealing with such a man. But money can matter more than Marxism, even to a Communist, Baar realized, and the Underground leaders must have been certain the sailor was trustworthy.

The sailor was a short, plump man in his late thirties with the nervous habits of sniffing constantly or rubbing the right side of his protruding nose with his forefinger. His name, or the name he gave Baar, was Robert Sopka, and he addressed Baar as Mr. Donoval, the name the guerilla was then going under.

The plan of escape Sopka proposed was a dangerous one. "The departure of my oil tanker is set for Thursday night," he told Baar. "That gives us barely two days of preparation. That in itself would not be much of a problem. But the real difficulty is that the crew is Communist, except for one other man whom we can trust. And then there is the chance that even at the last moment the whole trip can be called off."

"What does the boat carry?" Baar asked.

"It's going empty to Vienna to bring back oil from Zisterdorf."

"And how do you propose to get Michael to Vienna?" Baar made no mention of Father Michael's calling. Sopka had not indicated that he knew anything about the man he was to smuggle out of Slovakia and Baar reasoned that so widespread was the Communist search for Father Michael that the less Sopka knew the better. The priest himself kept out of sight.

The sailor put his cap down on the table and leaned forward on the edge of his chair. "Our big problem is getting him on board. Even with false identity papers we can't take him through the main gate of the harbor, because he would be spotted right away as being out of place. So we will have to get him over the iron fence at a point when the guards will be pacing somewhere else. This means you will have to come with me to see the exact location I have in mind."

Baar offered the sailor a cigarette.

"No, thanks," Sopka said. There was a trace of condescension in his voice as he said, "I have some Bulgarian cigarettes. Take one, please." The cigarettes testified to Sopka's travels.

Baar inhaled and sighed in appreciation. "When do you want to show me the spot?"

"If everything is set, I would prefer to do so right now."

"If everything is set?" Baar echoed. "I thought it was all agreed."

"Well, I mean the financial side of the thing," Sopka said, rubbing his nose.

"How much?"

"Ten thousand kronen," the sailor said, his eyes turned away from Baar.

Without batting an eyelash, Baar walked to his chest of drawers and took out an envelope. "How about five thousand now, and five thousand when we get the passenger into the harbor?"

"A deal," agreed Sopka quickly. He laughed nervously.

The two left the house and went on foot through the dark streets toward the harbor. Because the hour was late, they were stopped twice by the SNB and forced to show their identity cards. They were just going out for a beer or two, they told the police, at a bar near the entrance to the harbor where they were to meet several other sailors.

Behind the tall iron fence the Danube shone silvery in the moonlight. "You see that huge warehouse?" Sopka said, pointing to the dark contours of the biggest building Baar could make out. "Count three more warehouses ahead of that one. In front of the third warehouse we will start this operation. You bring your passenger to that spot at ten o'clock Thursday night and help him climb over. I will be on the inside. After he is in, he will be under my care."

With that understanding, the men parted, the sailor continuing on through the entrance and aboard his boat and Baar returning to the house on Vegelinova Street. One of the SNB patrols that had stopped him earlier noticed him again and a gendarme remarked, not in an unfriendly way, "That must have been a short beer."

"It was, indeed," Baar replied casually. "We got there just before the closing hour. I may meet my friend again Thursday night. Then we'll make sure to go earlier."

Baar added amiably, "Good night."

"Good night to you."

The satisfaction Baar felt now that he had arranged for Father Michael's departure vanished abruptly when he returned. The priest balked at leaving Slovakia.

"As long as there is one soul that needs me, I must stay here," he said. "I can only promise you that I shall try to go abroad when I am no longer needed. But please do not rush me to leave my country and my brothers."

Baar knew he could not force the provincial head of an order to leave the country against his will. Instead, he tried to reason.

"But look, Father, which is more urgent, the interest of the whole Church or the interest of a local flock that can find another priest? If you go to Rome, you can report on how the Communists enslave the Church and how they brainwash those who do not go along with them. The Holy Father no longer has his nuncio here as he used to. Who then can tell him of the true conditions here? Can I do it as a layman? Who would listen to me? Only you can do it with authority."

Baar's manner was intense and his argument compelling.

222

But Father Michael was still uncertain. The land was dear to him. This was the country of his ancestors, the land in which were imprisoned many of the members of his order. How could he, their shepherd, leave them? Would it not be a betrayal of the faith they showed when they elected him their Provincial. Yet it was equally true that the Holy Father was cut off from Catholics behind the Iron Curtain, that his nuncio had been expelled and his bishops jailed or removed from their positions.

"Father," Baar implored, "think of what so many of us have gone through to free you and bring the story of what has happened to the Catholic Church. And haven't you wondered how it is that we can have succeeded in getting you so far in the face of the Communists' efforts to halt us? Do you think it is just skill or luck that has brought you this far?"

The priest was silent for a moment. He said resignedly, "Since it seems to be the will of God, Jan, I shall then go."

Baar held his breath for a moment to suppress a deep sigh of relief. "You will sail for Vienna on Thursday."

At the appointed time, Father Michael and Baar left for the harbor. Baar made a point of taking a route he thought would bring them in contact with the same SNB patrol he had struck up an acquaintance with two nights earlier. An open, friendly approach was best designed to avoid suspicion, he thought. The SNB men were there all right and remembered Baar. They waved him on, not even bothering to inspect the identity papers of the tall, slender man, dressed in ordinary work clothes, who stood silently by as Baar chatted with the gendarmes.

In front of the designated warehouse, Baar halted. "Here it is, Father."

"So this is where we part, Jan." Father Michael embraced the guerilla who had done so much for him and blessed him with the sign of a cross on his forehead.

Sopka materialized on the other side of the fence. Crouching down so the priest could mount his strong, broad shoulders, Baar slowly straightened himself up, lifting Father Michael well above the fence top. The priest pulled himself over and tumbled down on the other side as Sopka helped break his fall. In a trice, Father Michael and the sailor were on the way toward the protective darkness of the warehouse. When Baar could no longer make out their figures, he vanished into the night.

Sopka made for the river bank with his charge. There he had a small boat waiting that would take them to the tanker. But as they rushed toward the boat, the large searchlight atop the main warehouse suddenly flicked on and started sweeping round the harbor area. The guards must have heard their steps!

Grabbing the priest by his sleeve, Sopka pulled him back to one of the smaller warehouses. There they hid in a combine that was waiting to be shipped to a collective farm in Russia. Sopka's nervousness increased with the passing time, for the tanker was scheduled to leave in less than two hours. There was no time to be lost. Straining to hear the voices outside the warehouse, the sailor did not notice Father Michael's eyes shut nor his lips move in silent prayer.

A car's motor could be heard through an open window of the warehouse. Then a deep voice booming instructions to start inspecting the warehouse two buildings away from where the two fugitives were hiding. The big searchlight was dimmed and Sopka relaxed a bit. He motioned to the priest the time had come to make a break for it and the two men jumped out of the combine, raced through the warehouse, squeezed through a back window and ran down the river bank to the small boat. Sopka rowed slowly to make as little noise as possible, but within ten minutes they reached the tanker.

Three short whistles by Sopka brought his associate to the deck near the stern of the boat with a thick rope. First Sopka, then the priest were hoisted aboard. Before either could ask, the other sailor said, "The crew is playing cards."

Without a word, the two sailors led Father Michael down

narrow iron stairs to the engine section of the tanker. The ship was driven by oil and since it was bound for Austria for oil, only one fuel tank was filled to lighten the load. Into the empty tank, which would be filled for the return trip with oil purchased from the Zisterdorf fields, the secret passenger was to be placed.

"This is not exactly the most luxurious passenger cabin," Sopka noted wryly, "but it will have to do." The priest handed him the rest of the money Baar had promised, with profuse thanks.

Sopka and his confederate unscrewed a small opening at the bottom of the empty tank and helped Father Michael squeeze through. The tank was so narrow that he could neither stand nor sit but was forced to half-stoop, his back against one oil-smeared side, and his knees against the other. The door was screwed back on loosely to permit at least a hint of air to enter the tank.

The oil fumes remaining in it turned his weak stomach. Here he had to remain at least until the Communist customs officials made their final inspection of the ship to make sure that nothing was being smuggled out of the country. From cabin to cabin, through the hold, even into the engine room, the officials went, knocking on machinery, opening doors.

"Holy Mary, Mother of God, don't forsake me," Father Michael prayed soundlessly, holding his breath and forcing himself not to vomit as footsteps neared the tank in which he had contorted himself. The steps grew fainter until he could hear them no more.

No longer could he keep the food down. He wretched violently, again and again. Thirty feet away, tending the engines, stood a machinist. But amid the roar of the starting engines, he heard nothing of Father Michael's agony.

Why didn't Sopka and his friend come to let him out? He had been breathing the air in the tank at a faster rate than it was seeping in and his chest soon began heaving as he struggled to breathe. He was certain he was going to die from lack of oxygen when he heard a hammer knocking on the wall of the tank. The knocking followed a pre-arranged pattern.

"Thank you, Holy Mother, thank you," he gasped, only half-conscious, as the door was unscrewed and air rushed in, air that was fetid to the two sailors outside the tank but smelled sweet and fresh to the struggling priest.

"We could not get away sooner," Sopka said apologetically. His confederate left to make sure the coast was clear. Father Michael was forced to remain inside the tank as Sopka stood guard, but at least the opening remained ajar and he could breathe freely. When the tanker was well inside Austria, Sopka's helper returned and the two men helped the priest out of the tank and brought him to an empty cabin where he went unnoticed for the rest of the trip.

When the tanker docked in Vienna, Sopka came to let the priest out of the cabin. But Father Michael was not yet going ashore. "Please, forgive us," the sailor said, "but we must be unkind to you again." The priest would have to wait until he could be removed from the tanker so that none of the other crew members would learn of his presence.

"I'm afraid we will have to keep you here on the boat in the bilges until the proper time."

With the ship at anchor, Father Michael lay in the bilges, in mud and water and oil. Finally at midnight of the day after the tanker had docked, the two men came to free him. All but a few members of the crew were ashore. Down the rope on which he had first come aboard Father Michael was now lowered into the shallow water. Ten feet above the Danube he lost his hold and fell the rest of the way. Coming up sputtering, he half swam, half crawled through the muddy water to the shore.

Oil and mud covered him and his clothes clung to his body. Dirty as the water was, he washed himself in the river, lightening by several shades the color of his clothes and the exposed parts of his body. Scurrying up the bank, he crossed a bridge and came to a streetcar station. While he waited for the car, he tried to cleanse himself further at a water spigot nearby.

A streetcar headed for the old section of Vienna finally arrived and he boarded it. The few people on the car at that hour stared at the wet, wretched figure who looked more like an outcast of society than the Very Reverend Father Provincial of a Catholic order. But he paid his fare and took a seat quietly, avoiding the gazes of his fellow passengers.

His destination was a sister monastery of his own order, located near the familiar Dome of St. Stefan. At three o'clock in the morning he knocked at the monastery door. No answer. He knocked repeatedly until a brother finally answered.

"I am Father Michael Bobula, provincial head of your order in Slovakia. I come from Bratislava and I seek admission here as my first refuge."

The monk stared incredulously at the ragged, filthy wretch of a man before him who pretended to be a head of the order. Father Michael looked at the bewildered brother with sympathy. He could not blame him for the obvious disbelief, for who indeed would take the bedraggled priest for what he claimed to be?

The door was shut gently in Father Michael's face.

Again he knocked until the brother reappeared, this time a look of irritation on his face.

"I beg you humbly to call your superior," Father Michael said, first in German, then in Latin. The tongue of the Church had the desired effect. When the startled monk heard the Latin words, he went to arouse his superior from sleep, but not before he had again shut the door with a request for Father Michael to wait there on the steps.

The superior, too, shrugged him off, even though he spoke in flawless and unhesitant Latin. "Many men besides our Holy Brotherhood," the superior said, "speak Latin these days, even the Communists."

He was about to shut the door once again when Father Michael, now desperate, recalled the name of an Austrian father with whom he had studied in Rome. "Is Father Adalbert here?" he asked. "He will know me."

A few minutes later a large, powerfully built priest came to the door. One look at Father Michael was enough. Father Adalbert broke into a broad grin, reached his arms out to embrace his friend and then, recalling the guest was now the head of the order in Slovakia, fell to his knees. Kissing the hand of Father Michael, he exclaimed:

"Laudetur Jesus Christum."

"In eternum," responded Father Michael. He had been recognized.

For several hours he had been on free soil, but it was not until this emotional moment, this moment when he and his brothers had given praise to God, that the realization flooded over him that he was now beyond the reach of the Communists. His new-found brothers led him, weeping, into the monastery.

Ten days later, clad for the first time in almost a year in the snow white habit of his order, he knelt before the throne of Pope Pius XII in Rome. To the Holy Father and other officials of the Vatican and to the general of his own order, Father Michael reported all that had happened to him and to the Church in Slovakia. There he completed his recuperation. There he advised the Pope on the ordination of secret priests and the consecration of secret bishops for Slovakia. There he studied Spanish, French and English. And then, after seven months in Rome, Father Michael sailed for the New World where today he still ministers to the faithful.

Book III THE NEW WARFARE

Though primarily an agricultural land, Slovakia has a rich industrial heritage. In the Middle Ages, she was known for her gold and silver. On the soil of Slovakia, the Fugger family of Germany built a branch of its vast mercantile and mining empire. In Slovakia, Empress Maria Therese opened Austro-Hungary's first technological university.

After the second World War, the Soviet rulers, uneasy over the proximity of Czech industries to the bordering West, began shifting more and more industry, including petro-chemicals, missiles and rockets, to Slovakia, which borders on the Soviet Union. Thus Slovakia became the home of the huge Skoda Industries; a National Academy of Sciences flourishes there; and new laboratories, operated not only by Slovaks but by Russian, Czech and German scientists, were opened.

It was this rapid growth of science and industry in Slovakia that pointed the way for the Underground's new role in the dark days after the futile Hungarian uprising in 1956, those days when the disillusioned rank and file of the Underground learned abruptly what their leaders had long known—that liberation was not close at hand, and that the battle against communism would be long and drawn out.

That the Underground's struggle would have to enter a new phase became clear. Large-scale guerilla warfare seemed to advance the Slovaks' cause little if any. Conventional sabotage was but a thorn in the Communists' side: bothersome but not particularly dangerous. Such tactics had succeeded in preserving the ideal of freedom in Slovakia but they had not toppled the Red rulers.

Now, the Underground's leaders decided, the Resistance must throw its resources into the broader battle between East and West. More particularly, into the new war for supremacy in science and technology, a bloodless war whose significance to the future of the world did not even impinge itself on the American consciousness until the Russians sent up their first Sputnik in 1957.

In this new kind of global struggle, as far as the Slovak Underground is concerned, the skill of its members would count more than their number.

10. Love for Sale

NOT ALL THE members of the Underground are noble, by
any means. But if a person is loyal to the Resistance, his weak-
nesses are tolerated so long as they do not endanger his colleagues. Nor are the Underground's exploits always successful.
Fortunately, however, some lesson can usually be learned even
from the failures. One of the most notable examples of these
aspects of the Underground involved Olga Gazdova.

Olga was a beautiful woman, too beautiful for her own good,
many said. She had hair the color of midnight that cascaded to
her shoulders. Her eyes were dark and fiery and her wide, full
mouth lent a suggestion of savagery to her vital, passionate
face. Her magnificent body moved with a sinuous grace that
seemed full of promise. Never could she walk, or rather glide,
into a room of people without bringing a halt to conversation
and the attention of all eyes, male and female. She was built
for love, many said of her, and they were not far wrong.

The beauty, if not the passion, was evident at an early age.
Olga was the youngest child of a wealthy family of central
Slovakia. Her father had married the only daughter of the
owner of the largest retail store in the town where they lived
and he inherited the store when his father-in-law died. Olga was
the child of her parents' old age and a more spoiled offspring
would be hard to imagine. Their only daughter, she was the
apple of her parents' eye and her whim was their command.
Expensive food and clothing, private schooling, vacations
abroad with her governess, nothing was too good for her. Even

in the lean Hitler years, Olga never knew the deprivations that many of her friends felt.

Then the Communists came to power and the Gazdovs' life of luxury was over. Their store was taken from them. But because they embraced communism, or said they did to save their skins, nothing worse than retirement on a small pension was their fate. Ashamed at their quick conversion to communism, and unaccustomed to the drab monotony of her new life, Olga decided to flee to the West. Like many of her Slovak brothers, she went to Vienna. The year was 1949, when she was just past twenty.

She settled in the American zone of the city, in a colony of other Slovaks. Though post-war Vienna was not the city of culture and *gemütlichkeit* it had once been, life there was not so lackluster and pallid as in Slovakia. Still, Olga went without the luxuries she had become used to. Austria's economy was barely getting back to its feet and much of the country's resources were being drained by the Soviet occupiers as reparations. Jobs were then difficult to get and those that were available were reserved for Austrians.

So Olga and the other Slovaks did as best they could. They lived chiefly on contributions from Slovaks who had gone to the West and from charitable organizations. Nylon stockings, cigarettes, medicines and drugs and other black market sundries were sent to the Slovaks, who in turn sold them in war-torn Austria for far more money than the contributors could have raised in cold cash.

And then one day, a member of the Slovak Underground approached Olga and changed her life. It was Jozef Maryan. He had been searching for just such a woman. He had heard of her wild beauty, and of her patrician background. By talking first with other Slovaks in exile in Vienna, he had reason to suspect she was unhappy with the hand-to-mouth life she led.

He came to the apartment she shared with another Slovak girl. The dark-haired Underground chieftain, who specialized in recruiting, began by inquiring politely of Olga's past and present. He wanted to size her up and confirm his secondhand impressions, and also to break the ice gradually. Finally he arose from his chair and paced around the room nervously.

"Olga, you are a beautiful woman."

She smiled as briefly as she could without saying a word. Her suspicions were immediately aroused.

"How would you like to undertake some special work for the Underground?"

Her eyebrows arched. No reply. Maryan was further discomfited.

"It is work of the utmost importance to our cause."

"What sort of work?"

Maryan stopped speaking in Slovak and abruptly switched to German. "We need someone who can move to the Russian zone of Austria and find certain things out from the Russians who are stationed there."

Olga thought for a moment. "Find out things how?"

Maryan averted his eyes. "Any way you can. Perhaps by being friendly with the Russians."

Being friendly, Olga reflected. Selling her body? Is that what he meant? She was outraged. She stared at him hard. He looked away at first, then stared back at her. The embarrassed silence confirmed her suspicions.

But perhaps she didn't have to sell her body, she thought. She was certain she could take care of herself. All her adult life, and many of the years before, she had been fending off admirers—though not all of them, to be sure. The idea that she would be a latter-day Mata Hari popped into her head. The vision appealed to her.

Maryan applied the clincher. "All we want from you is information. If the Russians want to give you gifts, well, that is none of our business. You will be free to keep anything you wish."

Olga's face was creased in smiles. The boredom, the want of luxury had left their mark. "When do I begin?"

Maryan grinned for the first time, too. He took out a handkerchief and wiped his forehead. Though he had a reputation for coolness and daring, he had never recruited such a spy before.

Olga was outfitted with false identity papers and passports. She was to assume the name of Helen Friml, an Austrian. Like children of all wealthy families in Slovakia, she had learned at least one other language. In this case, it was German. During her two years in Vienna, the harsh guttural edge of the tongue had eroded and now she spoke the softer German of the Viennese. That would help reduce suspicion.

There was little trouble smuggling her into the Russian zone. Following the advice of the Underground, she soon became a frequent visitor to the Imperial Hotel, headquarters of the Soviet occupation force.

The six-story grey structure on Vienna's spacious Ringstrasse earned its name by housing the great royal names of the last century. Built in 1864 as a palace for Duke Friedrich von Württemberg, it was never used by him. It was converted into a hotel and, alone among Austrian hotels, was allowed to designate itself *Kauserliches und Koenigliches*—Imperial and Royal Court Hotel.

Here Wilhelm I of Germany and the Iron Chancellor, Otto von Bismarck, came to stay when visiting Vienna. In a salon on the first floor, the Austrian-German alliance of 1879 was signed. The Imperial's guest book reeked with royalty. Wilhelm II of Germany; Edward VII of Britain; Empress Eugenie of France; King Alfonso XII of Spain and his successor, Alfonso XIII; Don Pedro, Emperor of Brazil; Sultan Abdul Hamid; the Shah of Persia; the Khedive of Egypt and members of the imperial houses of China and Japan—all inscribed their royal names on the book.

And then, the Russians came.

Periodically, the Russians held dances in the Imperial's ballroom, throwing them open to the young ladies of Vienna. The hotel was in the city's international zone, and Olga, or Helen as she was now called, could have attended even if she remained in the American zone to live. But any move to reduce doubt or distrust of her motives was deemed advisable.

To these dances Olga went and met Soviet officials and troops. Though she concentrated on the higher ranks, she was also friendly to the lower echelons, who were less likely to be suspicious, more grateful for her attention, and thus might let tidbits slip without knowing how they fit into a larger pattern.

Most of the men she found boorish and single-minded. Only the ones she judged less tiresome were allowed the favor of her interest. She kept several on the string at one time, permitting each to buy her clothing, perfume and all the niceties she had been used to but had been denied for too long. With adroitness that increased with practice, she was brought to bed by very few, and only in cases where it was absolutely vital to obtain information that could not have been garnered otherwise.

Perhaps several of the Russian officers suspected her of spying. So skilled was she at obtaining information in a casual, natural fashion that it is not possible to say for sure. But even if some did surmise the truth, they said nothing, perhaps afraid they themselves would be compromised, perhaps for fear of losing Olga's favors.

What the Underground desired most was information on Soviet troop movements in Austria and in the East European satellites. By taking note of the comings and goings of the men she befriended, she was able to piece together a considerable amount of data, for she was not at all unintelligent. Along with information from other sources, the Underground constructed a larger picture of Soviet deployment and passed it along to the West, chiefly through contacts in NATO Intelligence.

Though she enjoyed making a conquest, Olga was not cruel and most of her affairs ended only when her suitors were transferred elsewhere, usually with something to remember her by. To proposals of marriage, and there were many, she would reply sweetly as if she had never been so flattered before.

Never could she tie herself down, she was not the sort, surely he could see that, she told each prospect in turn, always adding that no one but he had ever made her think so seriously of the offer of marriage. The rejected swains would leave happily, their egos bolstered.

If anyone made trouble, if he refused to take no for an answer, if he demanded of her more time than she was willing to give, or if she simply tired of him, Olga had an unfailing way out. She would quickly strike up a friendship that blossomed into something deeper with that man's superior. The unhappy swain would run into excuses from Olga that she could not meet him that night as usual, or the next one. Soon his suspicions were aroused and he would follow her, only to discover that the man who accompanied her was none other than his overlord. Sullen but subdued, he would quietly fade away.

Olga became an artist at the game of love. Intuitively, she had developed a sense of how to make any man she chose fall head over heels in love with her. Her sheer beauty, of course, was enough to attract any man. But attraction plus passion do not always equal love and a man who was truly in love with her was easier to induce to part with information, whether consciously or not. Besides, there was a certain challenge in drawing a man beyond the stage of lust.

In the Soviet Union, beautiful young girls are schooled in the arts of love. The many cases, some told, most untold, of Westerners in Vienna and behind the Iron Curtain who betrayed their countries for such women attest to the success of the Russian "schools for love." What these women were taught formally, Olga learned by instinct and practice. The arrogant and ambitious she would flatter; in the handsome she would find hidden wellsprings of intellect; the shy and uncertain she would praise as virile; and to the grumbler she would offer a sympathetic shoulder. Rarely did she fail.

One day in 1954 Yuri Bedovsky entered her life and changed things abruptly.

Yuri was a colonel in the Soviet Army and a geological engineer. He was in his middle thirties at the time, a tall, gangling man with a thick head of blond hair and a boyish charm. His family was prominent in Soviet circles. Until his death a short time before, his father had been a leading scientist and his two brothers and sister were also scientists; the oldest brother was highly placed in the administration of Russia's space program. Yuri had been sent to Austria to see what could be done about improving oil production in the Zisterdorf fields, which the Soviets had taken as payment for war reparations. He was ambitious and hard-working and till then had little to do with women.

It was at a dance at the Imperial that Yuri and Olga met. She turned away from her partner at the end of a waltz and saw Yuri staring at her from the punch table, halfway across the ballroom. From his look, he must have been staring for a while, she thought. He did not turn his eyes away as she gazed back at him. But his look, she noticed, was neither arrogant nor lustful, as was usually the case. Rather, she would have sworn, he was staring wistfully at her.

A boyish smile crossed his lips as their eyes locked. He made no effort to approach her. Was he playing hard to get? she wondered. Or was he just shy? There was only one way to find out. Though he was not handsome there was a hint of strength in his angular face that appealed to her.

Olga walked slowly across the room, smiling rejections along the way at those who asked her for the next dance. As she approached Yuri the smile quickly vanished from his face. He turned aside awkwardly and poured more punch into the glass he was holding, which was already nearly full. So it was shyness after all, Olga said to herself.

"Hello." For a lark, she made her voice as sultry as possible.

Yuri was flustered. His mouth worked noiselessly before he mumbled a greeting in return, and Olga at once felt remorse for trifling with this man who looked like a boy.

She made small talk with him to put him at ease, smiled as

if it were the most natural thing in the world when he refused to dance and motioned him to sit down next to her on one of the chairs along the side of the ballroom. After he thawed out, he displayed a dry sense of humor, a quality not conspicuously notable in the other Russians she had met. Perhaps overcompensating for his initial shyness, he became voluble as she drew him out. When she heard of the importance of his job, she decided he was a potential source worth cultivating.

Yuri was unlike any of the other Russians she had let court her. He was cultured, sophisticated and considerate, a welcome change of pace. They discussed art and music, went to the Vienna State Museum, to concerts and galleries in the international zone. Finally she invited him to dinner in her apartment, a much more lavish one than the first she had lived in when she moved into the Soviet zone. There, after three bottles of French wine, she gently led him to bed in such a way that he was convinced afterwards that he had managed the whole thing quite well.

Though he was inexperienced, he was not naïve enough to think that he was the first or even among the first. Yet he treated her with the guilty consideration of a man who has taken a virgin and this endeared him to her all the more. And though he was not the first, he did earn the distinction unknown to him of being the first Russian she truly desired, and the first whom she felt impelled to seduce instead of fight off.

When the guilt passed, as it quickly did, Yuri found himself unabashedly in love for the first time. He showered her with presents, gloves, fine leather goods, jewels and even furs. He gave unstintingly, not to buy her love as his predecessors had done, but because he was a generous soul. She did not discourage him.

To Olga's delight, Yuri was not much of a Marxist. To be sure, he was a member of the Communist Party, but his attitude toward life was conditioned by membership in the scientific community. Like most true scientists, he had a curious mind that instinctively recoiled from dogma, from pre-ordained truth. Insofar as it was possible, he remained aloof from politics. Yet Yuri wanted to carve out for himself a great career in his chosen field and since he was a Russian that naturally meant his future lay in strengthening the might of the Soviet Union.

Olga did not usually speak with her lovers or would-be lovers of Marxism. It was not her view of history that interested them. But each one, perhaps suspecting deep down that she may have been planted by the ubiquitous Soviet secret police to check on their loyalty, did go through at least the motions of professing belief in the Communist dogma and its ultimate triumph. Yuri's indifference, by contrast, endeared him even further to her.

In fact, after several months, Olga began to wonder if she was not falling in love with Yuri. Never before, at least, had she been drawn to any man as she had been to Yuri. For the first time she felt a sense of guilt in her assignment and vowed never to pump Yuri for information. Her other suitors, meanwhile, were not immediately dropped. They were phased out— as one left Vienna, no other was chosen to take his place. By the end of the year, Yuri was the only man she was seeing regularly.

But Olga had not lost herself completely: she still encouraged him to bring her presents, not simply for her own enjoyment, for she had long since had more of everything than she could use, but to give to her less privileged Slovak friends.

Yuri proposed marriage and Olga seriously considered it. She delayed her answer. Time and again he pleaded—over and over she put him off. Her Underground friends had learned with dismay of her affair with Yuri and had even debated assassinating him to bring her to her senses. But they feared such a move would alienate Olga forever. Moreover, they still nourished the hope that Olga could never yield herself to any man for life.

It was in July of 1955 that Olga finally found out whether she truly loved Yuri or not. The time was shortly before the

Russians, along with the Americans, British and French, were to pull their forces out of Austria and leave her an independent country at last. The place was on a path in the park near the Hofburg Palace in the international zone. The occasion was Yuri's desperate, final proposal of marriage before he was to leave for home.

They sat on a bench, he clutching her hands tightly in his as if to convey the depth of his love through his fingers. He pleaded earnestly with her to marry him, his voice rising to a shout that brought the curious stares of passersby. She rose and walked onto the grass, shaking her head and saying, "No, no, I can't, I can't," repeatedly.

"If you really loved me," Yuri said, following after her, "you'd come."

"If you really loved me," echoed in Olga's mind. "If you really loved me," she repeated to herself.

She tossed her dark hair back. It came to her clearly then. She did not love him. Or at least not enough to live behind the Iron Curtain with him. The words were torn from her as if she had no control over what she was saying.

"I can't live in the East, Yuri. The thought of the drabness, of the stifling atmosphere there repels me. I wasn't made for that kind of life. Even here in Austria you can live better than in Russia. Once I go East, I would never be able to escape to the West again. I would never be able to go to America. I often dream of that, of going to America. I don't know how I could have ever thought of going East with you."

Yuri was stunned. Reading the expression on his face, Olga suffered a pang of remorse for her cruel but deeply felt words. They had been as revealing to herself as they must have been to Yuri.

He said nothing. She felt an urge to soften the blow, but the usual farewell, the admission that nobody except her current partner had ever made her think so seriously of marriage, would not work, she was sure. Quickly her mind sought other avenues.

"We can be married, Yuri, if you will stay in the West."

"What do you mean?" came the tortured response.

"If you leave the Soviet side and join our side. We can go to America to live."

Yuri's face paled. The "our side" was not lost on him. His mouth worked but no words came out. Finally, he turned on his heels and walked away.

Just as she had hoped. She knew he would reject out of hand her proposal that he defect. When he had time to think about it, Olga was certain, Yuri would convince himself that she was an imperialist spy, that she had never truly been interested in him for himself but only to induce him to betray his country. Then he would feel ennobled at the thought that he had turned away this temptress, that he had remained loyal to the motherland. In such an exalted state, the hurt that Olga had caused him would quickly pass away. And that would be the last she would see of him. Or so she thought.

But Olga had calculated wrongly. She had underestimated her own powers. She had become so used to men's desiring her body that she had assumed that was all Yuri wanted. Passion, she knew, was finite. It could be transferred in time to another available body. But Yuri loved her and love is infinite, and cannot be so easily dampened. Her absence proved impossible for him to bear.

Four months later he appeared suddenly at her Vienna apartment. At first he was calm, almost aloof. But he could not maintain such a pose in her presence. Soon he lost control of himself and embraced her fiercely. He couldn't live without her, he swore, life had lost all meaning since he had left. The clichés of romantic fiction found new truth on his lips. He kissed her again and again. First she tried to restrain him, then she submitted passively.

When she had quieted him down, he told her what had happened to him since their parting. He had managed to get himself assigned after several months of string-pulling to the Gbely oil fields just over the border in Slovakia.

He had thought it over carefully, and now he had decided he would go to the West with her. But not right away. He wanted to amass a large amount of money first. He did not want to sell his knowledge to the West, nor did he want to work at anything that could harm the Soviet. To start his life anew under such conditions, he reasoned, would take time and money and he wanted to go fully prepared. He would visit her as often as he could, bringing as much money as he could save out of his not inconsiderable salary, and she would put the money in a Swiss bank. When a sufficient amount had been saved, he would cross the Iron Curtain for the last time and they would go and live together in the United States or Canada.

As Yuri recounted his plans and deliberations, Olga analysed her feelings toward him. His näive assumption of her cooperation was touching. She still felt warmly toward Yuri, but now she was in complete control of herself. She could look at him objectively, or almost so. Furthermore, she had met someone else in the period of separation, an American businessman stationed in Vienna who traveled widely in the country for his firm. She thought she was in love with the American, who resembled Yuri in many ways. He was tall, shy but intelligent and conversant with culture. Even if she was not really in love, she was sure the American would soon ask her to marry him and eventually take her back with him to the United States. The prospect of crossing the Atlantic delighted her so much that she was willing to give her American suitor the benefit of the doubt of her love.

But Olga still harbored a vague sense of guilt about Yuri. She did not wish to hurt him again by telling him on the spot that she no longer cared, that she loved another. Besides, he might prove useful to the Underground. So she agreed to his plan. She would take his money and save it in the bank. But she would see to it that he never had too much to save. She would play him along, induce him to spend lavishly on her as he had in the past. He could not refuse her anything, she was sure, and that way it would be a long, long time before he could build up enough reserve to make the break. Perhaps by then his ardor would cool and he would change his mind.

The unwritten pact was sealed in Olga's bedroom.

Every few months Yuri would come. One time he received permission from his superiors to visit a doctor in Vienna, a specialist whose equal was not available in Prague or Bratislava. Another time he was allowed to spend his vacation in Vienna, for he was a trusted Communist. After a time, he no longer told Olga what pretext he had used to join her. She gained the impression Yuri had come in some illegal fashion, but she asked no questions and he offered no information. Each time, Yuri would bring his savings, and each time she would run through the money in short order over his feeble protests. Little was left for deposit, but what was there Olga scrupulously transferred to a Swiss bank.

During this period, Olga resumed her work for the Underground. There were no Russian officers to seduce any more, but she made herself useful in other ways. Her apartment became a rendezvous for couriers from Slovakia, or the first station for the Underground's railway to the West for those who fled Slovakia. The presents from Yuri were redeemed and helped finance the operations. Meanwhile, her romance with the American businessman was flourishing. She did not love him, she finally decided. She wasn't even sure she liked him as much as she did Yuri. But he appeared to be far richer and he was a sure path to a prosperous life in America. Still, she could not bring herself to pump Yuri for information on the Soviet oil situation as the Underground requested.

Then her American businessman was killed. Only, it turned out, he was not an American businessman at all. He was an intelligence agent who used the business connection as a cover for his work. One night, when he was supposed to be out of the city on a business trip, his body was found riddled with bullets in a Vienna alley. The story released by Austrian officials, of course, made no mention of his espionage activity. He was an industrialist, they said, who was murdered while defending himself against robbery by a group of thugs. But the word quickly spread in Underground circles of the victim's true identity. It was the Russians who had killed him.

Olga's point of view changed overnight. She did not blame Yuri personally for the death of her newest admirer. But her resistance to the Underground's pleading that she use her charms over Yuri to advance the West's cause broke down.

It was at this time that the Slovak Underground contacts in Vienna received a request from one of their leaders in the United States for information on a new turbodrill the Russians had perfected. The revolutionary drill supposedly enabled the Russians to drill oil and gas wells at a rate more than ten times faster than the best American rotary drill.

In 1956, an American machine-making firm actually purchased forty of these turbodrills from the Soviet as part of a deal under which it would be licensed to sell the drills in the United States. But it turned out that these turbodrills were of an older design; they had been used in Czechoslovakia as far back as 1950. The bit was inferior and held down the drilling speed of which the turbodrill was capable. Furthermore, information on how to operate the drill was withheld by the Russians.

Meanwhile, word filtered back through the Underground that a newer, vastly improved turbodrill was coming into use behind the Iron Curtain. It had an improved bit, made of synthetic materials and diamonds. Special heat-resistant steels had been developed for it, as well as a synthetic rubber that was supposedly well-nigh indestructible.

The U.S. Government was aware of the development of the newer turbodrill, but it was not considered a tool of war. So the Underground set out to obtain the drill and sell it to an American business firm. Its motives were threefold: to help raise money to sustain the Underground, which had found funds harder to obtain within Slovakia itself after the abortive Hungarian rebellion; to strengthen the West's industrial might; and, perhaps most important, to test the Underground's adaptability, to see if it could shift its main task from one of sabotage and harassment and military intelligence to that of espionage, of stealing the enemy's scientific secrets for the use of the West.

The Slovak Underground is broken into many cells, none of which knows much about the others. An Underground member caught by the enemy could, at most, be tortured into revealing the names of a limited number of fellow partisans. Only a few leaders know the complete extent of the Underground. Several different channels into the Underground were asked to obtain blueprints of the Soviet turbodrill. None succeeded.

Finally, the group of which Olga Gazdova was a member was contacted. Getting the plans of the drill was the first assignment she was given involving Yuri since she had lost her compunctions against using him.

They met as usual in her apartment, where she put on a performance worthy of the finest actresses. As they embraced on a sofa in the living room, Olga turned her face away from Yuri's and sobbed quietly.

"What is the matter, Helen?" he asked worriedly.

"I can't stand these hit-and-run meetings any longer, Yuri," she blurted out, her eyes glistening. "I want to go away with you to the West, where we can live together as man and wife openly and all the time." She stroked his thick blond hair.

"But we don't have enough money yet, darling." As an afterthought, he added, "Perhaps we can save up faster if I didn't spend so much on you every time I come here."

He regretted the words the instant they were out. Olga pulled away from him, leaped from the couch and headed toward the bedroom. As she ran, she broke down and wept loudly.

Yuri followed her. He sat on the edge of the bed where she had sprawled tearfully face down. Stroking her back gently, he kept repeating, "There there," and swearing he did not mean what he said. She turned over, looked up at Yuri soulfully, and pulled his face down to her breast.

245

"There is another way to get the money," she whispered into his hair.

"How?" His voice was muffled by her firm bosom.

"Perhaps you do not have money, but you do have know-how that can be sold for money."

She felt his body stiffen, but he did not raise his head from its fleshly cushion. After a long silence, he looked up at her. "It was only after great agony that I said to myself I would go with you to the West. But betray the Soviet I cannot do."

Her fingers tickled his ear as he spoke. She pulled him down to her again and continued talking as if he had not said a word. "I don't know much about such things, of course," she lied, "but you hear all sorts of stories in Vienna. I have even heard some Americans are willing to pay $5,000 for the plans of some new kind of oil drill you have." As she talked, her hands found their way inside Yuri's shirt and gently rubbed his back. Occasionally, she would dig her nails into his back, right above the buttocks, where she knew the sharp pain aroused his desire.

Yuri protested her suggestion. But she continued relentlessly. Gently, indirectly, she raised the possibility that she might have to end the affair. All the while her hands and lips moved over his body as if to show him what he would be missing if he lost her. His protests steadily grew weaker.

The human mind, driven by love and lust, is capable of almost any rationalization. First Yuri told her, and himself, that it was not so much the Soviet he was concerned about as his own family. What would happen to them if he were dis-covered to be a traitor? Then he reasoned that if he were care-ful, there was no need to be caught. If he escaped to the West incognito and kept quiet about it, perhaps his family would be spared. After all, they were important scientists and the Soviet could not afford to lose their talents.

Olga suggested and Yuri quickly agreed that a turbodrill was not really a weapon of war anyhow. It was not like giving the West the plans of a new missile or plane. Western engineers were not stupid, either. They would probably develop a turbo-drill sooner or later anyhow.

When Yuri left the apartment two hours later, physically and emotionally spent, he had agreed to secure the plans for the turbodrill.

Several weeks later, a long distance phone call from Vienna brought the Slovak leader in the U. S. and an American businessman on the first plane available. The American remained in a hotel while the Slovak leader and his Underground contact took a taxi that wound a circuitous path through Old Vienna, through the new city and into the outskirts. There, in the dark doorway of an old palace now owned by an Austrian attorney, was a large wooden crate. In it was the heart of the turbodrill itself, not merely the blueprints.

The crate was packed hurriedly into the taxi and brought back to the hotel where the American was waiting. He was calm and a trifle skeptical until the box was opened. But his composure disappeared once he saw what was inside. The turbodrill had been broken in three pieces by the jostling it underwent in its trip across—or under—the Iron Curtain. But all the vital parts were there. And the drill was plainly the latest model.

But the story does not end without a final stroke of irony. It was as if a Hollywood censor had gone over the script of a movie and decided that the climax must be rewritten so that immorality would not be rewarded. The drill is still in its crate, never used, somewhere in Vienna.

Once before, the State Department had rejected an American firm's request that Soviet technicians be allowed to come to the United States to give instructions in the manufacture and operation of the 1950-model turbodrill. The latest turbodrill had also come without detailed instructions on its operations or the fabrication of certain vital parts. There was little reason to expect the Government to change its mind the second time, especially in view of the method by which the latest turbodrill was acquired. And under such circumstances, no company can be expected to risk the capital required to bring the new turbo-drill home and try to duplicate it.

But the Underground does not regard the episode as a failure. It did not obtain the money it hoped for. It had not added to the West's industrial strength. But it had proved to its own satisfaction that it was possible to purloin scientific secrets from the Communists.

11. The Enemy Camp

WINE and liquor flowed freely at the Military Officers' Club in Dubnica. An old village ten miles north of Trenčin along the Vah River, Dubnica had been transformed into an industrial center by the Communists. Located there was the headquarters of the Military Technical Institute, which supervises research and production of military weapons in Slovakia. All the top Slovak officials of the Institute, scientists and military and civilian administrators alike, along with their wives, were at the party, tossing down drink for drink with the resident Russian scientists, who came out of their usual shell of isolation for the occasion.

For Colonel Rudolf Muran, a ruddy-faced man in his mid-forties who was head of the Institute, this was a joyous occasion. He had called the party to celebrate the completion of the prototype model of a portable carriage for intermediate-range missiles that could be moved on truck or train and quickly set up for use as a launching pad for the projectile. After a year of work, the model Muran's scientists had developed was now ready for production.

Muran emptied his glass of wine and soda and turned for a refill to Eugen Kalina, one of his personal aides. Kalina had worked assiduously in Muran's office since he came to the Institute several months before and the invitation to the party was tantamount to recognition of his labors and his status. Many a long evening he had remained to work late, refusing the extra pay to which he would normally be entitled.

Colonel Muran hoisted the glass his blond-haired aide

brought him. He motioned toward the clock in the room, which told that midnight had arrived. "Ladies and Gentlemen, Comrades. To the new day, which heralds the start of production of our new rocket launchers. To our ever-growing military power!" He swallowed the wine and soda and everyone else in the room followed suit.

Next, in accordance with an old Russian custom, came the hurling of the wine glasses at the roaring pot-bellied stove in the middle of the room. The purpose, as everyone gathered quickly, was to see what sort of design the few remaining drops of wine from the broken glass would make on the hot metal before evaporating. Among the Russians was a superstition that the pattern of wine drops might forecast the future. As with oracles from the beginning of time, the design, of course, was subject to all sorts of interpretations. But on the chilly October night, it seemed like a wonderful idea to the people gathered there.

Eugen Kalina did not believe in superstition. But to refuse to go along with the rest would draw attention to himself. And as any courier of the Slovak Underground knew, it was dangerous to appear different from the people around him. The ability to blend into his background had many times saved the life of Eugen Kalina, or to give him his rightful name, Filip Polhora.

Filip tossed his glass hard at the stove.

"Look!" exclaimed one of the Russians, pointing at Filip's glass. "It hit the stove and bounced off unbroken."

"And it rolls on the floor still whole," said another. There was surprise and consternation in the voice of the Russian who ran over to the glass to pick it up. The other guests in the room crowded around.

"What does it mean?" asked the wife of one of the Slovak scientists.

The Russian holding the glass did not answer. "This must be an unusual kind of glass. That would explain it," he said. But the glass was passed from hand to hand, and everyone could see it was just like the others that had been thrown and shattered.

The Russians, who had been boisterous all night long, turned suddenly silent. No explanation of the meaning of the unbroken glass was offered by them, and none of the Slovaks present dared ask. It was plain to see, however, that a pall had settled over the Russian guests. Filip was elated, for whatever it meant, the glass that would not shatter was obviously a good sign for him. His eyes flickered quickly over Colonel Muran's face, just long enough to notice a thin smile on the director's lips. His own face was expressionless as he lit a cigarette.

The ritual of the wine glasses halted abruptly and the orchestra was hastily reassembled. At a sign from the colonel, it began playing the lilting "Blue Danube Waltz." Muran started to dance with the wife of one of the Institute's scientists, then others, including the Russians, came onto the dance floor.

Filip stood alone. Sitting by himself on a chair against a wall of the room, he noticed, was the young lady who had recently been placed in his office as a clerk. Her name was Irma Mrazova and she was an attractive, slightly plump blonde.

What was she doing here? Filip wondered. Her rank as a clerk certainly did not entitle her to membership in this exclusive group. He had already begun to suspect that she was planted in his section at the Institute to spy on the technical personnel there, using her obvious charms to win the confidence of the men and reporting their political views to her superiors. Her presence at the party seemed to confirm his suspicions. Or was she invited only to provide an extra partner for the bachelors among the guests?

Such thoughts passed through Filip's mind as he looked at her. She was smiling at him and Filip got the impression her eyes had been fixed on him even before he turned to her. Walking up to her, he said: "May I have this dance?"

"I have been wondering, Comrade Kalina, why you haven't been dancing. Are you still thinking of your unbroken glass?" Her golden hair, worn at shoulder length, and her clear blue eyes reminded him of Leonora. He preferred Leonora's firm but willowy figure, though there was something to be said for the full ripe body, too.

"I worked more than twelve hours at the office today," he said, "and I don't know if my feet are still good for a dance." Gallantly he added, "But the fire in your eyes I am sure can bring anything back to life," and he whirled her onto the dance floor.

Spy or no spy, Irma was an enticing woman, mused Filip as they danced. She pressed her body close to his, smiling up at him, and he could feel her rounded breasts yield against his chest. Control yourself, he ordered himself.

It was with some relief that the dance came to an end and he could invite her back to his table for a glass of wine. One drink led to another, however, and then to a dance, and one dance led to another, all the while Filip was growing more conscious of the abundance of her body. It had been a long time since he had seen Leonora.

The joyous spirit of the early evening, meanwhile, had returned to the party as the incident of the unbroken glass was forgotten. As the clock struck three in the morning, Colonel Muran interrupted the festivities once more and with his inevitable glass of wine and soda raised, he announced:

"To the portable launchers, which at this very minute enter the production lines!"

"To the launchers!" came the response from the crowd.

It was just as each guest was raising his or her glass that the explosion came. A thunderous detonation rocked the room, spilling wine from uplifted glasses and shaking the dishes and utensils over the edge of tables. Ladies screamed and men shouted.

"What is it, Eugen?" Irma asked, taking his hand in hers as if it belonged to her.

"Don't worry, Irma," he soothed her. "It's probably only some mishap in the plant. In the stillness of the night the noise sounds much louder than it actually is."

"I wish you were right, Eugen, but nowadays one can never be too certain. The subversive elements never sleep."

Filip's assessment was obviously too mild. Without a word Colonel Muran and several of the other administrators ran out of the room toward the plant, a little less than a mile away from the officers' club. Shaken by the explosion, the rest of the crowd slowly began to disperse. The musicians packed their instruments and soon the reception room was dark.

After some hesitation, Filip decided to take Irma home. It might offer an opportunity to see if his apprehensions about her were correct, he rationalized. Irma clung to him, her soft body pressing against his in the chilly night, her step made uncertain by the alcohol she had consumed.

As they walked outside the club, fire engines and cars carrying security officers were seen rushing from all directions toward the entrance to the factory. The Klement Voroshilov Enterprises in Dubnica consisted of an Administration Building above ground, in which the Military Technical Institute was housed, and several weapons plants built right into the foothills of the Strazovska Hornatina Mountains. A tunnel behind the Administration Building led to the underground factory.

Filip longed to follow the fire engines into the mountains to see how successfully the plan he hatched with his accomplice had come off. Judging by the number and loudness of the fire brigade, the explosion had been a huge one. But Filip had to suppress outward signs of joy and anticipation lest he betray himself to his pretty companion.

Halfway to Irma's house, his ears picked up the sound of footsteps behind him. The muted quality of the sound indicated to Filip that their pursuer was trying to keep as quiet as possible, yet maintain his distance behind the pair. Filip pulled Irma's arm and speeded the pace.

"Honey, it's getting real chilly. We'd better hurry."

She smiled knowingly. "We can have some nice hot coffee in my apartment. And perhaps we can find some other way to warm up. There's no need for you to go back to the old section of town tonight."

He grinned and kissed her quickly on the run, but said nothing. So she knew where he lived, he reflected. Her own home was in the newer section of town, the part closest to the industrial complex; it was strange that a mere clerk rated a place in the new town, which was usually reserved for higher-ranking employees.

When they reached her home, she handed him a key and he opened the door. It came as no surprise any longer to see furniture and rugs that were obviously expensive.

"You have managed to do quite well for yourself, Irma," he noted.

"I am a bit smart sometimes," she said coyly.

Filip opened the bar in her living room and poured each of them a stiff drink of cognac. He had managed to stay sober so far, while she was quite drunk. Perhaps more liquor would loosen her tongue.

"Irma, you are not only smart, but beautiful and, I should add, irresistible."

Not very original and perhaps a bit heavy-handed, but the direct approach might be best for the tipsy Irma. He put down his drink and embraced her. She clung to him fiercely and their lips remained together for a long time. Those steps behind them outside had been forgotten.

Her next words brought the spell to an abrupt end.

"Eugen, I think I have seen your face somewhere," she said, suddenly trying to get out of his embrace.

"What?" The anxious words escaped his lips before he could think. His tight grip around her loosened.

"Your face, those eyes of yours, I have seen them somewhere, but I cannot recall where." She ran the tips of her fingers over his closed eyelids.

"Never mind where you have seen them, darling," he said. "Let's think of us right now." He filled up her glass again

254

while she put an American jazz record on the phonograph. Was she playing cat and mouse with him?

They sat drinking and listening to the music until it was over. She turned the machine off and moved toward him on the sofa, kicking her shoes off. So unsteady was she on her feet now that she fell down flat on her posterior as she hurled the second shoe off. She grinned foolishly and Filip gently lifted her onto the sofa next to him. Perhaps now she was drunk enough to begin questioning her.

Their hands roamed over each other's bodies as Filip talked.

He tried to mask his intent by asking questions that seemed only to show his personal interest in her. She answered in a thick voice, interspersing her replies with amorous cries and pleadings.

Skillfully he played her, never pushing his questions too far, never bringing her to too high a pitch of passion, alternating love and queries so that like Pavlov and his dog, she answered him almost eagerly in order to bring his hands on her yearning body once again.

Irma was the treasurer of the local unit of the Communist Party, he learned. Though Eugen Kalina was ostensibly a Communist, Irma had never heard any praise of the Party from his lips, so she knew he was not truly devoted to it, she told him. But she would gladly give up her position in the Party if it would please him.

Nonsense, Filip thought. She is trying to trap me.

Though he did not want to yield to the temptation of her body, Filip's will was weakening. Yet to end the love play abruptly might create a dangerous enemy. To succumb would be a breach of his love for Leonora. Create an incident, dampen her ardor, then pull back gracefully. That was it, he thought.

"Irma, I don't believe a thing you told me," he said, keeping his voice friendly and his arms tight around her.

"You don't believe me?" She pulled out of his grasp. "Let me up."

255

She straightened her hair and flared at him. "I'll show you," she tried to wink slyly but both eyes closed completely as she swayed. Her sense of her own importance had been called into question and she reacted as Filip hoped she would—with dividends.

From a drawer in the room she pulled a small notebook. "You see what I have here? A list of Underground agents and couriers. I have already discovered three and reported them to the State."

So she was a spy!

One name after the other she began to read off. Among them was Filip Polhora.

Had she seen a picture of him? That would account for her recognition. Did she know who he really was? As Eugen Kalina, his hair had been changed from dark brown to blond, from a regular haircut to a crew cut. His other facial features had been subtly altered, too. No, Filip convinced himself, she had not yet guessed his identity, but it might be dangerous to remain in Dubnica much longer.

Consternation gripped him as he heard the names of many of his associates run off her lips. Hiding his dismay, he laughed heartily, grabbing for the notebook in as offhanded a manner as he could contrive. "Honey, it's late, really. I had better go home. This little squabble has spoiled what was otherwise a most charming evening. Maybe we can meet again tomorrow night."

Irma refused to let the notebook loose. Better not push his luck, Filip thought, letting go. "Don't go, Eugen. That explosion has me worried. I am afraid to stay alone." Filip smiled and patted her shoulder. "It will soon be daylight and time to go to work." He kissed her on the forehead and started to rise, but she pushed him back. Her mouth sought his greedily, her teeth bit into his lips, her hand snaked between his legs—and the fire, rekindled, spread quickly in his loins again.

He threw her to the floor and wildly, as if he had no control over what he was doing, he tore off the undergarments she still

256

wore as she writhed in pleasure. Down, down, he bore on her, angrily, contemptuous of himself for succumbing, contemptuous of her for what she was, taking her in passion and hate until she groaned with pain and ecstasy.

Out in the street a chilly morning breeze blew in from the River Vah. Filip had not gone very far when he heard footsteps behind him again. Instead of hurrying, he turned a corner and came to an abrupt halt. In a matter of seconds, his pursuer made the turn and smacked right into him.

Even in the dim light Filip could tell immediately it was Robert Hladik, the head of the maintenance crew at the Voroshilov Enterprises, and a member of the plant's Underground cell.

"It was unwise of you to go with that girl," Hladik whispered.

"I know, but it was important," came Filip's hushed reply. "But now I think my days here are numbered. She may remember what we talked about when she sobers up."

Hladik nodded. They walked across Dubnica's main street to the old section of town along the banks of the Vah. There Filip had rented a room in the workers' quarters.

"Did you have any trouble?" he asked Hladik.

"No. Well, a little with the ignition cable. Nothing to speak of, really."

"Do you know what was destroyed?"

"We don't know exactly. But with so much explosive, we're pretty sure that just about everything in the section is kaput."

The pair found themselves at the shore of the Vah, whose cold grey waters flowed quickly by. "We had better meet with the rest of the men tomorrow night at the inn as usual," Filip said as the two men parted.

Since there were so few hours left before his usual waking hours, Filip decided to skip sleep. He showed up at his desk early that morning, after passing through the heaviest cordon of security officers he had seen at the Enterprises. Even his top clearance card did not prevent a search of his person, though that seemed to Filip to be locking the barn door after the horse was stolen. A few days earlier such a search might have found a miniature camera secreted in one of the sandwiches Filip carried in his lunchbox. But he had decided to play it safe as the day of sabotage approached.

No sooner had Colonel Muran come to work than his office was invaded by the Institute's top security officials. After half an hour, they came out of the director's room, several of them carrying files that Filip recognized as personnel reports on the employees of the factory and the Institute. Before the day was out, he had learned through the inevitable front office grapevine that not only had the prototype for the portable launching pad been destroyed but also all the machinery in one wing of the plant that was supposed to turn out the production models of the complex device. Not for several months could new machinery be supplied, even assuming a new prototype could be hastily devised.

Because there were half a dozen aides in the room in which he worked, Filip was forced to restrain his joy. The Communist cause had been set back. But more important, the sabotage and the investigation that was certain to follow would draw the attention of the Voroshilov Enterprises' security officials away from the chief purpose of Filip's mission—the theft of the Military Technical Institute's scientific secrets—and away from the heart of the Underground's espionage network there, which was the office of the director of the Institute himself.

The sabotage at Dubnica took place a year after Hungary's abortive rebellion in October 1956. In the spring of 1957 Filip Polhora told several of his comrades in the Underground that he had had enough, that he was going to flee to the West with Leonora. He had begun making preparations for the flight when word came that General Duplin, the shadowy figure Filip believed to be one of the top leaders of the Underground —if not the leader—wanted to see him. Only once before had

Filip set eyes on Duplin and the latter's request was not to be taken lightly.

For several days Filip waited in the home of an elderly couple in Bratislava to which he had been sent. Finally, the old lady went to his room, knocked and told him someone was waiting for him at the door. Downstairs he found a chauffeur who directed him to a Czechoslovak Army car. Wordlessly Filip dropped into the rear seat of the black limousine and was driven from the hilly area of residential homes through the busy streets of the city to the office of Major General Duplin, deputy commander of the Second Military District of Czechoslovakia. The district embraced Slovakia.

Through an arch leading into the courtyard around the military headquarters the car passed. The auto was General Duplin's own and the two guards at the gate saluted with their rifles without stopping it. Here he was, Filip thought, in the den of the lion. He tried to keep his face free of concern.

Ushered into an antechamber of a suite of offices reserved for General Duplin, Filip took off his hat, straightened his tie and seated himself in a comfortable armchair under a collection of pictures of the President of the Czechoslovak People's Republic and other Party notables. In a few minutes time, a short brunette came into the room.

"So you are the relative of the general, Comrade Mistrik," she said. "I understand you are a machinist. Well, despite his great responsibilities, the general is never ashamed of the less fortunate ones in his family."

Filip managed an indifferent smile. "We all admire our distinguished uncle who serves both the Party and the People's regime with such distinction." He could lay it on as thick as anyone.

"Would you mind, Comrade Mistrik, filling in this form," she said. "It's just a necessary routine, you know." The form was a familiar one. Name, occuption, place of work, relation to the person he wanted to see, subject of intended discussion.

"Family affairs," was his answer to the last one. All the answers he was to give had been arranged beforehand.

After the officer in charge of the general's bureau had signed the form, Filip was taken through a room filled with typists into another chamber in which sat two officers, a husky red-haired colonel and a slim, dark-haired major. There the female secretary's job ended, for the inner sanctum was firmly in the hands of military personnel.

The young major rose, bade Filip sit in an empty chair and said, "The general is in a conference, but it should be over any minute."

As he sat there, Filip was reminded of the only other time he had seen General Duplin. It had been many years before in Vienna when the Russians still occupied a portion of that city. The general's parting words on that occasion to a group of Underground workers came back to Filip: "Patience, patience and patience in all our undertakings. Suicide is not our business. We must wait and wait and wait."

There in the waiting room the word "suicide" ran through Filip's mind. In the room with him were two officers of the Communist-run Czech Army, who would only too gladly order him shot out-of-hand if they knew his true identity. All of a sudden, fear gripped him unreasonably.

Was it suicide for him to be there? Was a trap set for him? Was General Duplin playing a double role, seeming to run the Underground only to learn the names of the hundreds of dedicated agents so he could betray them? Beads of sweat formed on Filip's forehead as he felt a sudden urge to turn and bolt.

Then he relaxed once again. Perhaps it was just as well that he was leaving Slovakia, he thought. The years had taken their toll.

"Is it too warm for you, Comrade Mistrik?" the red-haired colonel asked.

"Yes, it is rather a warm day. Could I get a glass of water?"

The major handed him a tumbler filled with liquid from a jug on his desk.

After a short wait, the double doors leading into General Duplin's office opened and two Soviet officers, their tunics festooned with decorations, walked out. The colonel motioned Filip to enter, shutting the doors behind him.

Duplin's large frame seemed to fill the wood-paneled room. His thick black hair was liberally flecked with white. His face, set in a scowl, softened when he saw Filip. The general gestured to a large armchair that seemed to envelop Filip when he sat down.

Without a preface, Duplin plunged in. "So you want to leave us," he said. His voice carried a hint of irony.

Filip was awed by the presence of this patriarch of the Underground. He waited for Duplin to continue, but the general said nothing. Growing increasingly fidgety, Filip felt his self-control slipping away and the words tumbled out of his mouth.

"For ten years we've been fighting the Communists, for ten years our strength has grown, for ten years we've been preparing to overthrow them. We have waited for the day when America and her allies would wage a holy war of liberation and we would sabotage the railroads and the factories. But our comrades rebelled in Hungary and the West did nothing. Nothing. Only sympathetic words.

"What's the use of fighting any longer? We cannot overthrow the Communists by ourselves and the West will not help us. For ten years we have been living a delusion." Still the general said nothing, only stared at him.

"I've watched relatives and friends suffer and die," Filip went on. "For what? We are no closer to freedom than we ever were. I'm tired, very tired. All around I have seen other members of the Underground, the ones who are not wanted criminals, go back to their homes in the last few months. They have given up the fight. But there is no safe place for me in Slovakia. I want to go to the West. I want to get married and live in peace."

Even after the young courier finished, Duplin maintained

his silence until a sympathetic smile creased his craggy face. He leaned forward across the mahogany table that separated him from Filip and said in a low voice, "I brought you here today that you might see me in my difficult position. Everyone of us takes great risks, in our own different ways, in our fight against this evil we call communism."

"Platitudes," flashed through Filip's mind.

Duplin arose. He seemed to collect his thoughts as he paced the room, his hands behind his broad back. When he spoke it was not in direct answer to Filip's remarks. Or at least it did not appear to be.

He began by recounting the large and growing power of the Warsaw Pact Armies, stopping occasionally before a large wall map of Europe to document his point. How puny the Resistance seemed, Filip thought as he listened, against this colossus grown even stronger than he had imagined. Next Duplin turned to the West. He told his guest the West was growing "soft," that its military and political strength, as compared with that of the Communist bloc, was receding, that it had lost its sense of urgency in the international struggle.

"Perhaps he will want us to disband and fight no more," flitted through Filip's mind as Duplin made it seem the victory of communism was inevitable. The young courier moved uneasily in his chair.

"My boy, you must not be dismayed by what I have said." It was as if Duplin had read Filip's mind. "I have told you all this to emphasize the importance of the Underground. It is precisely because things are so dark that it becomes more important than ever to keep on with the Resistance."

Filip's arched eyebrows asked the obvious question.

"If the Underground were to vanish in Slovakia, wouldn't the people become convinced once and for all of the ultimate triumph of communism? Certainly, they have become discouraged since Hungary. Perhaps their faith in the Underground has lessened. But as long as the Underground can harass the Communists, as long as it can broadcast the truth to the people on the secret radio, as long as it can bring the priests of the Church of Silence to the people, then the spark of hope will still remain, the hope that someday we will be free again. The Underground keeps that spark alive. If we were to quit the fight, hope would vanish and the people would succumb in their hearts to the Communists.

"Keeping the people's hopes alive is only part of the Underground's job. We have a more important task now, and it will force us to recast our thinking. We must no longer think of only Slovakia's fight to be free. We must think of the free world's battle and gear the Underground's activities to this broader struggle. We must awaken the West to the growing might of the Communist bloc and we must seek to strengthen the West."

"But how can that be done?" Filip interjected vehemently. "We have blown up trains and carried out hundreds upon hundreds of riots and local revolts and acts of sabotage. Yet we never have succeeded in arousing the West."

Duplin sat down again, facing Filip. "Science and technology. This is the answer. The struggle between communism and the free world will be decided, I am convinced, in the laboratory. The West is only beginning to realize this. It is convinced of its own superiority in science and it cannot take the Russians seriously. But that is a mistake. I have heard the Russians will send a rocket around the earth before the year is out. Perhaps that will shake the West out of its smugness.

"The job of our Underground now must be to demonstrate to the West the scientific strength of the Communists. And we must go one step further. We must carry the secrets of Communist science and technology to the West."

Filip found his interest aroused despite his intention to leave Slovakia.

"Yes. We are in an excellent position to do that in Slovakia. There is hardly any type of weapon or military research that isn't being produced or performed one place or other in our country. We are already organized in many of the plants, but the emphasis has been on sabotage. Now I am not proposing we abandon sabotage by any means. But blowing up a machine or even a wing of a plant only slows the Communists down temporarily. It is nothing more than a needle in the bear's foot.

"But stealing a scientific secret, that is another matter. If we can bring to the West the blueprints of a new missile, or a new weapon, or Communist research on atomic energy or plastics, then we are adding to the base of Western strength. If the West can harness its own scientific skills, and we can give to the West the best of Communist science, then it stands to reason the West will be stronger than the Communists."

"But that will take time, General," Filip complained.

"Yes, my impatient friend, that will take time. That is the first lesson the Underground must learn if it is to continue to be effective in the future. I have counseled patience and more patience for years, but some of your associates have never been able to learn the lesson. To try to change things overnight is to commit suicide.

"Our struggle against tyranny will be a long one, Filip. It has already lasted a thousand years, so why do you get discouraged if success doesn't come quickly? You may not even live to see Slovakia free yourself. But the fight must go on. We must think of ourselves as part of the whole free world, and not just as Slovaks. We can never be free ourselves unless freedom comes to the whole Communist world."

Filip sat in silent reflection. After a while, he asked somewhat abashedly, "What would I do in this new Underground?"

"The same Underground, Filip," Duplin replied quickly, "the same Underground, but with a new way of doing things, a new emphasis, a new goal." He paused to let that sink in, and said: "We want you to reorganize our cell at the Voroshilov Enterprises at Dubnica. Our men there are prepared to perform acts of sabotage. We want them to think also of stealing Communist scientific secrets and passing them along to the West. Your job would be to arrange this new way of operating."

"Voroshilov," Filip echoed. "That's where the Military

264

Technical Institute has its headquarters. I would need top security clearance to get in there."

Duplin smiled. "We are not without resources, Filip. The director of the Institute is one of us, Colonel Rudolf Muran. He has asked for a new personal aide, and I think we can get that job for you—if you want it, that is."

"Who is Colonel Muran?" Filip wanted to know.

Muran was a professional soldier, Duplin told him. Before the war he had attended Hranice, the West Point of Czechoslovakia, and continued his engineering studies at the Technological University at Prague. When Hitler took over Czechoslovakia in March of 1939, Muran and others fled to Poland, leaving their families behind them, to continue the war against Germany. When Poland fell, Muran decided to go to Russia, assuming naïvely that the Russians would act as big brothers to the smaller Slavic nations and welcome him happily.

Between Podvolociska in Poland and Russia flowed a small river that posed no problem to cross. Muran and his friends took off all their clothing, placed it in bags and walked naked into the river, holding the bags above their heads. No sooner had they reached the halfway point across the river, however, when a powerful voice from the Soviet side was heard: "Hands up, who are you?"

"We are Slavs," Muran shouted, "and we want to go over to your side."

"Drop your clothing into the water and keep your hands up," came the reply.

What could Muran and his colleagues do? To go back to Poland meant captivity. So they continued into Russia where they were met by a group of soldiers and marched naked for three miles to the nearest village. Children and old folks ran out of their houses to spit upon them and curse them as spies.

Muran and his friends were tried and found guilty of entering the country illegally and sentenced to hard labor in Soviet prison camps for ten years. Separated from the others, Muran spent the next four years traveling from one forced-labor camp to another, from Odessa to Moscow, by cattle car to Kolyma in northeastern Siberia to the gold mines of Khatanga in north central Siberia and to the coal mines of Pechora in Arctic Russia.

Finally in 1943 Stalin recognized Czechoslovakia and a Czech embassy came to Moscow. In early 1944 Muran's letters to the embassy brought results at last. He was freed to join one of the Czech units that were formed in Russia to fight the Germans who were deep inside Soviet territory. Muran remained with his unit in the Soviet, but other Czech units were dropped behind enemy lines in Czechoslovakia for partisan warfare. These units sparked the Slovak uprising in 1944, tying down three German divisions, and formed the nucleus of the group that was later to lead the Czech Army to embrace communism.

After the war ended, all Slovaks in Russia were sent back to their country, as were other Slavic nationals. Because of his anti-Communist leanings, Muran quit the army and looked for work. But the best job he could get was as a factory hand; although the Communists had not taken over the country yet, his lack of loyalty to the Party barred him from using his engineering skills to gain better employment.

But in 1948, after the Communists took over Czechoslovakia, Muran changed his tactics. He was as unalterably opposed to communism as before, but he agreed to join the Party for his family's welfare; his oldest son, for example, would not have been allowed to go to the University if he was not a Party member.

The Czech Army was only too glad for Muran to return. He spoke Russian fluently and his technological training was needed, since the Army was to control the production of military weapons and military research. Great new industrial plants were being built in Slovakia, at the Soviet's instigation. Muran got his old Army rank back and was sent to Russia for a year to learn Soviet methods. When he returned, he was placed on the board that ran the Military Technical Institute in Dubnica and eventually worked his way up to the directorship.

In this position, Muran was privy to the most important work going on behind the Iron Curtain in missiles, aircraft and other weapons. Throughout the years he had managed to keep in contact with the anti-Communist Underground and the labor cell that had been set up at the Voroshilov Enterprises came under his wing. Now the time had come to take full advantage of Muran's position, and Filip had been tapped to bring this about.

"Just how will you get me into Voroshilov?" Filip asked Duplin.

"You will apply for the job as aide to Colonel Muran. Your name is Eugen Kalina, a loyal Party member. Your parents were killed by the Germans during the war for helping the Resistance. You've had clerical experience in Eastern Slovakia, which is a requirement for the job. We will provide you with all the papers and our people in security will see to it that your information checks out when your application is forwarded."

"This Kalina is a fictional creation, no doubt," Filip said.

"No," Duplin said. "He is real. That is why I do not anticipate much trouble when Muran selects you for the job and sends your papers back for processing. Kalina's hair is a different color than yours, and his face is longer and thinner, but such things can be altered without too much difficulty. In most other ways, the two of you are quite alike—age, height and weight, physical structure and so on."

"Where is Kalina now?"

Duplin looked straight at Filip so the latter would be sure not to miss the point. "So far as anyone knows, he is vacationing in Eastern Slovakia. That is what he set out to do. But he will never return. We have seen to that. Eugen Kalina will turn up next in Dubnica."

Filip stared back at Duplin silently. After a moment, he

said, "You must have been quite certain that I would change my mind about leaving Slovakia."

The burly general rose from the table once again. "We never lost our faith in your devotion to Slovakia, Filip." Duplin's voice betrayed emotion for the first time.

"Well," Filip said with a grin to hide his own inner turmoil, "at least I will be something else than a courier now. I am thirty-two years old, and that is past the retirement age for couriers."

The night after the sabotage at Voroshilov, Filip and his colleagues met for their customary evening of card-playing at an inn in the old section of town, as unconcerned as if the explosion had never happened. Hladik, Jan Dubrava and Juraj Koren sat at the table with Filip, while four eager kibitzers provided a protective wall around them. While they played, they plotted.

The group of eight men made up the most important Underground cell in the Voroshilov Enterprises. From Colonel Muran, Filip had received the names of the seven others, all of whom had top security clearance and were admirably situated to perform acts of sabotage. All were maintenance men, with access to every part of the underground factory among them. They could wander around the plant without attracting more than a cursory glance from the other workers or guards.

Never did the cell meet in private, for if someone had ever learned of such a meeting suspicions would have been quickly aroused. Instead, the members congregated nightly in the inn for beer and card games until their presence became so customary as to be ignored—even by the STB men who occasionally visited the place.

Though he was not a member of the Underground, the innkeeper was a man who sympathized with the Resistance and could be trusted. He kept an empty beer barrel in the cellar of the tavern, near the men's room, and it was this beer barrel that served as a "dead mailbox" for transmittal of Underground messages.

Into this beer barrel Colonel Muran managed to plant microfilmed copies of secret documents—progress reports on missiles and other weapons, for example—or of reports he himself had drafted describing the character and personality of leading Communist scientists under his aegis. Muran never dropped the documents into the mailbox in person, and neither Filip nor any other member of the cell had ever found out who the contact was. So many men passed by the beer barrel on the way to the toilet that it would have been impossible to identify the contact unless an all-night guard were kept. And although Filip was curious, he realized the less he knew about the other Underground member or members working for Muran the less he or his cellmates could reveal if captured.

Other dead mailboxes were also located around Dubnica in ever-changing places—in an out-of-the-way hole in the grey wall that surrounded the centuries-old church in the heart of the old town, in the hollows of trees, or the underside of a truck belonging to a trusted cousin of one of the cell members. To these places, Filip brought the rolls of microfilm he himself had shot.

As special assistant to Muran he was one of six men who worked in a large room full of filing cabinets, separated only by a chamber of female secretaries and clerks from Muran's office. In these filing cabinets were recorded most of the goings-on in the defense plants and military research branches in Slovakia. Not quite everything. The projects of topmost secrecy were kept under lock and key in Muran's own office.

But there was enough in the filing cabinets to keep Filip busy for months. With his specially built microfilm camera, he would snap pictures in the rare moments during regular working hours when he was alone in the room. When he had been working at the Institute long enough to be accepted as a regular, he asked and received permission from Muran to work overtime. Sometimes one of the other special assistants would stay late, too, but usually Filip was left alone to do his work. Once a worker won top security clearance, he could leave the plant without fear of personal examination, though Filip's lunchbox contained a false bottom in which he hid his camera just to be sure.

Since he did not want to hold onto the undeveloped microfilm any longer than necessary, Filip placed it at least once a week in one of the dead mailboxes. There the microfilm was picked up, usually by Jan Dubrava, the small shifty-eyed little man who served as courier for the cell. It was said of Dubrava that he loved his motorcycle more than his wife. His associates never denied the legend, in fact they encouraged it, for Dubrava's preoccupation with his motorcycle made it seem perfectly natural when he took off nearly every weekend for a trip to Bratislava, some 110 miles away. There, Dubrava left the microfilm that Filip and Muran had taken and other Underground members sent the documents on to the West.

In the inn that night, Filip told the other members of the cell that he was leaving Dubnica for fear that he might be unmasked. He made the news known matter of factly as he dealt out a card to each of the other three players. With faces equally expressionless, each player lifted a corner of his card.

"Hladik will be in charge when I leave," Filip said through lips that barely moved. Hladik was easily the most intelligent of the remaining group. "I think it might be best to lay low for awhile now. I don't know if the man who replaces me will be one of us, but in any case you will at least keep getting reports in the beer barrel." Filip did not mention Muran's name, for only Hladik among the others knew the role of the director of the Institute. Filip dealt another card to the players, face up. "From time to time, someone from the Underground will be in touch with you with new instructions. Whoever he may be will work through Hladik."

"Twenty-one!" Dubrava exclaimed happily as he uncovered an ace in the hole to go with the king showing on the table. He raked in the coins and stood up, saying, "I think I will skip my chance at the bank tonight. It's getting quite late."

The others mumbled agreement or disagreement, according to their fortunes that evening, but all rose to depart.

"Until tomorrow night," Filip said amiably.

Now all that remained for him before leaving Dubnica was a final talk with Colonel Muran.

The next day just before lunch, Filip walked into the room adjoining his where Irma Mrazova worked and found her putting on lipstick. When she saw him she started powdering her face furiously.

"Don't be angry, Irma," he pleaded.

She continued to ignore him. He moved close to her desk and said cajolingly, "How about joining me this evening for dinner at the Zavodna Jedalen?"

"Will it be like last night? I was expecting you to call."

"I'm sorry, Irma, but I wasn't able to see you. I was terribly tired from the night before and I went to bed early. I assure you that I will not disappoint you tonight," Filip promised.

Irma brightened. "Let's try it then. But don't disappoint me this time."

"I will meet you at the restaurant then, at eight." Filip left the room.

Actually, he had no intention of meeting Irma, for it was that night that he planned on leaving Dubnica. Uncertain whether he had kindled Irma's love or suspicion, or perhaps a mixture of both, Filip played it safe by tying her up while he would be making his escape. While she was waiting for him in the restaurant, perhaps with STB men planted nearby ready to pounce, he would be heading toward Bratislava.

Filip spent the morning waiting to see Colonel Muran, who was kept busy in one conference after the other. Finally, at 3 P.M. Muran was free and Filip, carrying a pile of papers, rushed into Muran's secretary's office asking to see the director.

"You know he is very busy, today, Comrade Kalina, and he

does not want to be disturbed. Can't it wait till tomorrow?" the secretary said.

"I don't think so. A report came in this morning about the A-9 and A-10 rockets from the Prakovice proving grounds. There have been some enemy acts there that should be brought to his immediate attention."

It was a lie, but a clever one. The atmosphere at the Institute headquarters was still permeated with tension after the sabotage of thirty-six hours earlier, and a report of Underground activity at any plant under control of the Institute was cause for concern at the highest levels. Muran's secretary went into the director's office, came out again quickly and ushered Filip in.

He stood at the colonel's desk, but Muran did not ask Filip to sit down for he did not want an important official to come into his room and find him granting such a courtesy to a subordinate employee, a civilian at that. Nor could Filip be allowed to remain in the room long; lower-ranking workers just didn't stay there more than a few minutes.

"What is it?" Muran's manner was almost brusque.

"Sir, the purpose of my visiting you is to tell you I am leaving tonight. The cell is working smoothly now and Hladik will take over for me. Things are—well, getting too hot for me. It would be a good idea if you fired me."

"The same idea occurred to me last night," Muran said. "But I was not sure if your work here had proceeded far enough along so that you could leave. Since it apparently has, Filip, consider yourself fired." Muran laughed soundlessly.

"Before you go, however," he added, "perhaps you had better stop at the inn once more. I have no doubt your successor will be an able man, but since you are leaving anyhow I think I had better microfilm some reports this afternoon I had been intending to shoot in a more leisurely way. That way you can take them all at once instead of having them passed in several batches."

Moving closer to the desk, Filip said in a low voice, "There

272

is one more thing, Colonel. Beware of Irma Mrazova. She is an informer."

"Don't you think I know?" Muran replied. "Something will have to be arranged."

He stood up, the two shook hands and wished each other luck, and Filip was gone. The meeting had lasted less than three minutes.

Back in his own office, Filip put on a long face as he began packing the few personal belongings in his desk. His co-workers, who knew where he had been, crowded around curiously.

"I was fired," Filip told them. Why? they wanted to know. Filip shrugged, "The colonel was not satisfied with my efficiency."

Filip's colleagues expressed their sympathy, unfeigned, because they knew that to be fired meant that he would have difficulty finding a corresponding job and in fact would have to look for manual labor. But by the time the commiserations were over and Filip stopped at Irma's desk to break the news, he almost believed his bad fortune himself.

"I would still like to have dinner with you," he told her. "Perhaps with your connections you might be able to help me find a new job."

Eagerly, Irma said she would help. They would talk it over at the restaurant.

From his apartment room, where he packed a few more possessions, Filip went to the inn around 6 P.M. to meet his cronies. In a loud voice, he told them, "I was fired today. Perhaps some beer and a good game of cards will help me forget my trouble." In a low voice once the dealing began, he said to Dubrava, the motorcyclist, "Pick me up at nine tonight. I want you to take me to Trenčin to catch my train there, just in case the boys in green are at the station in Dubnica."

While one of the four men who formed the wall around the card-players sat in for him, Filip visited the men's room in the cellar and returned with the microfilm left by Colonel Muran.

At 8 P.M. he excused himself and shook hands warmly with each of his friends.

As he gripped the hands of his collaborators, Filip's emotions were mixed. Here were skilled workers, men of above ordinary intelligence, who in the space of several months had been molded into an efficient operating unit in the Underground's new warfare. The ease with which they were able to shift their goals and *modus operandi* was a source of considerable pride for Filip. Yet the satisfaction in a job well done was diluted by the sadness he felt at having to leave them. Sadness and a tinge of jealousy at their opportunity to continue the work at Voroshilov, unsuspected and unwanted by the secret police.

Filip rose and left for the apartment. What would Irma be doing now? She must be getting impatient at the restaurant. Colonel Muran, he was sure, would not inform the STB of his dismissal until the next morning when he would be far from Dubnica. But what if Irma had taken the initiative herself when she learned he was fired and called in the STB?

By the time he reached the apartment, he had convinced himself he would find the authorities waiting for him. But they were not. Hastily, he taped Muran's latest microfilms to his body, burned the remaining tape and other possibly incriminating papers, made sure his revolver and knife were in position for instant use, then left. He walked down by the River Vah and, when he was sure nobody saw him, dropped his microfilm camera, hair color dye and other materials he had used in his current disguise in a weighted bag.

Then back to the apartment house to wait for Dubrava. Still no sign of Irma or the STB. It would be wiser, Filip thought, to hide in a dark doorway across the street where he could keep an eye on visitors to his own building. But no unusual guest had called when Dubrava drove up with a roar ten minutes later. Carrying only a little hand bag, Filip mounted the back seat of Dubrava's motorcycle and off they went.

In twenty minutes, they reached the railway station at Trenčín, where a loudspeaker was announcing the arrival and departure of trains. One would soon be leaving for Bratislava,
Filip's destination. But there, near the lines of people in front
of the ticket windows, were four SNB men. They were pacing
up and down looking for any "wanted" criminals skipping
town, a customary police practice.

Filip turned to Dubrava. "You'd better buy my ticket for
me. I'll be wandering around the station wherever there is a
crowd of people. Just hold onto the ticket on the platform
near the rear until I come and take it from you."

Dubrava did as he was told. As the Bratislava Express
chugged into the station, a crowd of passengers descended on
the train, jostling Dubrava, who held Filip's tickets above his
head. A man with his nose encased in a bandage came up to
Dubrava and grabbed for the ticket, but the short motorcyclist
pulled it back in time.

"It's me, Kalina," the face behind the bandage said excitedly.

Indeed it was, Dubrava now saw with his mouth agape. He
handed the ticket over to Filip, who ran for the door of a third-
class car as the train started to pull out of the station.

The best defense against discovery is sometimes a good of-
fense, Filip knew. So he acted accordingly. Pointing to the
bandage on his nose, he talked about his ailment to everyone
on the train who would listen. He had to go to specialists in
Bratislava to get it treated, since his condition could not be
cured by anyone in Trenčín. Loudly and continuously, he
talked about his nose to the point of boredom.

He talked about it to the police who boarded the train at a
control point along the way for a routine look at the passengers. He told them what his doctor had told him. He told
them what his friends said when he started on his trip. He
described his symptoms. He asked the police if they had known
anyone who suffered from the same trouble. He chattered so
much that the police fled from his torrent of words.

The passengers on the train could not help but laugh and one policeman, shaking his head, turned to another and said of this buffoon: "What a crank! I'm glad I don't have to travel with him."

Filip had no trouble at all on the trip to Bratislava.

12. Ordeal

FILIP remained in the Slovak capital for several weeks. By the time he had been there a few days, he was certain, Irma Mrazova would have checked the picture files of the secret police and discovered that Eugen Kalina and Filip Polhora were one and the same. The heat would be on.

Aboard one of the small boats laid up during the icy months in Bratislava's winter harbor, where Filip now hid out, he would be safe for awhile, he thought, or at least as safe as any Underground agent could be when the police were searching intensively for him. Enough food to last almost a month had been laid in and the stay would give him time to change his appearance so that he looked like neither Filip Polhora nor Eugen Kalina.

He let his crew-cut hair grow longer and washed the blond coloring out. Through a contact with the Underground in Bratislava he managed to obtain a light brown hair dye and spectacles. He also grew a mustache. It was not the best of disguises, but it would have to do.

To pass away the time and keep his mind sharp in his self-imposed solitude, Filip filled page after page with information as best he could recall from the files of the Military Technical Institute. He wrote on long sheets of paper, filling only the top half before going on to the next sheet. That way, after he had finished a particular topic, he would go back and read what he had written and when he discovered a fact or two he had left out he could fill in the blank space.

The mental exercise also served another purpose. Filip could not be sure that the undeveloped microfilm would come out readable, or that the film might not be damaged in transit across the watery Iron Curtain, or that the couriers themselves had not been cut down while trying to cross to the West. By writing down all he could remember, he would serve as a personal backstop to the microfilm.

Pushing himself to remember everything, Filip would close his eyes and imagine himself in a classroom. His teacher was asking questions, and he would answer them.

"What is the shell structure of the A-9 missile? Of the A-10 missile?"

"Can you tell its composition, thickness, design and resistance to temperature?"

"What is the temperature resistance from cone to last stage?"

"Manner of joining, releasing and firing for each stage?"

Filip knew the answers, and he smiled at his imaginary interrogator for even daring to suspect his ignorance. But then the teacher asked him, "Can you describe the manner of using preceding stages as firing platforms and all the problems related thereto?"

His mind was a blank. He tried to answer, but all he could do was stutter a few meaningless words. How stupid could he be, he berated himself. Well, he consoled himself, perhaps Colonel Muran's microfilm would have the answer.

Day after day Filip wrote, until even his dreams were affected. In his sleep he would fill sheet after sheet or answer questions like a child learning his catechism. But the dreams did not disturb him. Recording the secret information from Dubnica was a labor of love and his conscious and unconscious merged into one. Dreaming for him was living and his living was dreaming for just one goal, the successful completion of his assignment.

Only one thing about his dreams of technology bothered him. He discovered one night, when he jolted himself awake after failing to answer a question, that he was talking in his sleep. Although no one but Underground contacts ever came aboard the boat, one could never be too sure. So Filip decided from then on to place a cloth over his mouth each night when he went to bed to prevent talking out in his dreams, or at least to render his words inaudible.

After some time, Filip accumulated a large sheaf of notes. He could not, of course, carry so many records on his body when he crossed the Iron Curtain, so he read the material through once more, emplanting it in his memory, then burned all the papers. Once he reached the West, he would dictate it all into a recording machine. Only the microfilm from Colonel Muran escaped deliberate destruction.

By mid-November, he was ready to leave Bratislava. He had received a new set of false identity papers and got word to stop at the home of an Underground contact at Malacky for the latest information on conditions in the dangerous Zahorie border zone along the Morava River. The order suited Filip perfectly, for Malacky was only five miles from Levary, where Leonora lived, and he decided without telling the Underground that he would detour briefly to see her. It had been many months since their last meeting.

The evening train took him to Malacky without incident. He went on foot to the outskirts of the town where Anton Sivak, his contact and an old friend, lived with his family. Cautiously he walked in the darkness. A thin layer of soft falling snow gathered on the badly paved streets. Filip turned into a narrow lane past dark and cheerless houses, hearing only the occasional barking of a dog or the crying of an infant.

For no reason he could consciously think of, a feeling of loneliness and despair suddenly overcame Filip. Was it a premonition?

At last he came to a whitewashed house, marked by two weeping willows in the front. No sign of danger so far. He raised his hand to knock at the heavy front door, then changed his mind and tried the knob. It was strange that the door was open, but he entered.

There in the sitting room, apparently waiting for him, was

279

not only Anton Sivak, but three strange men whose expectant looks immediately signaled danger to Filip.

This is the end, he thought as his pulse jumped. STB men, the State secret police! Control yourself. Keep panic out of your voice. Smile, look friendly, not scared.

No word came from Sivak's icy lips. Was it a trap? Doubtless. Sivak's silence revealed as much as the presence of the strangers.

No time to think or analyse. Instinctively, Filip acted. The STB men were obviously expecting him, but Sivak had not yet pointed the finger. Perhaps his disguise would work. He had to talk first, and fast, before Sivak did, before an innocent word from his friend gave all away. It was his only chance.

"Anton," Filip cried heartily, forcing a smile and holding out his hand. "I'm so glad I found you home. I thought you might be out drinking with the boys."

"Since when do you wear glasses?" was all Anton replied. The question rocked Filip anew. What kind of question was that for his contact to ask? It was a remark you would expect of an enemy, not a friend, in this situation.

Barely able to control himself, Filip managed to answer, "My eyes have been going bad. A specialist made these glasses up for me two months ago." His teeth clenched as he restrained himself from going at Anton with bare hands.

The police were eyeing Filip closely, but apparently had not yet made up their minds about him. Jumping at their indecision, he said, "Come, Anton, my girl is waiting for me at the inn. Why don't you join us there?"

Sivak was silent for a minute. If he was a traitor, Filip thought, he would give me away. Sivak's eyes were troubled. "I can't go now. Perhaps I will meet you later," he said weakly.

Trembling inwardly, Filip shrugged, turned around matter-of-factly and started out of the room. With his back to the police, he closed his eyes, expecting a bullet to hit him. But none came.

In the hall, Sivak's younger sister, Amalka, suddenly materialized and walked with him to the door. The police would not shoot while she was close to him, he thought.

"Goodbye, Jan," she said in a voice that could be heard in the sitting room. "I'm sorry you can't stay longer."

Then, offering her face to Filip so that he had to bend down to kiss her, she whispered when he was close, "Filip, you have been betrayed. Anton has turned traitor. They know about you and the whole ring." He noticed tears in her eyes.

It was dark and snowing harder when he went out the door. Walking at a normal pace to the gate of the fence, he suddenly vaulted over it and ran, ducking behind the first garden wall he came to. From Anton's house came shouting, a girl's scream, then shots.

Across yards and gardens, over a small brook, in and out of underbrush Filip sprinted, holding his revolver in hand but never firing it lest he give away his position. His speed was too much for the police, who had left their car some distance away from Sivak's house so Filip would not be alerted to danger. Helped by the wind that blew snow drifts over his tracks, he shook his pursuers.

He kept running nevertheless for half an hour through birch woods, swamps and meadows until he saw a barn. As he approached it, a German shepherd dog who had escaped his anxious eye leaped at him, growling. The dog was chained and could not quite reach him, but his barking might wake up the owner who, in the Iron Curtain buffer zone, was probably a loyal Communist. To retreat might not stop the growling soon enough.

Muttering friendly sounds, Filip gingerly moved nearer and, as the dog sniffed him, gently stroked the dog's testicles. The German shepherd quieted down, yapping contentedly, and rubbed his head against Filip's leg.

The courier patted his newest conquest, who settled down quietly at his post, and slipped into the barn to rest and to think. How much did the police know? Did they know about Leonora and her father? Had they arrested her already, perhaps killed her? It would have been easy to get panicky, but Filip forced himself to think calmly, to reason things out.

Anton's treason haunted his mind. Why had Anton betrayed him? He had known the border zone contact since school days in Bratislava. They had always been friends, though Sivak had never done well at the University, neither in grades nor in attracting friends of either sex.

Perhaps that was it. Perhaps jealousy of Filip turned Sivak into a turncoat. The envy of college days might well have grown in the years afterwards as Filip became a courier and Anton was kept in the dangerous but relatively dull job he still held. Now he was getting back at me, Filip reflected.

And yet, Anton did not give him away while he was in the sitting room with the STB men. Why? Filip thought he knew. Sivak lacked the guts to betray him to his face; the guilt Sivak must have felt at becoming a traitor would have weighed against his informing on Filip in the latter's presence.

Filip could picture in his mind Sivak turning to the STB men, after the courier had left the house, and only then stammering out:

"I'm not sure, but I think that man who just left may have been Filip Polhora. I couldn't tell because he was wearing a disguise."

That would explain the shouts and shots soon after he left Sivak's home.

But what would happen to Sivak's sister, Amalka? The STB men, remembering her actions, would certainly know she had helped Filip. But thinking of what he had left behind solved nothing, Filip realized. He was in a dangerous spot, and he shut his mind to such thoughts.

As for Leonora and her father, Filip was fairly certain Sivak did not know that Karol Danko was another border zone contact for couriers. Such contacts operated independently of each other through Bratislava, or whatever large city or town near the border served as headquarters for the local branch of the

Underground railway. Again, the principle that the less an Underground member knew, the less he could reveal.

But Sivak might be aware, Filip suddenly recalled, that Leonora was his fiancée. Many of his friends knew that, even though Filip had been careful to hide the fact of her father's role in the Underground. Would Sivak send the police to Leonora's house to wait for him? It was a strong possibility, but nevertheless Filip headed for Levary when he left the barn.

His flight from the STB men had already taken him in the direction of Leonora's place. For another hour he walked through the snow, making use of any cover he could find, until he caught sight of the towers of the baroque church that towered over little Levary, resembling in the darkness a mother hen watching protectively over her chicks. Running when he was behind cover, crawling through the snow when he was out in the open, he came nearer her house.

It seemed to Filip then that he was approaching paradise. Here was his beloved Leonora, patient, never-complaining Leonora, here was the house that had become dearer to him than the one he grew up in. Now he would see her again after a long separation, he thought, as the blood pounded in his head.

He had just reached the wooden fence that separated the garden from the fields behind Danko's house when he saw them. Figures furtively crouching around the house. The police, obviously. So Sivak *had* sent them there after all.

For a second Filip was tempted to shoot his way to the house. If he was to die, it should be at Leonora's feet. But that would help no one, he realized.

Shaken, his paradise now turned into a hell, he turned away. Casting one last backward glance in the hope of catching a glimpse of Leonora, he began crawling across the field back to the woods.

But ahead of him, barely distinguishable against the dark background of the trees, he could make out other figures spread some distance apart from each other. More police.

Somehow, without realizing it, he had managed to get past them on the way to Leonora's house. Should he push his luck and try it going back?

No. How could he? It was foolish to expect a second success. Was his assignment doomed then?

A few feet from where he lay on the ground he spied a wheat pit, half hidden by some bushes. In Slovakia, farmers who do not have a barn dig a hole in the ground to store their wheat through the winter, and cover it with boards. Filip's luck had still not run out.

The boards seemed frozen stuck to the ground and Filip's hands were numb with the cold. But with strength derived of fear, he managed to lift two of the boards, slither into the pit and let the boards drop gently back into place as the falling snow quickly covered his path. He was safe.

Thank God, the pit was full, he thought as he burrowed deep into the mountain of golden grain. Completely surrounded by the wheat, he would get at least some protection from the cold. Moreover, by submerging his head in the sea of gold he could escape the prying eyes of the police should they look into the pit.

It was no accident that Karol Danko's pit was so full. The Underground saw to it that he was well supplied. Had he not met his wheat quota the farm would have been taken over by the State and though he might still be allowed to till it, the Underground would find it too dangerous to use for its purposes. Each succeeding year, Danko's quota was raised by the State, raised in fact to a level his farm could not possibly meet. But the Underground always gave him money to buy wheat elsewhere so that he would have enough to deliver to the State.

The black pit in which Filip found himself was about ten feet in diameter and ten feet deep. Between the top of the wheat and the boards were two feet of air. At first he tried to keep motionless, to breathe as quietly as possible so that the police would not hear him. But a fit of sneezing seized him

284

as the grain got into his nose. He pinched his nostrils to stifle the sound until he thought his ear drums would pop.

Had Filip known the suffering he would have to go through in the pit, he might have tried to shoot his way out after all. Day after day, Filip Polhora remained in the pit. The grain stuck to his clothes, to his face, to his hair. Each time he risked lifting a board to look around, he saw the police still there.

The cold and the hunger were indescribable. He had to concentrate all his effort on keeping alive—to move his arms and legs, fingers and toes so that they would not freeze. He tried eating the wheat, but it was dry and unpalatable and it was all he could do to work up enough saliva to swallow it. Occasionally he would risk sticking his hand above the surface of the ground and pulling back snow to suck or mix with the wheat to soften it and make it more edible.

Twice during the week, the police opened the pit and stuck forks into the wheat while Filip pulled his head underneath and held his breath. Fortunately, their pokings were only half-hearted.

By the fourth day, nausea and pains in the stomach were Filip's constant companions. He thought of Leonora, imagining one minute she had been killed or captured by the Communists, then in the next instant envisioning her and himself together somewhere happily free of their tormentors. So near to her now, and yet so far.

If he ever came out of this alive, he swore to himself, he and Leonora would flee to the West. For four years now theirs had been a hit-and-run love. Months might go by before he would pass through Levary to see her. Never could he stay more than a day or two. A few hours of love, a tearful parting, and away he went on his assignment.

Never would she raise the question of marriage, knowing that he was a fugitive from law and could not settle down anywhere except as a guerilla in the mountains, where men did not take wives.

Always it was "one more assignment" and he would take

her West, but the one more assignment led to another which he could not turn down. He could not bring himself to abandon Slovakia as long as there was still some hope of freedom. Nor did Leonora press him to.

Thoughts of death also filled Filip's mind as he lay there amid the wheat. To climb out of the pit meant certain death, perhaps mercifully quick. To remain there meant slow death. Either way, his mission would end in failure and the work of Colonel Muran and the labor cell at Dubnica would have gone in vain.

Yet even now, as always when he faced death, he thought of others and how much they depended on him. Leonora . . . the Underground . . . Slovakia. He could not let them down. Failure was worse than death. Stay alive, stay alive, he willed himself. And yet it would be so easy to shut his eyes and let his spirit drift gently, ever so gently, into a quiet, tempting sleep that would end his agony forever.

He jerked himself awake. It was the evening of the seventh day. Breathing seemed to come easier now, and the numbness that came over his body wiped away the pain. Was this the way it was before death?

Forcing his unresponding body up, he peered over the edge of the pit. No sign of the police. Had they given up, or was it just an hallucination? Had they decided that, since he was warned at Sivak's house, he had fled the area? Filip had no way of knowing, but it was a chance he had to take.

He raised himself out of the pit by sheer will. His legs felt like wooden boards when he tried to walk and he stumbled like a drunken man. But he was past fear. He knew he had to get out of the pit, or die. Beyond that, he could not think.

He staggered to the house. It was dark inside. Had Leonora and her father been taken away? A few more agonizing steps and he was at the rear window. He raised his arm, rapped weakly on the glass, and then fainted.

The next thing he knew Leonora was holding him in her arms, holding his cold hands in hers, pressing his frozen cheeks to her warm ones, sobbing uncontrollably. And then she was dashing about for warm clothes to put over his face and hands, for something warm for Filip to drink. He was dimly aware that she took off his shoes and soggy clothes, made a bed for him, propelled him with her father's help into a warm bath, did a hundred things at once, all the while crying and smiling and holding him.

Tucking him into bed, she sat beside him till he fell asleep.

Filip slept soundly through the night and much of the next day, while Leonora stood guard, pacing the house on tiptoe, looking out the windows to see if the police had returned. During the week before she and her father had seen that their house was under surveillance but there was nothing they could do about it. The police had never entered their home, nor had Leonora and her father tried to leave except for routine chores around the place. The police eyed them suspiciously as they moved about the farm, but said nothing. When Leonora or her father asked what was wrong, the police would simply shrug their shoulders in silence.

The second day of Filip's recuperation, Karol Danko left the farm and made his way through the countryside he knew so well to learn the movements of the border guard and plan a route of escape for Filip. While he was gone, Filip and Leonora spoke of a million things, of their love, of what had happened to each in the intervening months. Leonora listened patiently while he recited all he had memorized from the files of the Voroshilov Enterprises. When his memory faltered, and he would grow angry with himself, she would laugh and tease him to change his dark mood until he grinned and pulled her down on his chest to kiss and embrace.

At ten that night, they heard a knock on the door, which was bolted from the inside. Immediately she grabbed his hand and pulled him to the chimney her father used to smoke hams and sausages. She had planned it all beforehand for just such an emergency. Inside the chimney was a ladder Filip climbed until he found a niche where he could hide without being seen from the bottom. His pistol was ready in his hand.

But it was only Leonora's father. With a feeling of relief Filip came down from his hiding place, black with soot, to Leonora's laughter. The merriment, however, turned abruptly to tears when she learned from her father that Filip, weakened as he was, would have to make his break across the Iron Curtain before the next dawn.

Suddenly and unexpectedly the illusion of safety, the unreal atmosphere, cast by love, of the last two days vanished as the three sat down to discuss the hard facts of their plight. Why had the police withdrawn from the house? Would they be back? When? Were they watching the house from a distance?

There were no answers to those questions, and so after a while they stopped discussing them. The police were wherever they might be, and there was nothing anyone in the house could do about it except get Filip away before they returned. Filip and Leonora held hands while the escape plans were being laid. They both knew that he could never come that way again—that it might be a long time before they saw each other again.

"Why don't you and Leonora come with me?" Filip blurted out.

It would be impossible for all three to cross the icy Morava in safety. Surely Filip knew that, Karol reminded him gently. In his condition, Filip would have trouble enough getting to Austria himself.

"But you are in danger if you remain here," Filip argued. "The police will be back. At least can't you leave the farm and go somewhere else to live?"

Karol paused only momentarily, for the idea had already occurred to him. "To flee now would be a confession of guilt. If the police knew what I was doing, they would have arrested me by now. Besides, I cannot abandon the Underground."

I cannot abandon the Underground echoed in Filip's ears. He was moved by the matter-of-fact way Karol had said the words. No bravado. Simply, but deeply felt. They filled Filip with guilt over his resolution, sworn in the wheat pit, to flee to the West with Leonora after his current assignment was over.

Karol arose before Filip could say anything. "It is two o'clock. Time to go."

Leonora ran for her coat. "I'm coming with you as far as the river," she cried.

Her father tried to dissuade her. He told her it was too dangerous, but she would not listen nor did Filip have the heart to argue with her. "At least," Karol Danko said in rueful surrender, "we can have a little hot tea and rum before we start."

It was snowing when they left and the flakes, driven by the wind, stung their faces. The moon, dimmed behind clouds, gave a silvery cast to the white landscape. Trees, houses, the distant mountains, all appeared in hazy outline in the muted light. Cautiously the three picked their way along.

The canal they had to cross was frozen and Leonora slipped. She grabbed at Filip and the two fell into a heap, laughing like two children on a lark. But Karol hushed them, for soon they would be at the river.

Karol knew the schedule of the border guards to the second. That was his business. He also knew, for he had arranged it, which patrols would be induced by the Underground sympathizers among them to gain respite from the snow and cold by visiting the barn of a friendly farmer, where a bottle of Slivovitz awaited them. If things went according to plan, two searchlights in the towers overlooking the Morava would also stay out of action for five minutes.

But still the guards might change their routine, as they did sometimes, and there was no time to waste. Karol was impatient with Leonora and Filip as they drew near the icy river and the moment the two lovers had been dreading came.

They stood on the river bank and threw their arms around each other. Suddenly, Leonora cried:

"Take me with you, Filip. Oh, take me with you!"

He pressed her to him more tightly, gripping her arms until she winced in pain. He let go, then cupped her face in his hands and kissed her tenderly on the lips, on the forehead, on her eyes.

His voice was choked as he said gently, "I can't, Nora. You know that. There is nothing in the world I would rather do. But I can't."

Filip pointed to the river. The temperature was near zero and ice had formed along both banks. But in the middle of the river the current flowed swift and dark and cold.

"We don't have a boat. You would never make it across."

Filip held her close once again, kissed her for the final time. He could feel her warm tears on his cold face. "I swear I will come back and take you the next time." And then they broke apart.

Taking off his shoes, into which had been sewn the precious microfilm, Filip tied them around his neck and crept out onto the ice. He took a last look back and saw Leonora standing on the shore with her father, blowing a kiss to him. For the rest of his life he would never forget her forlorn look, like that of a tiny child tearfully watching his father depart for work, as he did every day, but still not sure of the father's return.

Filip's eyes moistened. Perhaps she could have managed to swim with him across the Morava, he thought. True, she would have encumbered him and endangered his vital mission. But was it right to put the mission before her? His mind filled with such confusing thought, Filip failed to notice the ice thin out as he crawled and before he knew it he fell into the icy water.

He gasped with the cold and swallowed water before recovering himself. Then he started to swim. Soon he could feel numbness creeping over his arms and legs. Sharp pieces of ice afloat in the swirling waters stabbed him. Fighting the swift current that carried him downstream, he had to swim two feet for each foot he narrowed the distance between Slovakia and Austria.

There came the point when he was no longer conscious of

the cold, when he felt strangely warm and sleepy, when he wanted only to close his eyes and rest. That was the danger point. That was death sweeping over the weakened courier, the time when it is easier to die than live.

Again he thought of how his death would hurt the things and people he loved. Now a new idea sustained him. As he reached out with his arms and kicked his feet, he was convinced that a force greater than his own was helping him, that God kept him alive because He intended to use him in some way. How else could Filip explain his luck in eluding the STB at Leonora's house, the strength that carried him through seven days of slow death in the wheat pit, that had enabled him to cross the Morava River time after time under conditions as challenging and dangerous as now?

It was this conviction of a supernatural guidance of his life that revived his flagging stamina and spirit and kept him from yielding to the sweet temptation of death. Certain now that Leonora would never have reached the far shore with him, Filip summoned up the last reserves of his strength and pulled his arms through the water, first one, then the other, steadily, mechanically.

Not until he reached the Austrian shore did it penetrate his consciousness that shots had been fired at him from the Slovak side. Had the guards who shot at him caught Leonora?

In the moment of his triumph, Filip felt dejected and alone.

13. An Inside Job

DR. ANTON HOLY was a brilliant man. To his co-workers at the Research Institute for Plastic Materials in Bratislava, he seemed the epitome of the cold-blooded unemotional scientist. Though still in his twenties, he was known as The Old Man behind his back. His skin was unnaturally dry and he was never known to smile. He spoke slowly and in carefully measured words, and it was obvious that he was thinking all the time his lips moved.

Yet beneath the cold exterior resentment, jealousy and ambition tortured him. Of Slovak peasant stock, he had the native shrewdness of his ancestors. If he was hurt, the wound would never heal. Conscious of the great sacrifices his family had made to pay for his education as a chemist at the Technological University in Bratislava, he was shattered when the farm his parents owned was taken over by the State. Though the farm was anything but prosperous, it had been in the family for generations and it offered his parents a status in the village that vanished when they were forced to become common laborers in a nearby mill.

Outwardly he showed no resentment. But inwardly he seethed. He refused to join the Communist Party. Although he had risen to the post of one of four assistants to the director of the Research Institute, he knew he could never reach the top position without Party membership. This angered him all the more. Occasionally he allowed himself the luxury of imagining the overthrow of the regime, when the Communist di-

292

rector of the Institute would be removed and he, because of his obvious skill, would be named the successor.

The work of the Institute was of vast importance to the Party and to the Government. Each succeeding convention of the Communist Party in Czechoslovakia called for a manifold increase in the production of plastics. In a country of Czechoslovakia's industrial strength and ambition—every bit as much as the Soviet, she was the arsenal of the Communist world—raw materials were consumed greedily, and raw plastics were replacing metals in many facets of weaponry and consumer use. Much of the work in developing new, tougher plastics went on in Dr. Holy's Research Institute.

For awhile, Holy thought of somehow hampering the research. But after considerable self-scrutiny, he decided it would not do much good. Sooner or later he would be caught in the sabotage effort and end up as an unnecessary martyr. He preferred to live.

Perhaps he could defect to the West with all the vital results of the work of the Institute. But then much of the work was yet to be finished and who would continue the research he had already begun? He did not rule out the idea as an ultimate solution, however. It was another reason not to apply for Communist Party membership, a thought he coolly entertained in moments when ambition overcame resentment. As a member of the Party, he knew, he would have difficulty getting a visa to the United States even if he could manage the escape. Only the important Red intelligence agents, or the big fish in the Communist pool, Holy was aware, could defect to the United States without visa problems. He doubted he was important enough to merit the red carpet treatment.

Frustrated as he was, Holy was ripe for picking as a source of scientific data for the Underground. And the man who picked him was no less a personage than Lt. Col. Robert Pokorny, the chief of the State Secret Police, the STB, of Bratislava.

Pokorny was one of the authentic heroes of the Slovak

Underground. During the second World War he fought with the guerilla army against the Nazis. When the war ended, the partisans split into two opposing factions—one run by Communists, the other by Church-inspired anti-Communists. Pokorny's sympathies were with the anti-Communists, but he soon saw the Communists would win out, as they had done in Poland, Hungary and Yugoslavia. So he pretended to side with the Reds and worked his way up to a responsible position in the Communist group that took control of Czechoslovakia by coup d'état in 1948. For his work, he was offered the position of STB chief for Slovakia, subordinate only to the Commissioner of Interior for Slovakia.

It was a cruel and trying choice. He knew if he took the job he could be neither inefficient nor soft lest he arouse suspicion. Yet the post offered too important a chance to aid the anti-Communist Underground to turn down. He accepted. Though he never personally ordered, or even witnessed the torture of enemies of the Communist State, he knew he could not prevent his underlings from employing such time-honored methods of seeking information or confessions or inflicting punishment. Only rarely did he compromise his high office by directly helping individual Underground members. Over the years he gained a reputation for crisp and efficient leadership among fellow Communists.

Only one failure marred his record. This was his inability to capture the enemies of the State who for years had been able to broadcast anti-Communist propaganda over a clandestine radio station right in Bratislava itself. Several times a month, the secret station would come on the air. On holy days, it would urge the citizens of Bratislava to remember St. Cyril and St. Methodius, who brought Christianity to Slovakia a thousand years earlier and had remained ever since symbols of Slovak nationalism.

Or the clandestine station might broadcast the names of apparently harmless citizens throughout Bratislava who were actually spies for the State. Each block in the city had its undercover spy who reported any treasonable words or un-usual goings-on to the secret police, such as the appearance of expensive clothes on an ordinary laborer, which might indicate he was being paid to work against the State. Collaborators in other parts of the country were named, too, by the secret sta-tion. Although the broadcasts did not carry far outside Bratis-lava, the names of the spies were duly noted and passed by courier or by word-of-mouth to the proper area, where other secret radio stations tipped off the local citizenry.

The reason for Pokorny's failure to apprehend the operators of the secret station was simple: Pokorny himself ran the clandestine radio.

With his trusted chauffeur, Pokorny would make recordings of his messages at his home. Sometimes he would speak in a disguised voice, sometimes the chauffeur. Then while his un-marked STB sedan was out prowling the streets of Bratislava, Pokorny would turn on the radio transmitter located in the trunk of the car.

It was obvious to the police that the transmitter was located in Bratislava. Had it been stationary it would have been run down by the police in no time at all. But it was always on the go. To confuse matters further, Pokorny would broadcast in-structions to the two dozen or so other STB cars patrolling the city, sending them every which way, usually away from his own car.

The irony of it all delighted Pokorny: while his disguised voice, berating the Communist regime, was coming over the regular radio, his STB voice was barking out instructions over the police radio, cursing the traitor to the State.

Pokorny and Anton Holy were cousins. They saw each other occasionally for drinks or a meal at a restaurant. Their conversation was usually constrained, for while Pokorny could and did ask Holy about his research, the latter did not feel it proper to ask Pokorny about his STB work. The safest ground, and the one that usually took up most of their dialogue, was about the peasant lives of their youth.

It was while they were discussing their parents that Holy blurted out his resentment at the State for taking away his family's farm. Holy, in a dark mood of self-pity, had indulged in a rare bout of overdrinking and Pokorny, who had a keen insight into the human soul, took him from the bar at which they had met to his own apartment. The STB chief had sensed, even before this latest meeting, that something was troubling his young cousin.

The moment the words were out Holy bit his tongue. Here, in the presence of one of the most powerful men in the State, he had voiced anti-State sentiments. The sudden fear he felt, the sinking feeling in his stomach, sobered Holy up more quickly than any home-made remedy could. But to his surprise, Pokorny did not pounce on him. Instead, the STB chief uttered words of sympathy.

Cryptically, Pokorny said, "There are many like you, in highly placed positions, who feel as you do about the State."

Holy was puzzled. Then it struck him. Pokorny was simply appearing to sympathize with him in order to draw him out. If he fell for the bait, if he uttered any more anti-State remarks, he would be signing his own death warrant.

"I think I had better be going," he said, rising from his chair.

Pokorny smiled enigmatically but said nothing as he showed Holy out.

The young scientist lived in fear the next two weeks, waiting for the director to call him into his office and tell him his services were no longer required. Or maybe even worse. Holy's imagination was beset with fantasies of imprisonment and torture. Even his colleagues remarked on Holy's jumpiness whenever one entered his office. The nervousness was so unlike the cool, calculating assistant director.

Then one day the phone rang in his office. It was Pokorny on the line, full of wisecracks, making no mention of Holy's indiscreet words. "When can we get together?" Pokorny finally asked.

"Just the two of us?" Holy asked incredulously.

"Yes. It's about time we had a heart-to-heart talk. How about my apartment tonight at eight."

Pokorny took Holy into his confidence that night, and Holy in turn spilled all his venom at the State and voiced his frustrated ambitions. Pokorny revealed his role as operator of the clandestine radio station, much to Holy's delight, and then proceeded to the main business of the evening: the time had come to use the radio to pass onto the West the scientific knowledge of the East. And Pokorny had decided to start with the plastics research going on at Holy's institute.

The conference dragged into long hours of the night. When they parted everything was agreed upon. Holy promised to carefully avoid Pokorny in the future. A go-between, the chauffeur of the STB chief, would bring information from Holy to Pokorny.

Holy returned to his laboratories serene once again. Now he was getting back at the State, perhaps hastening the day when it would collapse and he would get his rightful due.

It had been Holy's habit to work often in the evenings, so no one took special notice as he gradually increased the number of days he worked overtime. Around the Institute he had always had the nickname of *bifler,* which roughly translated means a cross between an eager beaver and a workhorse.

As assistant director, Holy had access to all the drawers and safes in the director's office. He would stay in the labs until the last worker in his section went home, then quickly steal into the director's office. Using a camera might be too risky. His eyes were his camera and his memory was his film.

Taking out the files one by one, he studied them on the spot and memorized them until he knew all the formulas. When late at night he left the gates, guarded by sentries, he had nothing whatever to show—no papers, no film. Everything was in his head. At home he would quickly write down what he had learned that day, stuff the papers into an envelope, seal it and put it away. Once a week Pokorny's chauffeur would come to Holy's apartment and pick up the envelope.

Slowly but surely, all the results of the research already completed at the Institute was transferred to Holy's apartment and thence to the West. Each Saturday, Pokorny's secret radio would transmit some anti-Communist message into which Holy's information, in code, was carefully blended. Across the Austrian border in the little town of Hainburg, ten miles from Bratislava, a Slovak refugee would pick up the program on a listening device and send the coded parts on to Vienna. Periodically, couriers from Bratislava would bring changes of code to the Underground contacts in the Austrian capital, just to play it safe, but the Communists never did realize what was going on.

At the end of four months all the worthwhile information in the director's office had been sent to the West. But Holy had become so exhilarated by his success at espionage that he refused to quit. If he sat back and waited for research under way to be completed it might take weeks or months before he had anything new to pass over to Pokorny. So impatient was he that he determined to get hold of incomplete research, partial solutions to scientific problems, and make them available to the West, too, on the assumption that researchers on the other side of the Iron Curtain could build on the start made by Communist scientists.

To further such aims, Holy began courting young ladies who served as laboratory technicians at the Research Institute. He was not the most attractive of men, but as the assistant director of the Institute he was regarded as quite a catch by the women. Being logical about it, he courted the ladies one at a time. He'd date one, take her to a dance or a restaurant, bring her small gifts, such as a bag of oranges, which were a rarity in Slovakia, or a box of chocolates. Never would he raise the question of marriage directly. Instead he would implant the idea deftly in the flattered girl's mind by commenting that he could never marry until he realized his scientific ambitions. And the young lady, excited at the prospect, would piously commend Holy for putting science ahead of marriage.

Once the young lab technician was ensnared, Holy would casually ask her to show him the work she was engaged in. The young ladies, of course, did not initiate research. They merely performed the tests and made the measurements ordered by the scientists under whom they worked. But they usually had a pretty good idea of what their superiors were looking for, and even when they did not, Holy could draw his own conclusions from the information the girls supplied.

Perhaps the elaborate romantic groundwork was not wholly necessary. As an assistant director, Holy's request might have been regarded as not unusual, had he made it directly. The young ladies may even have swallowed a contrived excuse to explain why he did not want them to tell their superiors of his interest in their work. But the preparations were Holy's calculated way of playing it safe, of making sure the girls would cooperate and keep their mouths shut to boot.

One by one, Holy wooed the female technicians, extracting all the information at their disposal, then dropping the current flame for another. He made a point of remaining on friendly terms with the jilted ones, who were too impressed with his position to make a fuss when his attentions waned. Furthermore, they were not anxious for the scientists for whom they worked to learn of their betrayal, though they never really regarded their actions in such strong terms. Actually, over a period of months, Holy gained the reputation among the girls in the Institute as a Casanova and each of the women who had been the object of his attentions gained a certain prestige in the eyes of the others.

Every Friday night Holy passed on research data to Pokorny's chauffeur the STB chief would tape a program in his apartment. Then on Saturday afternoon he would transmit from the station built into his STB car. Things appeared to be going smoothly.

But unknown to Pokorny, the Central Government in Prague had quietly stepped in. The scandal in Bratislava had grown into a national disgrace. That the secret radio was being used to transmit vital scientific data to the West was not even known, so far as the Underground has been able to find out. The revelation of the names of Communist plants and collaborators, to be sure, hindered the STB and reduced the risk of many Underground operations. But the overwhelming impact of the clandestine station was psychological. It was living proof that the spirit of resistance to tyranny could not be snuffed out, that the Communists were not omnipotent after all. Other secret stations flourished in Slovakia, but the existence of one right in the capital city itself, right under the eyes of the regional headquarters of the secret police, stamped it as something special.

Drastic steps had to be taken. A contingent of secret police from Prague, which controlled STB operations in Bohemia and Moravia, the two western regions of Czechoslovakia, was sent to Bratislava by the Ministry of Interior. Had Pokorny known of the move, he would have protested mightily, for the STB in Slovakia was supposedly autonomous and the equal of the STB in the western half of the nation. It was as if the police of New York were sent to California because the law enforcement officers of the latter state could not solve a puzzling case.

After listening to the secret broadcasts for several weeks, the agents from Prague came to the conclusion that a member of the STB was involved. For one thing, the accuracy of the names of Communist informers indicated that someone with access to STB files in Bratislava was feeding information to the broadcasters. For another, the agents found it hard to believe that any station could function within the confines of a city, even one that always seemed to be on the move, and elude trained secret police for so many years—unless, that is, someone was subverting the STB from within.

The agents from Prague could have shown themselves, of course, and ordered all the STB cars searched. But secrecy was essential. If all the members of the secret police learned that one of their number was the villain behind the clandestine radio, the news might eventually leak out. Disgraceful as the secret radio was already proving to the State, the shame would be multiplied many times over if the public was to learn that an official of the STB was involved. Thus open and dramatic steps to flush out the traitor had to be rejected.

Patiently the STB men from Prague observed the comings and goings of their colleagues from Bratislava. Enlisting the cooperation of the Ministry of Interior, the investigators arranged for a series of conferences to be held on Saturday afternoons during the time the broadcasts were usually heard. At these meetings, Interior Ministry officials from Prague would hold seminars on law enforcement, modernized methods of police detection and other perfectly logical topics for groups of STB officers. Never was exactly the same group invited more than once; various permutations and combinations were tried.

Careful records were kept and checked against the operation of the clandestine station. When certain of the conferences were announced several days ahead of time, the secret transmitter broadcast on a different day of the week than Saturday. When certain ones were announced at the last minute, the Underground radio did not transmit at all. The attendance list of each of the meetings in question were checked to see if any one name, if any one STB official of Bratislava, appeared at all the sessions.

One name did without fail. To the amazement, anger and chagrin of the probers, Lt. Col. Robert Pokorny, the chief of the Slovak STB himself, was their man.

The investigators from Prague were now ready to move. At 1 P.M. the following Saturday, just as Pokorny was preparing to take his car from its garage and broadcast, he received an urgent phone call from the Interior Ministry's Bratislava office telling him to report there for an important conference. Pokorny hid the tape he had prepared in his apartment and left for the office, assuming the meeting would be no different from the others he had been attending.

Ironically, the tape that week contained what perhaps would have been Holy's greatest scientific coup. He had got hold of the theories and initial formulas of a plastic material that could withstand both great heat and near-absolute zero cold without losing its shape or physical properties. The work was not quite finished but enough research had been successfully completed to point the way. Into a sealed envelope and then into the hands of Pokorny's chauffeur went the information.

Pokorny must have suspected something was amiss when he saw none of his fellow STB officials at the conference. Only he. But there was nothing he could do except play along and listen to various proposals for improving the efficiency of his group's operation. The advice involved administration and was so innocuous that his suspicions were further raised.

The discussion was prolonged till 3 P.M., long past the time when the secret radio would usually have broadcast. When it was clear there was to be no broadcast that day, the Prague agents arrested Pokorny's chauffeur as he waited in the car in front of the Interior building, forced him at gunpoint to yield the key to the trunk and discovered the incriminating evidence.

Pokorny was never seen again in Bratislava. From usually reliable sources, the Underground learned he was whisked by special plane from the Vajnory airport in the Slovak capital to Prague. There he was tried in secret and executed in secret. The manner of his death was violent and brutal, for he was left to the secret police to kill and the STB does not treat lightly those within its ranks who are traitors. Pokorny was beaten by fist and club into a bloody pulp.

His execution—by hanging according to the official announcement—for unspecified charges of treason against the State was recorded several weeks later in the Communists' organs. No one would ever know of his role in Bratislava's secret anti-Communist radio, or so the Government thought.

But Pokorny was not the only member of the STB, not even the only highly placed official of that organization, who was also a loyal participant in the Underground. Another STB officer passed on the story of Robert Pokorny to the Underground, which took pains to see to it that Pokorny's heroism—and the vulnerability of the Communist rulers that it revealed—did not go unnoticed. By courier, by word of mouth, by secret stations in other parts of Slovakia did Pokorny's exploits become widely known throughout the land.

As for Holy, the logical scientist soon realized what must have happened when Pokorny's chauffeur failed to show up in the next few weeks to collect the envelopes he had prepared. Holy burned the papers he had filled out, calmly took a two-week vacation that was owed him and fled Slovakia across the Morava River. After spending several months in Austria and Germany, he eventually reached the United States where, under another identity, he is now working as a chemist in the research department of one of the country's largest makers of paper products.

14. Flight to the West

TWO MONTHS after he brought the microfilms from Dubnica to Vienna, Filip Polhora was on his way back to Slovakia. This time his assignment was one he had decided upon himself: to bring Leonora back to the West.

Ahead of him lay the prospect of an excellent job in the United States. He looked forward to a life with Leonora free of constant flight and perpetual danger, and a position with a missile-making firm that would enable him to continue the fight against communism in a different way.

In Vienna, Filip stayed at the apartment of Lisa Heinrich, a beautiful young actress. Lisa had no official connection with the Slovak Underground, which was precisely the reason Filip's orders directed him to her. His assignment was so important that, with Anton Sivak's treachery, it was reckoned safer to avoid his usual Underground contacts in the Austrian capital.

Lisa Heinrich was regarded as trustworthy. As a matter of fact, she was a first cousin of none other than Col. Rudolf Muran of Dubnica.

Her apartment on the Schwarzenberg Platz, just a few hundred yards from the Belvedere Palace where the Austrian peace treaty was signed, was furnished in old-fashioned splendor. Filip slept on silk and damask and a crystal candelabra hung from the high ceiling of the huge apartment. Oil paintings purchased with Lisa's earnings as an actress adorned the walls.

The apartment was a perfect stage setting for Lisa. She carried herself with quiet grace and poise, an air of serenity that seemed of a bygone era. Hazel eyes, beneath auburn hair cut short, dominated her intelligent face.

When Filip arrived and she saw his haggard face, testifying clearly to what he had gone through, she put him to bed immediately with a glass of warm milk, warned her maid not to answer the door to anyone she did not know and left for the hospital that was run by her husband, one of the country's best-known physicians.

Even to her husband she did not confide about Filip's mission. She simply told Dr. Heinrich that a friend of her cousin's had fled Slovakia and described Filip's condition.

Under Dr. Heinrich's care and the ministrations of his wife, Filip's strength gradually returned. Security measures were strictly observed. While he was convalescing, he was not allowed outside the apartment and no one except the Heinrichs and their maid and governess could enter the guest room in which he stayed; no outsiders were even told that the Heinrichs had company. Vienna, though no longer an occupied city, was still full of spies and agents of both sides in the Cold War, and violent unexplained deaths of non-Austrian nationals was not uncommon.

In a week, Filip was ready to start talking of his mission. Lisa, meanwhile, arranged to get the microfilm developed and to borrow a projector. The technical details of what Filip had brought from Dubnica were, of course, beyond her ken, but her quick mind easily comprehended the enormous importance of his catch.

The big problem was whom to give the secret data. Other Underground contacts in Vienna were forbidden. The U.S. embassy, or the embassy of another Western country, was the obvious choice, but a direct approach was inadvisable. Austria was now a neutral country and if an Allied diplomat was caught dealing with an Iron Curtain Underground, international repercussions would surely follow.

Though Filip did not know it then, the State Department would have ruled out direct contact with the Slovak Underground for yet another reason. Since Woodrow Wilson's day, United States policy has been to support a unified Czechoslovakia; by dealing with the Slovak Underground, which generally favors a separate Slovakia, the State Department feared it would seem to imply support for Slovak independence.

Lisa had the answer. She would summon Stefan Ilok, whom she had met years before at a party in Vienna after her first big stage success at the Burgtheater. They had seen each other frequently after that whenever Ilok traveled to Vienna, and he became fast friends with Dr. Heinrich, too.

Ilok was now in business in the United States, as far as Lisa knew, but she was also vaguely aware that he had some sort of connection with the Slovak Underground. Filip quickly endorsed Lisa's suggestion, and the young actress, acting on impulse, decided to place an overseas call to him rather than write.

"I shall fly in this Saturday," Ilok promptly agreed. Though Lisa was reluctant to speak other than in the most general terms of Filip's information, Ilok knew she would not have called unless she had something of the utmost importance.

With him, Ilok brought two men. One was Benjamin Lee, the Washington representative of a large American aircraft manufacturing firm that was putting more and more of its facilities into missiles and rockets. Lee was a hard-shelled, cautious type whose knowledge of U.S. weapons and defense planning equipped him to assess the value of Filip's data. The other was Howard K. Low, a New York investment banker of un-bankerlike enthusiasm and exuberance. If Lee's company was to undertake any new projects as a result of what Filip revealed, financier Low would be ready with the capital.

Filip, meanwhile, spent the intervening days, and part of the nights, once again putting down on paper everything he could remember from the files of the Military Technical Institute. Putting pencil to paper for hours on end served to keep his mind from dwelling continually on Leonora.

On the Saturday that Ilok arrived with Lee and Low, Lisa

arranged for them to meet for supper at Vienna's famous Hotel Sacher. The conversation opened with idle pleasantries, but Filip was too pent up to let that continue for long. He had already waited ten days in Vienna for this moment. In a low voice that could not be heard at the next table, he outlined in a stilted but unhesitant English the type of data he had ferreted out of Dubnica; the details would come later.

From the very start of his revelations, Filip held his listeners enthralled. So absorbed, in fact, that they did little justice to the *coq au vin* and *Sacher torte,* the celebrated chocolate sponge cake, placed before them. Ilok could tell from the intense look that replaced the gentle skepticism on Ben Lee's dour face that the Underground had struck paydirt.

From the hotel the group adjourned to Lisa's apartment where Filip projected the microfilm on one of the few bare spots on the walls, interpreting the words for Ben Lee and Howard Low. Pausing only for a round of cognac, Filip then began dictating all he had written down on paper the preceding days into a recording machine the visitors from America had brought with them. He spoke in Slovak; Ilok, meanwhile, whispered a running translation into the ears of his two friends.

Long into the night Filip went on. After breakfast the next morning, he recalled other things that had slipped his mind and put them on tape, too.

It was an amazing *tour d'horizon.* Filip told of the intermediate-range missile-launching sites in Czechoslovakia and other satellites, and of the portable launching system the Communists had devised that did away with the need for fixed pads, as were used by larger ground-launched American missiles at that time. The location and description of defense plants in Slovakia; the Communists' spectacular achievements in new high-temperature steels and other heat-resistant materials; the friction and jealousies that prevailed in joint ventures among Soviet and satellite scientists—all these Filip recounted to his awed and silent listeners.

When he was finally through, Howard Low stared at him

hard and long, then shook his head as if in disbelief. "Filip," he said in a voice lowered to hold emotion in check, "I think you may have helped give us in the West the kick in the pants we need."

Shortly thereafter, the information Filip smuggled out found its way to the Pentagon, where it fit into the mosaic of bits and pieces furnished by other sources. Further verification of the extent of the Soviet's capacity to destroy Western bases in Europe and Africa with intermediate missiles was passed along to the House Appropriations Committee by Congressman Daniel J. Flood, a Pennsylvania Democrat from the Wilkes-Barre area, which is heavily populated with Slovaks who work in the coal mines. It was not long afterwards that the U.S. began closing down bases in North Africa, and Congress voted extra funds to speed development of the Polaris submarine and intercontinental missiles to be fired from the United States, thus reducing the West's vulnerability in Europe to Soviet weapons.

For Filip, the success of the mission brought a more personal result. So impressed with the courier was Lee that he offered Filip a job in America as his personal assistant. Among other things, Filip would help Lee analyze the information the firm received from various sources on weapons development and research by the Communists.

The decision was an agonizing one for Filip. He sat there quietly in Lisa's apartment, first torn one way, then another. A decade of his life had been invested in fighting for Slovakia against her Red rulers and one does not turn his back so easily on the actions of his manhood.

"The Underground keeps the spark of hope alive," General Duplin's words came back to Filip. "And if we were to quit the fight, hope would vanish and the people would succumb in their hearts to the Communists."

But the mesmerizing physical presence of Duplin no longer swayed Filip. And each time he saw Leonora, patiently waiting for him, and then had to leave her, the urge to go to the

West grew stronger. Now that her house had been kept under Red surveillance, her life might be in danger. Besides, he would still be using his considerable experience and talents on the West's behalf.

"I accept your offer with gratitude," Filip finally told Lee. "But there is something I must do first. It will take me back to Slovakia. One final mission, and I will join you in the United States."

"A woman?" Low asked perceptively.

"Perhaps." Filip smiled but said nothing more.

Filip did not go back immediately. First he had to regain fully his stamina, for the task of bringing Leonora back would call for all his physical as well as mental adroitness. He would be driven to the Prater, Vienna's largest park, where he would run and run until his feet were leaden and his lungs ready to burst. He would swim in the indoor pool at the Diana Bad, a public bathhouse, always with someone trusted to watch over him. Later, Lisa took him to Carinthia in the Austrian Alps, where her family owned a small estate. There Filip skied over the roughest terrain, there he ran and fought with dogs.

But everywhere he saw Leonora's face before him. In the snow, in the pine trees, in the hills. Why was there no word from her? It seemed as if the earth had swallowed her.

He would have liked to strengthen his body further, but he could wait no longer. Shortly before Christmas he returned to Vienna. To go back to Slovakia, he would need new identity papers. Contrary to his orders, he contacted the Underground cell he usually worked with in the Austrian capital, much to the surprise of the members of the group, who had not even known Filip was in Vienna. Olga Gazdova, Stefan Zubak and the others urged him to delay his return, for the whole border area around the Morava River had been reinforced by contingents of the dread STB, the secret police.

But Filip, eager now to build a new life for himself and Leonora in the West, was not to be dissuaded.

At least, the Underground cell decided, Filip would not follow his old routes. Communist police would be waiting for him in Zahorie, no doubt. In fact, the entire Slovak border had become too dangerous for him. It was resolved that Filip would take the long way around to Levary, crossing from Austria to Bohemia in Western Czechoslovakia, then make his way to Slovakia.

Before Filip left, he attended a New Year's Eve party in Olga Gazdova's home in Vienna, where many of the Slovak exiles gathered. Perhaps the knowledge that he was about to undertake his last mission in Slovakia made him too sure of himself, too relaxed to be cautious. Perhaps he drank too much. Whatever the reason, Filip spoke too readily of the route he would take once he was inside Slovakia, although he did not realize his mistake at the time.

After all, he was among his own people and he had no reason to doubt any of them. The wine flowed, merriment reigned and their curiosity seemed only natural to Filip. Not until days later when he harvested the consequences of his loose talk did he recall that one of the exiles, a small dark man named Jan Magala who lived off the other Slovaks, had remained sober while the rest drank, had seemed a bit more inquisitive than the others.

The memory of that party and his loose tongue there would haunt him forever.

On January 2, 1958, Filip left Vienna with a sense of expiation of guilt, for this trip was for Leonora who had waited so long and suffered so much for his sake. He took a train to Gmund in Austria, near the Bohemian border, and from there, set out on foot for Ceské Budějovice in Southern Bohemia, a trip that took him through the mountains and forests that spanned both sides of the Iron Curtain.

To the person who sees the barbed wire barriers for the first time, the view is awesome. Three rows of wire greet him. The first is five feet high. Three feet further back is the most frightening of the wire fences, the one that is electrified. Almost seven feet tall, the middle barrier is the most closely knit with wires running not only horizontally, as in the other two fences, but vertically, too, so that the result resembles a grid. Set another three feet back is the third wire barrier, much like the first. Behind the Iron Curtain are watchtowers some twenty to twenty-five feet high.

To the experienced courier, the wire curtain is somewhat less awe-inspiring. Penetrating it takes courage, coolness under fire and a capacity for split-second timing. But having crossed the Curtain a number of times, the courier comes to regard it as just one of many obstacles, the most dangerous perhaps, but still only one of a number he will encounter on a mission.

Actually, the middle fence is rarely electrified by day, when few people dare escape under the watchful eyes of the border guards. Night is the time for breaching the Iron Curtain. Even in the darkness, the central barrier is not fed electricity constantly, for the expense would be enormous. Sections may be electrified at random at night, or the switch may be thrown when border guards discover that some unauthorized person is near the Curtain, or when an escapee steps or trips over one of the wires scattered throughout the border area and sets off a warning signal.

The particular section of barbed wire Filip broke through that night was not electrified, but had it been he was prepared to cope with that menace, too. From Underground contacts at Gmund, he had learned in which horizontal poles of the electrified fence fuses were located that could be disconnected to shut off the current for the sections of the fence nearby.

The Underground had also provided Filip with a map showing the location of the minefields and signal wires in the area near the Iron Curtain, information furnished by Underground members planted among the border guards. The details of the map had been memorized by Filip, yet the possibility always remained that a mistake had been made, or the location of the mines or tripwires changed. His teeth clenched and body tense, he alternately crawled or sprinted when the map showed large areas free of danger, until at last he saw the woods three miles into Bohemia that signaled the end of the minefields.

When Filip's train arrived in Bratislava it was night again. Straight to his hideout, a large house in Zahradnicka Street, he went. But from some distance away he saw a group of men in front of the house. They were dressed in plain clothes, but the casual way they were milling about the place was an obvious sign to Filip they were police, probably the secret police.

He turned to walk away. But it was too late. He had been spotted.

"There he is."

Filip ran. They called on him to stop, and then started to shoot. He dodged around a corner, into the basement of a building, out a window and through a back street. He slowed down his pace as he approached a main thoroughfare. So far he was in luck. The police could not be seen behind him.

Hailing a cab, he ordered the driver in a voice loud enough for bystanders to hear, "Take me to the railroad station, quick. I've got to catch a train."

But once he entered the cab and the driver started up, Filip drew his gun and poked the barrel against the back of the driver's neck. "Don't go to the station," the courier said. "Turn north and drive toward Pezinok."

Calmly, the driver protested he did not have enough gasoline.

"I don't care about that," Filip said. "If you want to live, drive as far as you can."

Out of Bratislava the cab headed, until after several miles it reached a point where the nearby forest ran right down to the road. There was no sign of human habitation and Filip ordered the driver to stop the cab and let him out.

Reaching into his pocket, the courier brought out a handful of bills and offered them to the cabbie. But the driver shook his head.

"If you were an ordinary criminal fleeing the police, you would not offer me money," he told Filip. "So you must be fighting the Communists. In that case, I don't want your money. You are a brave man and I am glad I could help you."

They shook hands and the driver turned back to Bratislava.

Alone once again, Filip walked into the woods, still trembling from the excitement of the escape. After an hour on foot, Filip could keep his eyes open no longer. He threw himself down on a bed of pine needles, buried his face in his forearm and tried to keep the discouraging thoughts away.

Would he ever reach Levary and Leonora? Would she be there waiting for him? How did the STB find out about his hideout in Bratislava?

Filip was quite certain that Anton Sivak knew nothing of the house on Zahradnicka Street. But who then could have tipped off the enemy? As sleep invaded his consciousness, Filip had the hazy recollection of talking about the hideout quite recently to someone. But who, and where?

He awoke at dawn, unable to control the slight shivering of his body in the icy air. He knew he must go some place where he could warm his body, where he could relieve his hunger. A farmer's house, perhaps, if he could find a reliable one. He was out of the border zone now, where most of the farmers were loyal to the regime, and there was a good chance he might find a peasant who sympathized with the Underground. Farmers everywhere behind the Iron Curtain, he knew, were the most discontented group.

On the outskirts of the first village he came to, two small farms straddled the dirt road. Well, one was probably as good as the other, Filip thought, as he went around the back of the farm to his right. A few chickens that scrambled away as he approached were the only sign of life.

He knocked at the kitchen door, which was opened almost immediately by a slight but wiry old man. The farmer looked at the haggard, trembling visitor before him calmly, then said politely, "Yes?"

"Praised be Jesus Christ!" Filip said. If the farmer was not a Communist, then chances were he was sympathetic to the Church. "I have come looking for work," Filip lied, "in return for food and lodging."

The farmer stared at him long and hard before replying. "We will see about the work later. But come in and sit yourself down and join us in breakfast."

The old peasant's eyes, which seemed to look right through him, made Filip nervous. But the smell of bacon and coffee wafting to the door from the kitchen was too much to resist. He entered, nodded to the farmer's wife, accepted her offer of a wash-up, and sat down with the two elderly people at the table. Weak as he was, Filip reasoned, the two would be no match for him if it came to that.

Wolfing down the food hungrily until he noticed the farmer peering at him with those penetrating eyes, Filip slowed down his eating. Not a word had been said during the meal, which increased his anxiety.

"I can do any kind of farm work," he volunteered, as he downed a second cup of coffee.

Bluntly, the farmer said, "You are running away from something." There was no trace of a question in his voice, nor any sign of fear before the fugitive.

Filip hesitated momentarily, then decided to admit he was in flight. But instead of telling the truth, he concocted a wild story in which he lost his job, could not get a new one and was forced to steal food from the State warehouse to feed his wife and three children, but was caught in the act and somehow managed to elude his pursuers.

All the while he listened, the farmer nodded his head and smiled. It was a curious smile, though, Filip noted, and he was not at all sure the farmer believed a word of what he had been saying.

Again, abruptly, without warning, the farmer struck home. "You're the one who escaped from Bratislava, the one the

314

radio says is a tool of the Western Imperialists and a traitor to the State."

If he had kept his wits about him, perhaps Filip could have brazened out his lie. But he was in no condition to think clearly. He leaped from his chair, knocking it over behind him, and pulled out his revolver, pointing it at the farmer.

The woman screamed but the farmer stared at the gun without apparent concern. His eyes held a look of fatalism. They had seen much agony and sorrow and now they seemed to say, Whatever will be, will be.

To Filip's surprise, the old farmer chuckled.

"Son," he said, "you don't have to tell me anything. If you are an enemy of the Communists, you are welcome here. As our guest, not as a farmhand."

Filip's eyes were riveted on the farmer's face. Was it a trick to put him off his guard? No, the courier became convinced, here was an honest man if he had ever seen one.

Filip lowered his gun. But just to make sure, he kept it in plain view tucked into his belt.

The farmer smiled broadly now. "You are a lucky man," he said. "My neighbor across the way is a Communist, one of the few in the village. Had you gone into his house . . ." The shrug of the shoulder was eloquent.

As they sat and talked, the last lingering doubts of the farmer's trustworthiness vanished from Filip's mind. The farmer's story was a familiar one. Pressured by the arrogant agents of the Farmers Cooperative, who had never done any farming themselves, into giving up his ancestral farm to the State, he refused, only to be given quotas that increased each year until they were impossible to meet. This would be his last year of independent farming, and then the State would take over, and he and his wife would till the land that once was theirs for barely marginal wages.

"But you are not doomed yet!" Filip exclaimed. Impulsively he reached into his pocket and brought out two hundred American dollars, part of what Howard Low had given him in

315

Vienna. "You can hold onto your farm a little longer if you have enough money to buy more pork, and eggs, and wheat and potatoes to meet your quota. Here, this is for you."

Over the farmer's protests, Filip pushed the money on him. The farmer's eyes now lost that look of calm acceptance and were filled with tears of gratitude. The money could delay the inevitable only temporarily, but behind the Iron Curtain each bit of joy, each day of independence was to be seized.

American dollars were in great demand by the Czechoslovak Government for international trading. They could not be spent by individual citizens, many of whom received money from relatives in the United States, but were traded in for Czech currency at State banks or State-owned stores known as Tuzex. For Filip, carrying American currency was quite dangerous, for if he had been caught in any compromising situation the bills would have stamped him a Western agent. Yet he usually carried U.S. dollars with him on missions, along with Czech currency, for they made the best bribe.

"How can we repay you?" the farmer asked Filip.

Though he had handed over the money out of generosity with no thought of reward, Filip spoke impulsively again. "You can, if you will take me in your carriage to Levary or close to it across the mountains."

The trip would be a slow and dangerous one, for much of the fifty miles went over winding roads through the Little Carpathians. Moreover, the farmer, whose name was Gerdelan, would have to explain away two days of absence from his farm.

Yet, without an instant of uncertainty, Gerdelan replied. "Why not? When do you want to go?"

"Let me rest here one day," Filip said, "and then we can go tomorrow."

That night as he lay in bed, thinking of Leonora, Filip felt luck was turning again in his favor. By the same time the next day he would see Leonora again, hold her in his arms, at the house of sweet memory. And then he would bring her to the West. With such delightful visions, he fell asleep smiling.

It was dark when old Gerdelan's carriage drew into the outskirts of Levary. The farmer drove into a narrow lane, where there was no sign of life, and stopped. Alighting from the carriage, he walked onto the street that ran perpendicular to the lane, peered in both directions, but saw no police or any other inhabitants. It was the supper hour.

Hurrying back to his hay-laden carriage, he mumbled out loud, "It's time to feed the horses." Looking around one more time to make sure no one was watching, he drew back the canvas cover from the pile of hay.

"It's all right," he whispered as he lifted some hay.

Filip quickly arose, took the grey cover under which he had been hiding and draped it over the two horses standing in the chilly air, while Gerdelan gave them their feed. A quick handshake, some whispered words and Filip was off.

His heart was throbbing as he left Gerdelan. Soon the familiar church that towered over Levary came into view; its huge clock had just sounded 8 P.M. Halting at each intersection to listen for sentinels, finding none but feeling uneasy at their absence, Filip moved on until suddenly he saw Leonora's house.

It was completely dark, inside and out.

"Perhaps they're already sleeping," Filip thought, but the idea carried little conviction. Had he come all the way in vain? He quickened his pace, jumped over the fence into the little garden in front of the house, ran to the side where the room in which Leonora slept was located, not even bothering in his haste to check if any police were waiting in ambush.

His hand was trembling in anticipation as he raised it to rap on Leonora's window. But then, before he lowered his hand, he saw the white paper on the side door of the house. Approaching it, he noticed the paper had been stuck to the

317

door with wax; three corners were still firmly attached to the wood, the fourth flapping loose.

In the darkness he could not make out the writing, but he realized, with a sudden sense of foreboding, that the paper must have been an official one. Though no wind blew, Filip felt as if he had been struck by an icy blast. He staggered back, afraid to read.

But read he must. He pulled a box of matches from his pocket and tried to light one. His hands shook and he had to light another match, then a third before he could make out the words:

THIS IS ENEMY PROPERTY
CONFISCATED BY THE STATE.

Leonora had been lost! His life suddenly seemed to lose its meaning.

Out of force of habit, he pulled himself back to her window and rapped on it. It was useless, he knew at heart, but so many times had he knocked in the past and so many times had Leonora rushed to the window to answer that for a brief second he almost convinced himself she would come to him again. It was, in any case, a symbol of his loyalty to Leonora.

There was no answer to his faint knocking.

Perhaps he had not rapped loud enough. Perhaps she was in, but did not hear. Perhaps only her father had been arrested and declared an enemy of the people and she had been allowed to remain. Frantically he searched the ground around him until he found a stone. With it he tapped three times on the window.

A dull echo came back.

Again he tried like a man possessed, louder than before.

The silence seemed to mock him.

What was he knocking for? Why was he waiting here? Did he want to attract the police? The idiocy of his actions struck him as he recovered his senses. Watching the windows for a sign of life, he made his way toward the front of the house where, on the door, was the same official notice sealed in wax.

The words filled him with rage and despair. His hands clenched and unclenched and he wished at that moment that he could kill those who had desecrated the sanctuary of his love. But all he could do to relieve his frustration was tear off the official notices, an act that brought him little relief.

Suddenly, from the street, there came the sound of steps. His hand slipped into his pocket, wrapped its fingers around the handle of his gun. At least he could shoot down the imposters of justice.

But it was only two women in heavy cloaks. Filip put his gun back and flattened himself against the side of the house. As they passed, he could make out their words.

"Poor Leonora," one said, "now without mother and father."

"Such a fate," the other agreed, "such a cruel fate."

But that meant she was alive! Filip ran after them unmindful of the danger of being seen, but the two women, frightened by this wild-looking man running toward them, quickened their pace. They were no match for the frantic courier, however, and he quickly caught up to them and blocked their way.

"What do you know about Leonora?" he demanded. His disheveled look terrified them, but they could see he was no servant of the State.

"Tell me quickly," Filip implored. "Please tell me."

The taller of the two ladies looked around first to be sure no one was listening, then told Filip what she knew. Leonora's father had been killed two months earlier when he was caught with an Underground agent near the Morava. (It must have been only days after he had left Levary, Filip figured, before he had had a chance to send word to the Underground to avoid Karol Danko's house for a while.) Leonora, meanwhile, had not been arrested but had left the house after it was taken over by the State.

"But where is she, tell me," urged Filip impatiently.

"We only know that she ran away," the tall woman shrugged. "Where, no one knows."

As if she had second thoughts about talking to the distraught stranger, the woman grasped the hand of her companion and pulled her away. Filip stood in silent thought as they left. Walking quickly down the street, the women turned for one last look at the lonely man standing in despair in front of Leonora's house, then disappeared around the corner.

Where would she have gone? Her only aunt, the one in Bratislava, had died a year before. Filip's mind raced over the narrow range of possibilities as he hurried through the streets back toward Gerdelan and the carriage.

Of course, he thought, how silly of me, how utterly silly!

To Gerdelan, "Uncle, can you take me to Malacky? I must take the first express to Prague. I believe there is one at ten-forty. Can we make it?"

"It's not so far," Gerdelan said after a moment's calculation. "Besides the horses are fed and rested."

Filip resumed his position under the cover on top of the hay. He had suddenly recalled that months before, during one of his brief idylls in Levary, he told Leonora that if anything happened to her father she was to go to Prague, to the home of Jan Baar's cousin, and wait for Filip there. He could not be sure that Leonora would remember the advice, given in a moment when there was no danger, when they were speaking of their love and the future. But it was the best Filip could think of as he lay on the hay.

Gerdelan bought the ticket at the Malacky depot for Filip, who was the last man to get on the train. For reasons of economy, the train was not lighted, except for the dining car, and most of the passengers were already asleep. Filip found a seat and tried to calm himself down.

By five-thirty the next morning, he was in Prague. He ordered a taxi to take him to Baar's cousin's house, then changed his mind. It would be cruel to awaken Leonora at such an early hour, he thought, and besides he could do with a bit of a rest and freshening up before he saw her. So he ordered the driver instead to another hideout in Prague, reflecting ironically as he traveled that he could have saved time and anxiety had he gone directly to the Czech capital across the Bohemian woods instead of the long way round via Levary.

At his hideout, Filip bathed, slept till noon, then groomed himself so that he looked like any other burger. A cab ride brought him to the apartment of Jan Baar's cousin, which Baar himself often used as a base on his Underground missions. Baar's cousin lived there with her husband.

Tensely, Filip alighted from the cab two blocks from his target, walked up and down the street several times on the lookout for police, then approached the house cautiously. Even then he waited in the shadows of a nearby doorway for twenty minutes, watching the passersby. At last he swung into the hall of the house, ran up the first flight of stairs expectantly and scratched on the door softly.

An attractive woman in her mid-thirties opened it. "We were expecting you, Filip, to warn you," the words tumbled out in hushed tones. She closed the door quickly behind the courier.

"To warn me? Why?" Filip asked as he was ushered into the living room.

"The STB were here two days ago and again yesterday. They said they wanted to see my husband, Frank, but they searched the whole place after I told them he was still at work. Frank is certain they were expecting to find someone else."

Filip sat down, stunned. This was the last thing he had expected. Only then did it dawn on him the extent to which he had been betrayed. He remembered it all clearly, now— how he had mentioned the hideout at Bratislava and the one in which he now sat, at the New Year's Eve party in Vienna, how one man, Jan Magala, was not drinking like the rest, but instead asked question after question, in casual fashion to be sure, about his hiding places. And Filip, stupidly, unthinkingly, had told him!

The other hideout in Prague, the one from which he had just come, he had not mentioned that night in Vienna. It was just pure luck that he had not. And that one had gone unmolested by the Communists. That was the final bit of proof that someone in the Vienna cell was a traitor. Word would have to be sent back.

Then, gingerly, afraid of what the answer would be, Filip asked, "Is Leonora here?"

"She is," Margita Jakubik said, and Filip exhaled a sigh of relief. "She went to do some shopping. She should be back by four, when Frank will return. She wasn't here when the police came to search, thank God. She . . ."

Margita was interrupted by a knock at the door, a peremptory knock. The police again? Where could he hide?

Noticing some wool and knitting needles lying loose on a table, Filip quickly picked them up and threw the bundle into Margita's lap. "I'm your customer," he whispered urgently, and went boldly to the door, while she pretended to be knitting busily. In Slovakia, consumer goods come at a premium and it is quite customary for women to supplement family income by knitting socks, sweaters, scarves and other woolen goods at home.

It was the police. Two men in green barged past Filip, one shouting at Margita, "Is your husband not yet at home?"

"He has a late shift today," she answered. "Why don't you come tomorrow. He will be here for sure," she said quietly as she straightened out the knitting in front of her apparently impatient customer.

Interrupting the conversation, Filip said grudgingly, "All right, Mrs. Jakubik, but if the gloves are not ready tomorrow, I will not accept them or pay you for your work. Goodbye." He turned and walked out.

"You see how fresh this gentleman is?" Mrs. Jakubik commented to the police. "What does he think I am, a machine?" She grimaced at the door as Filip slammed it shut.

For the moment Filip was in the clear. It seemed obvious

that Frank Jakubik and his wife were being allowed to go free only until he would be caught in their home, then all three would be taken into custody. And what of Leonora? If she was there, too, when Filip was captured, she would be arrested, too.

From a doorway across the street, he saw the two policemen leave. Leonora was due back at four, almost two hours away. Instead of returning to the apartment, Filip decided to buy a ticket at a nearby movie theater and lose himself in the dark anonymous crowd there.

Filip's mind covered all the angles as the Russian movie flickered on the screen. According to Margita Jakubik, the police had come to their apartment only one time each day, ostensibly looking for her husband. They might frighten the Jakubiks into flight, Filip reasoned, if they came more often, so there was an excellent chance the police would not come back again that day. In that case, he would meet Leonora and take her away immediately from the hornet's nest.

Impatiently he fidgeted in his seat waiting for the fourth hour after noon to arrive. The minutes passed too slowly for him. He longed to hold Leonora close to him again, to whisper words of reassurance into her ear. At last four o'clock came and he left the movie house with relief.

He walked at an even pace, though he wanted to run, making sure to appear no different from the citizens strolling around him. As he approached Jakubik's house, he automatically filed the street scene in his mind for future reference. A playground dominated the center of the square on which the house was set. Snow had begun falling and children were throwing snowballs at each other. It was a peaceful scene, deceptively so.

Once inside the apartment house, Filip rushed up the stairs, rushed past Margita Jakubik at the door, rushed into the living room.

This time he was not disappointed. There Leonora stood, her eyes aglow. His powerful shoulders dipped, his arms went around her waist and he lifted her off her feet, up, up, until his head was buried in her chest. All without a word. Then, he lowered her gently and they stood quietly looking at each other.

Unashamedly, he drew himself on his knees and, kneeling before her, he sobbed, "Leonora, oh, Leonora, I will never leave you any more!"

He pressed his face against her thigh as she caressed his hair tenderly. She could feel his chest heaving. Gently unclasping his hands from behind her waist, she lowered herself to the floor next to him and they sat there, the two of them, crying, unconscious of any other presence in the apartment.

"My poor Filip, my Filip," Leonora cried. "Now we have only each other. Nothing else matters. Just us."

From the well of their recollections of past tragedy their words came. For Filip the chains of his sense of duty and responsibility to country had been burst at least temporarily, and he cursed the fate that seemed to contrive against their happiness.

But now he was in the hands of the beloved woman who had waited for him patiently. "Today, darling, we will leave, today and not tomorrow, never to leave each other again," he whispered.

She took her white handkerchief and dried his eyes, then hers. They stood up, he with sadness still etched on his face, she with a smile, faint at first, but growing more radiant on her beautiful face with the promise of a new life ahead of her. Her happiness was infectious and soon Filip's face was creased with laughter. He held her close and kissed her, then turned around abruptly, remembering again where they were.

"Where is Margita?" he asked.

"She wanted us to be alone. She is in the bedroom."

As they walked toward the bedroom, they heard a key turning in the front door and Frank Jakubik, a tall saturninely handsome man, came in. He had never seen Filip before and he eyed him suspiciously. Before he could say anything, Leonora announced:

"Frank, this is my Filip."

They measured each other with long glances, liked what they saw, then shook hands warmly.

"Margita," Jakubik shouted, "where are you hiding? Bring two goblets for Filip and me and let's have a shot of good strong Slivovitz. No Prague beer for us, but good Slovak Slivovitz."

While the two men drank and exchanged reminiscences, the two women busied themselves in the kitchen. Leonora, with her coat on, rushed passed Filip and Frank, explaining that she was going to the store to get some of the famous Prague frankfurters for supper.

"Don't stay out long, Nora," Filip shouted to her back.

She had been gone hardly five minutes when a sharp knocking on the door brought the conversation between the two men to an abrupt end.

"The police," Frank said.

"Hide Filip in the closet," Margita proposed, running in from the kitchen, but Filip did not approve. He looked out the window at the back of the house. It was still snowing but the way looked clear.

"I will leave through the back," Filip whispered to the Jakubiks. "Perhaps I can catch Leonora on the street." He opened the window, paused briefly to measure the long drop, then jumped, bending his knees as he fell to cushion the shock. He rose unhurt, gun in hand, ready to shoot it out if the police stopped him. But there were no troopers to be seen. Over a fence he vaulted, then ran behind two houses in back into a cobblestoned lane.

In the meantime, the police were searching Frank Jakubik's apartment once more.

"We saw a man who looked like Filip Polhora enter this house," one of the two troopers insisted. They were not the same police who had been at the apartment earlier.

"We know nobody named Filip Polhora, I swear it," Frank said.

"You can look in every room," Margita volunteered. "There is no one here, and there has been no one."

When they finished poking around the apartment, Frank said indignantly, "I told you he was not here. You have torn the house apart. I am a peaceful man and I have to be at work early tomorrow morning. Put everything back where you found it, or I shall report you to the officials in the morning."

"Shut up," one of the police retorted hotly. "We know what we are after. Just go ahead and report us if you dare."

In a rage now, Frank shot back, "Out with you, and let me eat my supper and get some sleep."

The air of injured innocence almost worked. Momentarily, the police were ready to believe nothing was amiss. But then one of them, noticing the back window still ajar, peered out and saw footprints underneath in the snow. They were obviously freshly made.

"Ha!" he exclaimed, a satisfied grin on his face, "I suppose you can explain that." He pulled Frank abruptly over to the window and pointed down.

Frank looked sternly at his wife.

"So," he shouted, his eyes blazing, "Your lover has been here again!"

Margita began to weep. She clutched at her husband.

"Please! Please!" she cried. "Don't be angry, Frank. He came just a little while before you did, but I told him to leave me, I told him I didn't want to see him again, ever. I promised you I would break off with him, and I did tell him to go away, Frank! I did send him away, please believe me!"

Frank stared at her coldly, obviously not believing a word she said. The police watched in silent fascination.

Margita's eyes pleaded with Frank, but to no avail. Breaking into deep uncontrollable sobs, she ran to one of the policemen and threw herself into his arms. Utterly confused, the trooper put his gun away and patted her back gently. "There, there," he soothed her.

Just then they heard shots from the street. Filip, failing to find Leonora, had circled back to the front of Jakubik's house again, hoping to waylay her as she returned. But unknown to him, STB men, the secret police, had accompanied the uniformed SNB troopers to the house. Across the square they had been hiding, in the recessed baroque archways of the former patrician homes now converted into apartment dwellings, ever since Filip entered Jakubik's house shortly after 4 P.M. that afternoon. From their protected positions, they opened fire on Filip.

Only one thing could save him, Filip saw in a twinkling. He ran straight into the playground, where the children were still tossing snowballs at each other, and stationed himself in the middle of the youngsters, brandishing his gun. They looked up at him in horror and he was ashamed of himself for endangering their lives. But the instinct of self-preservation was too strong.

"Don't move," he ordered the children, trying to keep his voice as gentle as possible.

"Don't shoot," came a shout from the STB men across the street.

"Come out, you can't get away," another loud voice was heard.

Filip stood his ground. Their warnings and curses beat on him like hailstones, but the police did not fire. Even the Communists would not risk hitting innocent children.

Yet Filip could not remain here forever. One of the smaller children, perhaps too young to know what was going on, drifted away from the group. The other children watched the tot walk away, then turned their eyes back to Filip to see what he would do. Filip could do nothing.

Another slipped away, then a third. In his budding panic, he even forgot Leonora.

There was still one more chance. Only four children were

left around him, too scared to risk leaving him. One of these he swept up suddenly in his arms and whispered to sooth him, "Don't be afraid. We can play Indians."

The other two boys scattered and Filip was left alone with his young hostage. Still the STB men did not fire.

Out of the playground he walked, down the street toward the main thoroughfare, carrying the youngster. If only he could reach the crowded boulevard, he might lose himself in the mass of people.

But the same thought occurred to his pursuers. From behind their safe positions they came hurrying after him. Afraid they would lose him, the STB men opened fire again, child or no child.

Filip whirled to face his pursuers. At last they were out in the open, half a dozen of them. He fired quickly, to the left, to the right, and two of the secret police dropped in their tracks. The others ran again for cover.

Now he dropped the child gingerly to the ground, patted his head and sent him off with a gentle push on the backside. Then he ran, bullets flying close, down the last few yards of the side street, onto the busy avenue. He waded into a crowd of people, which quickly broke apart when they saw the gun he waved, then re-formed when he had passed. Dodging and weaving he went, always sure to be near to a group of people to discourage any shooting at him.

A streetcar clattered down the street, stopped to pick up passengers, then started up again. On the dead run Filip lunged at the pole of the rear platform, clutched it and lifted himself up before the car had gotten up a full head of steam. For several blocks he rode it, putting more distance between himself and the two STB men still afoot in pursuit, their way hampered by the crowds.

Then off Filip jumped when he caught sight of an empty cab on another side street. Putting his gun away, he entered the cab, caught his breath momentarily and said to the driver, "Olsanske cemetery."

The driver turned around and looked at him questioningly.

"It's the anniversary of my mother's death," Filip explained, and the driver started off. Through the rear window, Filip could see no sign of the STB men.

In the misty moonlight, Filip rubbed his eyes. He had dozed off for a few hours. As he came to, he looked around for the good farmer Gerdelan's carriage, expecting to find himself in the hay, under the covers, on the way to Leonora's house in Levary. But there was no hay, no carriage, only a dark and empty graveyard. The memory of what had happened at Levary, and afterwards, returned to him in a tumble of images, as if he were having a confused dream.

He closed his eyes again to clear his picture screen of a mind, then opened them. The watch on his wrist that beat its steady tick-tock as he held it up to his ear, the wetness on his face quickly convinced him what he had gone through was not a dream, but a nightmare of reality. He dried his face, rose slowly and looked around, seeing the forest of monuments and gravestones interspersed with bushes, all covered with snow.

The lonely sadness of the place fit his mood perfectly. Leonora, he knew, must have been caught when she returned to the Jakubiks, along with her hosts. She would be imprisoned for a long term, perhaps even put to death in the angry uproar that would follow his escape—if he escaped.

But wait. Perhaps she had heard the shooting in front of the Jakubiks' house, realized what must have happened and turned away to flee. It was a faint possibility, but Filip's frenzied mind grasped at faint chances.

His emotions told him to turn back to search for her. But where on earth would she go, where would he look for her? Reason ordered him onward to the West, where he could wait until he heard about her, one way or another.

Remaining in the cemetery would do him no good. The police, he was certain, would organize an intensive search for him throughout Prague and its environs, and it would be best for him to start immediately for the German border.

How fragile is the thread that binds the mind. In the following days as Filip made his way westward, thoughts of Leonora, thoughts of paradise gained, lost, regained and lost, drove everything else from his mind and threw him into despondency. By nature, he was not self-pitying, but now he wondered if any man since Job had been buffeted by fate as he was. The unrelenting pounding of his memory distracted him, dulling his senses until his actions came not as carefully thought out moves but as mechanical responses. Only the instincts deeply ingrained in him as a creature of prey saved him during those days when his mind strayed from the road of sanity.

Outside the Olsanske Cemetery he hailed a cab and forced the driver to drive him beyond Beroun toward Pilsen, before he ran out of gas. Filip held a gun at the cabbie's head until he became convinced the driver was indeed as sympathetic to the anti-Communist cause as he swore.

Once near the border, Filip decided it would be safer to go on foot. Much of Bohemia was strange country to him, but like many Slovak nationalists he did not want to entrust his neck to any Czech if he could help it. Preoccupied as his thoughts were with the loss of Leonora, some remote cell of his mind told him to avoid the highways. Cutting across farms and meadows and forests, occasionally chancing sparsely traveled dirt roads, always ducking into the underbrush or behind trees when he heard the sound of a motor or the hoofbeats of a horse coming, Filip marched westward instinctively.

Once in a moment of mind-wandering, he relaxed his ban on seeking the help of strangers. Weary and footsore, hungry after days with only a few bites of a chocolate bar to eat and melted snow to drink, he flagged down an old farm truck that was going in his direction. Lulled by the steady low hum of the tires, Filip shut his eyes irresistibly and dozed off sitting up. What would have happened if he had fallen into a deep sleep he would never know. But he was dimly aware that the truck was coming to a stop, and he awoke suddenly as he sensed rather than felt the farmer lean over him and try to pull out the gun stuck in Filip's belt that had become exposed when the truck rounded a curve.

Filip's hand shot out and gripped the farmer by the wrist as the latter's fingers tightened around the handle. The farmer was a well-built man and Filip was weakened by deprivation and fatigue. But the tight confines of the truck cab reduced the physical advantage, and Filip's sudden movement had caught his assailant off guard. They grappled, each with a hand on the gun, a shot was fired and blood spurted out of a gaping hole torn out in the farmer's side, pouring onto Filip's clothes and the truck seat.

Resisting the temptation to drive the truck himself, Filip maneuvered it off the road where it could not be easily seen by passersby. The shock of the close call cleared his mind temporarily of Leonora and he swore to himself he would keep on foot the rest of the way, and forego even the back roads that began to thin out as he climbed upwards into what he calculated must be the start of the Bohemian Forest, which spanned the Czech-German border.

Higher and higher he climbed, sometimes knee-deep in snowbanks that slowed his progress to a crawl, never knowing where he was but always heading due west. In his lucid moments he noted the pristine loveliness of his surroundings, but such intervals were increasingly rare. Try as he might, he could not shake from his mind his last conversation with Leonora. Over and over he heard himself saying, "We will leave today, not tomorrow, never to leave each other again."

He tried to climb faster. Soon he came to a large flat rock, covered with snow, that formed a natural seat. Brushing off the snow until he uncovered the moss-encrusted rock, he sat down heavily. Instantly, memory flooded his consciousness, memory of Leonora lost.

But now he did not try to banish it from his mind. He let

the agonizing experience live again, welcomed it eagerly. Now suddenly the other experiences of his life, the close brushes with death, the feats he had performed in the fight for Slovakia, the brief shared moments of love with Leonora, all these Filip relived as he sat there. He had reached the bottom of despair. Like Job, he saw now, he must learn to endure travail without questioning God's will, to trust in God's inscrutable ways, to be confident that there was divine purpose even in the sufferings he bore.

Despondency gave way to exhilaration and he rose quickly from his perch. A half-frozen man should not lie down in the snow, he told himself, and he purposefully continued on his way. From the overhead sun he could tell it was noon.

By now, he figured, he should be quite close to the Bavarian border. But where was the barbed wire barrier that identified the Iron Curtain?

Over the next slope, he saw off in the distance a small village. Better skirt it, he thought. Probably a Czech border town. The Curtain couldn't be far away.

Bypassing the town through the adjacent pine forest he plowed onward in the snow. There, atop the next rise, he saw them, the Czech border guards.

Curious, he mused. Their uniforms didn't look like the ones Czech border patrols usually wore. Even at a distance, he could see the coats the troopers wore were noticeably longer than the Czech coats. Cautiously moving closer, he noticed now that the troopers' hats sloped upwards to a narrow top, unlike the Czech head coverings, which had a stubby cylindrical shape.

Were those really German troops ahead of him? Had he crossed over the Iron Curtain without knowing it? He turned backwards, sweeping his eye to the right and left. Yes, there they were, to either side, the high granite border stones, jutting through the snow, that marked the line separating Czechoslovakia and West Germany. They were behind him. He was in Germany.

Joyously he began running toward the German troops, raising his arms to wave at them. He opened his mouth to shout, but all that came out was a faint croak. They had not seen him yet.

Suddenly Filip dropped his hand. He ducked behind a tree to get out of their line of sight. Why turn himself over to the German border guards? It was an unthinking, impulsive gesture. They would take him to a refugee camp, where he would remain for months until he could get out.

Because a job awaited him in the United States, there was no doubt he would eventually be released. But there was something degrading, Filip reflected, about being herded through a refugee camp. He was a proud man and he viewed himself not as a refugee from tyranny, helplessly seeking the mercy of the German Government, but as a fighter for the free world, able to stand on his own two feet, now about to change his arena of battle.

So Filip avoided the guards, with little difficulty, and walked on, hoping to reach a town where he could board a bus or train for Munich. And as he walked, the wonder of his escape struck him. To his feverish mind, it seemed a miracle that the barbed wire barrier had miraculously disappeared.

Not until later did he learn there was no magic involved. He had simply, fortuitously, crossed the Czech-German border near the little town of Eisenstein, one of the few points where no barbed wire had been thrown up.

Eisenstein was split in two by the border, but since its lumber industry and farming required continual passage back and forth between the two sections, the Czechs did not put up barbed wire. Instead they protected the border with troops, allowing free movement to citizens of both parts of the town who had the proper passes. For several hundred yards of thick forest on each side of the town the border went unmarked by barbed wire and thinly guarded. Through this gap Filip had traveled.

But as he marched into Germany, that day, he was convinced God had parted the Iron Curtain for him, as he had parted the Red Sea for the Children of Israel. Perhaps it was a fatigue-induced delusion, but it seemed clear to him that God had given a sign Filip was to proceed to the West to fulfill his mission on earth.

And yet, what was that moaning sound behind him? He whirled around, but he saw no one. Was it the wind, or Leonora calling him?

15. The Choice

FOUR WEEKS after his flight from Prague, Filip was resting at the Vierjahreszeiten Hotel at Munich.

He had made contact with the Vienna cell of the Underground, warning it of Jan Magala's treachery in revealing Filip's secret hideouts to the Communists in Czechoslovakia.

Through the Slovak colony in Munich he had sent word to Ben Lee in the United States that he wanted a bit longer to decide on the offer of a job. From Howard Low and John T. Kmetz, an American labor leader of Slovak ancestry, came more funds to sustain him in the meantime.

Then one day Jan Baar arrived at the hotel. Filip had been anxiously awaiting some word of the aftermath of his escape and he fired questions at Baar even before the guerilla-turned-courier had a chance to seat himself.

"Frank Jakubik was hanged," were Baar's first terse words.

"What about Leonora?" Filip asked fearfully, neglecting in his anxiety to express his regrets at the death of the husband of Baar's cousin Margita.

"Leonora and Margita are in jail, twenty years." Baar lit a cigarette, offered one to Filip, then fished out a paper from his pocket.

"This is from Leonora. It was smuggled out of her cell."

Filip tore it out of Baar's outstretched hand.

My beloved,
  When there is no other way, at least I can fly towards you with my thoughts to tell you that I am constantly with

you and that I love you—the same as it was the first day we met.

Perhaps you will never read these lines. But I write them anyway for I am crumbling under the burden of our life, and in writing to you I try to keep up the hope of that day when we will not be separated any longer.

The thought of you is the only light that keeps me alive in my dreadful confinement. Though I have no inkling where you are, I call you often for I know that you hear me. I fear only that you are sick—I cannot admit to myself that you might be in chains, nor do I dare to think you might already be covered with the black earth.

If you are alive, I know that you will wait for me until I am free. I shall wait for you all my life. I go to sleep with your name on my lips, imploring God to protect you. And in my dreams, when I see you, I kiss your tired eyes.

Do not forget me, my beloved, for you know that you are my only hope.

Forever yours,
Leonora

Filip looked up at Baar, but his friend had quietly left the room to leave Filip alone in his suffering. He sat down on the edge of the bed, gazing at the wall with unseeing eyes, and wept soundlessly.

When Jan returned, Filip had composed himself once more. There was a look of cold determination about him, a look that told of a decision made and a mind cleared of confusion.

"How soon can we go back, Jan?"

Epilogue

Yes, the Underground still fights on in Slovakia, tapping the scientific strength of the Communist empire for the benefit of the West. And the Church of Silence still ministers secretly to the faithful, nourishing their hope of freedom.

But the struggle of the Slovaks is not unique. Events similar to the ones you have just read about have no doubt occurred, or will take place, in Poland, in Hungary, in the Ukraine, East Germany, Cuba, indeed in almost every land that lives under Communist domination. I have told the story of the Slovak Underground not to glorify my native land, but to exalt man's indomitable resistance to tyranny everywhere, his unquenchable yearning to be free.

G7